SHUT UP, HE EXPLAINED

A Ring Lardner Selection

edited by Babette Rosmond
and Henry Morgan

SHUT UP, HE EXPLAINED

CHARLES SCRIBNER'S SONS

New York

Acknowledgements

To Bourne, Inc. and Warock Music, Inc. for six lines from "Lullaby of the Leaves."
Copyright (1932) in the United States, jointly owned by Bourne, Inc., and Warock Music, Inc.
Copyright for all other countries of the world owned exclusively by Bourne, Inc., New York, N. Y.

To Harms, Inc. for two lines from "Night and Day" by Cole Porter. Copyright 1932 Harms, Inc. Reprinted by permission.

To Leeds Music Corp. for the lines from "Pu-leeze! Mister Hemingway!" by Milton Drake, Walter Kent and Abner Silver. © Copyright MCMXXXII by Leeds Music Corporation. © Copyright renewed MCMLIX and assigned to Leeds Music Corporation, New York 36, New York. All rights reserved. Used by permission.

Printed in the United States of America
Library of Congress Catalog Card Number 62-11355

Contents

SHUT UP, HE
EXPLAINED

Introduction
by Babette Rosmond

When *The Love Nest and Other Stories* came out in 1926, the famous introduction (see page 7) caused The New York Sunday Times Book Review to comment on Mr. Lardner's untimely death. (Most untimely, since he died in 1933.) The Book Review supplements have their perspective and Lardner had his. This collection is based vaguely on the premise that the two factions aren't ever going to get together.

Followers of book reviews may be Serious Readers (of Durrell, Riesman, Angus Wilson), or Readers Who Like Humor (Amis, de Vries, James Gould Cozzens). They are also guided by magazines printed on bad-complexioned paper; the followers, too, would have believed in the Master's early passing. This book is for the furtive minority who don't know about anything except what they don't like. Some of this faction may even now be under the innocent impression (promulgated for years by the others) that Ring Lardner was essentially a baseball writer. This book contains none of the baseball stories and none of the often-reprinted classics like "Golden Honeymoon," "The Love Nest," "Haircut," etc. It is an incomplete, indoor Ring Lardner designed to remind our furtive minority that this man was way ahead of his time in nonsense-humor, free association, or whatever you choose to call it. And you get into trouble right there, for, as Robert Benchley pointed out in his introduction to *Strictly from Hunger* (by S. J. Perelman, one of *our* people), Lardner wouldn't have dreamed of classifying himself as anything at all.

A book reviewer in San Francisco wrote a column recently about a work by John O'Hara. Part of it went like this: " 'Being a cheap, ordinary guy,' O'Hara said, 'I have an instinct for what an ordinary guy likes.' Ring Lardner might have put it this way, too."

Shut Up, He Explained was assembled in the hope of proving

1

that Ring Lardner would never in all this world have said anything of the kind. He knew above all else that he was not cheap or ordinary; the ungrammatical writing he occasionally affected has as much to do with his own ideas of style as the 1961 Minnesota Twins have to do with the 1927 New York Yankees. He was a great purist. (He offended Scott Fitzgerald by telling him that Fitzgerald used words incorrectly.) But Lardner did fool people . . . mostly because he didn't believe in making himself expensive. He was probably the only author ever born who wouldn't discuss his work with anyone, except, near the end of his days when he spoke to his son John about it in some detail.

My colleague and I began in a rosy dream of "talking to his contemporaries and. . . ." Well, James Thurber said he never met Lardner; Dorothy Parker said she never really knew Mr. Lardner well at all, not at all; Mrs. Samuel J. Lanahan, who was Miss Fitzgerald, said, "But I was only two when we lived next door to each other in Great Neck, and I don't remember him or anything about him." So much for his contemporaries.

The point we are making is: nobody writes this way any more. For a golden while there was *The New Yorker* of the nineteen thirties. They printed pieces by Benchley, Thurber and Perelman that clearly showed the influence of the Master. But where are they now, the people with the perfect ear and the see-through eye? The only practicing author who approaches it is a man Lardner would have shot on sight: Vladimir Nabokov. The outlook is different but the equipment is familiar. Mr. Nabokov perceives somewhat bizarre aspects of daily life; Lardner was a man of stern morality (he referred to himself in his radio columns as "comstocky"). The wayward Eileen in *June Moon* comes off badly, and then there was Ring's campaign, also in *The New Yorker* radio columns, against improper popular song lyrics . . .

All we really have to offer here is a glimpse of a first-rate mind in exercises ranging from superb to medium. For those who are interested in biographical details there is no more accurate collection of facts than Donald Elder has put together in *Ring Lardner* (Doubleday, 1956). Most readers know the famous short stories. Some of what we have here may sound familiar, too, or dated, or questionable, but the Ear and the Eye are at work in all.

Introduction
by Henry Morgan

If faces tell you anything, maybe Ring's face had a lot to say. He looked like a rather handsome cross between Buster Keaton and Ned Sparks. He wasn't bitter at all, any more than W. C. Fields was bitter. Or William Schwenk Gilbert. It's just that there are always those among us who have a fairly low opinion of the human race and are still amused by it.

Most major religions seem to agree that an Almighty put people on this fine piece of real estate and that the nonsense which followed was created by humans . . . . get the picture? It was people who drew lines on maps, then separated themselves into large cliques and started fighting. People invented haves and have-nots, soreheads and poets and Communism. And while it may be true that an Infinite Wisdom created a lot of damned fools, it was compensated for a bit by seeding among us a handful of witnesses who are at once loving and wary of their fellows, who see clearly the folly of the whole proposition, and can be funny about it.

Ring was one of the handful.

When Will Rogers said, "I never met a man I didn't like," he was hacking his way into the hearts of the witless types we still see around, running elevators and, often, large corporations. It is assumed that a man who likes everybody is himself automatically likeable. When, for example, a public entertainer sprays a maudlin 'God bless you' over twenty million TV watchers he's telling them they're lovely merely to insure the return of the compliment. And to be liked is generally considered to be what Arthur Miller's Willy Loman said it was . . . . the most important thing. When Rogers made his famous statement he was a mite forgetful, since he'd already written a magazine piece in which he mentioned quite a few people he *didn't* like. (A saner point of view and more to his credit.) To love 'everybody' implies a certain lack of discretion. The

3

usual audience for anything whatsoever contains, so medical author-
ities have guessed, a minimum of one out of ten who are certifiably
insane. Scattered among the non-certifiable are shoplifters, well-
poisoners, voyeurs, stock brokers, and plain, everyday goofs. It takes
a big man to bless 'em all.

Ring never made any wild statements about loving everybody.
People disappointed him. It is these disappointments which turn
some men into cynics, some into suicides, and some into satirists.

At the exact moment at which a bright boy discovers that his
father doesn't really know everything, the dice begin to teeter. Consider. Everyone is born to grow up inadequate, in the over-all sense,
and everyone finds his own way 'out'. Some wear little masks which
they put on at sunrise. Some steal. Others become grand, and
there's always a man in the White House. But *all* spend part of the
time being foolish or pompous or just plain moronic. Inevitably
the path to 'out' is cluttered with pettiness, greed, idiocy, and in-
justice.

The dice are beginning to tilt. If the boy is cold inside, and
cheap, he may become a cynic. If he is warm and has some values,
he may become a humorist. But if he is very bright, and very
loving, and continually disappointed, he may become a satirist.

Ambrose Bierce said that a cynic was "a blackguard whose faulty
vision sees things as they are, not as they ought to be". Another man
said that a cynic knows the price of everything but the value of
nothing. Bierce himself was a cynic by the second definition.

Mark Twain, the dear man, was a master humorist who avoided
the satiric by being too kindly. When, on occasion, he moved into
that field, he sounded a bit mean. This, according to our thesis,
was at those times when he felt most grievously disappointed.
Perhaps it would help if this were charted. . . .

CYNICS	HUMORISTS	SATIRISTS
Arsonists	Benchley	Lardner
Kidnappers	Thurber	Swift
Marie Antoinette	Perelman	Fred Allen
Fagin	Robert Moses	Fred Allen
Khrushchev	Weathermen	Mencken
Iago	Butchers (retail)	

This sort of hasty arrangement must ignore the different degrees with which we are not at the moment concerned: the burlesque, wit, clown, joke-teller, farceur. Naturally these classes tend to overlap and in Ring's case you could often split the difference. He was a wit and he wrote a good deal of burlesque. He even wrote what today would be termed 'non-objective' humor. And that is something else.

Good writing, like music, speech, painting—has rhythm. It is based, possibly, on the beating of a heart. When this rhythm concerns itself with reproducing the spoken word with (what seems to be) accuracy, we say that the writer has an ear for the spoken word. Ring had an ear, all right.

Once in a while, as you enjoy your way through this book, that ear may give you a bit of pause. Some of the small change of conversation is lost as time shuffles along and an occasional locution may surprise you. No matter. That's exactly the way it *did* sound, just the other day.

You may know that Ring drank a lot and played poker. I never heard of anybody who drank *and* played poker who didn't like people.

Introduction
by Sarah E. Spooldripper *

It is hoped that a careful reading of the stories collected in this book will dispel the general illusion that in his later years Ring Lardner was just a tiresome old man induced by financial calamity and a fondness for narcotics to harp constantly on the futility of life on a branch line of the Long Island Railroad. In these tales we see the old fellow as perhaps not lovable, but certainly irresistible. There was an impishness in him that fascinated. It was part of his charm.

I know it for truth that from fifty on he indulged to an alarming extent in the lesser opiates, eating aspirin as if it were so much mud and seldom laying aside the all-day sucker which he plopped into his mouth the instant he had finished his breakfast. Lardner always bolted his food. He was afraid the rats would get it. It was part of his charm.

Appearance of "The Love Nest," the short story from which the book takes its name, in *Cosmopolitan Magazine,* created a furore on the east bank of the Hudson, commuters of that neighborhood nearly coming to blows in arguments over the identity, in real life, of the tale's principal characters. Two old cronies who had played halma together night after night for nearly a week suddenly began making faces at one another, hiding each other's gloves, pinching each other's forearms, and altogether making a fiasco of the entire relationship. The author heard rumors of this feud and others and knew their cause, but kept his own counsel till the last day of his earthly career, when he confided to me that the Lou Gregg of the story was President Fillmore and the Mrs. Gregg, Mary Lewis.

It was in the middle of this work that the rivalry between Lard-

* Miss Spooldripper lived with the Lardners for years and took care of their wolf. She knew all there was to know about Lardner, and her mind was virtually blank. It was part of her charm.

ner, Scott Fitzgerald, and Opie Reade for the love of Lily Langtry reached its height. During a dinner party at which the then raging beauty and her raging suitors were all present, the toastmaster, Gerald Chapman, asked Miss Langtry to rise and drink to "her favorite." The muscles of Fitzgerald and Reade were taut; Lardner's were very flabby.

After a pause that seemed to endure all night but really lasted only half that long, Miss Langtry got up, raised her glass and said: "I drink to Red Grange. Heston may have been his superior on defense and Coy, Thorpe, Eckersall, and Mahan more versatile, but as a common carrier I take off my hat to the Wheaton icemonger."

Miss Langtry was deeply interested in college athletics and it was she who christened a certain New Jersey town Rahway because it was en route to Rutgers, Princeton, and the University of Pennsylvania.

Her response to the toastmaster's request affected her three swains variously. Reade arose and told the story of the two half-breeds, Seminole and Deminole. Lardner and Fitzgerald took up rotation pool, and weighed themselves once a week. Every so often they became maudlin, or, better still, inaudible.

An insight into Lardner's true character may be obtained from the correspondence which passed between him and Mrs. Patrick Campbell while he was writing the story "Haircut" at Atlantic City.

"Dear Ringlets," wrote Mrs. Campbell (it was a name she had for him), "don't forget 'Miss England' while playing around with 'Miss America.' "

"Dear Pat," was Lardner's reply, "am having a 'swill' time, but I do 'Miss England' and indeed I would walk a mile for a Campbell."

On the back of the card was a picture of Young's Million Dollar Pier.*

"Haircut" was written under a severe strain, the writer having just engaged in a violent quarrel with John N. Wheeler, then editor of *Liberty*.

* This correspondence and other mash notes written by Lardner and his admirers were obtained from the street cleaners of East Shore Road, Great Neck, where the author threw all his mail, and are printed with the permission of Judge Landis.

"Why didn't you lead me a spade?" demanded Wheeler.

"I was out of them," was the infuriating reply, and in a moment the two were rolling on the floor, with Wheeler's dice.

The character of the doctor in "Haircut" was a composite "photograph" of Mrs. Campbell and the Shuberts. It was Lardner's favorite among all his fictional characters, or, as he called them, "my puppets."

"Which is your favorite among all your 'puppets'?" I once asked him as we jointly gave the wolf a sitzbath.

"The doctor," he said.

The wolf was really the chief interest in Lardner's life. I have never elsewhere seen such a whole-souled comradeship as existed between the Master and this sinister pet. He was always hoping it would have a baby which he would have christened the Wolverine as a memorial to his native state.

Lardner's adoption of the beast was characteristic of the man. One afternoon in October while Mrs. Lardner (he always called her Junior as she was two or more years younger than he) was making out the May checks, she suddenly looked up from her work, sobbing, and said:

"Husband!"

"Yes, Junior. What is it?"

"I am overdrawn."

"You stay indoors and brood too much," replied Lardner. "A little exercise and a few pleasures would restore the bloom to both those cheeks."

"I am not referring to anything physical," said the little woman. "I mean there is less than no money in the bank."

At that moment there was a scratching outside that could not have been the children, as they had all had their baths.

"What is that noise, Junior?" inquired the Master.

"I will go and see," said the Madam, sliding headforemost to the front door, as she was a great admirer of Frankie Frisch.

She returned in a moment, sobbing louder than ever, with the news that the wolf was at the door.

This was the beginning of a friendship that the less said about it the better. But I suppose I ought not to complain, for the wolf's advent into the home was responsible for mine and it is not every spinster who spends the latter days of her life under such pleasant conditions as existed in the household of Ring Lardner, God bless him!

The story "Reunion" followed a visit paid the Lardners by the little woman's sisters and their husbands, all strict Swedenborgians and innately opposed to meat-eating and outdoor sports. Lardner was, of course, a devotee of golf and considered days spent indoors as days wasted. So it was torture to him, this prolonged sojourn of his in-laws, and "Reunion" was penned in a spirit of bitterness. The character of Mrs. Stu Johnston's brother is a composite of G. P. Torrence of Indianapolis, Robin Hendry of Detroit, H. W. Kitchell of Evanston, and F. R. Kitchell of Hingham, Mass., all of whom married sisters of Junior.

In re Lardner's golf, the following amusing anecdote is recounted:

Lardner was playing a mixed twosome with Mayor Walker of New York. They were both playing a Spalding mesh ball, which is how they got mixed. Coming to the fifteenth tee, they had halved the preceding three holes and Lardner could not remember whose turn it was to drive first.

"Your honor?" he said to the Mayor.

"Yes?" the Mayor replied. "What can I do for you?"

It is incidents like this that paint the man in his true colors. He was forever blowing bubbles. It amounted to a whim.

The romance of "Mr. and Mrs. Fix-It," without ranking with Lardner's best or with his most popular compositions, and betraying here and there a less persistent hold on character than is usual with him, is still a fascinating story, full of his peculiar sensuousness and pathos, with striking scenes vividly portrayed, and an advance on his previous farces as respects his constantly growing power of imaginative description.

Publication of this story in *Liberty* caused an estrangement between the Master and the Grantland Rices, who were unmistakably the parties inspiring it. So accurately were their characters and idiosyncracies depicted that they recognized themselves and did not speak to Lardner for a week. This was considered a triumph by the Master.

"But the lesson was all lost," he told me afterwards, when a reconciliation had been effected. "They knew I was writing about them, and now they are right up to their old tricks again, dictating where we shall buy our shirts, how to discipline our kiddies, what road to take South, what to order for breakfast, when to bathe in what kind of bath salts, and even how often to visit the chiropodist. It is an intolerable example of maniacal Southern hospitality."

He proceeded to a fresh attack, turning out "Who Dealt?" Mrs. Rice is unquestionably the first person in this story, the one who tells it; either she or Ruth Hale or perhaps Mrs. S. B. Thorne.

There is an interesting fact connected with the story "Zone of Quiet." It was written outdoors during the equinoctial gales. Nearly every other sheet of copy was blown away or destroyed by stray dogs, and when the manuscript finally reached Ray Long, editor of *Cosmopolitan*, over two-thirds of it was missing. Mr. Long thought this all for the best as he was crowded that month. Mr. Long is related by marriage to Mr. O. O. McIntyre, which is considered a horse on both of them.*

Most of the stories making up this volume are noticeably shorter than those Lardner wrote in the early days of his tepid career. This is due to the invention and perfection of radio. Not content with purchasing one of the standard radios on the market, the Master, who, like Jane Cowl, was something of a mechanical genius, made his own set and installed it in the suit of pajamas which he habitually wore nights. At first he was unable to get any station at all, and this condition held good up to the day of his death. But he was always trying to tune in on Glens Falls, N. Y., and it was only in his last illness that he found out there was no broadcasting station at that place. His sense of humor came to his rescue in this dilemma.

"Junior," he said to his wife, "they tell me there is no broadcasting station at Glens Falls."

"Am I to blame for that?" retorted the little Nordic, quick to take umbrage.**

"No," he answered. "It's Glens Falls."

Those of the tales in this book which have not already been mentioned were dashed off after the Master had contracted the cold that

* Strangely enough, Mr. Long's favorite amusement is horseback riding, so the innuendo is not so far out of the way. He is known as a keen whip around Greenwich and, during the winters, when he lives in town, can be seen in Times Square almost any morning astride his imported hunter, "Black Oxen," directing the traffic and selling tickets to the Field Day at Jamaica.
** Junior was an inveterate umbrage taker and frequently took more than was good for her.

resulted in the fatal attack of conchoid, a disease which is super-induced by a rush of seashells to the auricle or outer ear. Present during the last hours were only myself and the wolf, Junior having chosen this time to get a shampoo and wave in preparation for the series of dinner dances that were bound to follow.

"Edna," whispered the Master as he lay there idly watching the doctor change a tire, "to-morrow I will be all right again and you and I will get in a taxi and be ourselves."

He called me Edna only when he was up to some devilment. It was his way.

The Master is gone * and the next question is who will succeed him? Perhaps some writer still unborn. Perhaps one who will never be born. That is what I hope.

* The joke is on Miss Spooldripper, for she is gone too. Two months ago she was found dead in the garage, her body covered with wolf bites left there by her former ward, who has probably forgotten where he left them.

The Young Immigrunts
by Ring W. Lardner, Jr.
WITH A PREFACE BY THE FATHER

In 1919 a mysterious ten year old young lady named Daisy Ashford published a book called The Young Visiters, or, Mr. Salteena's Plan. The work was a tremendous success. Sir James Barrie wrote the preface for the first edition, and the public decided it was really Sir James himself who was curtseying behind the pseudonym. Well, there really was a Daisy Ashford, and very few people remember the whole affair; but we may say that it had a deep influence on The Young Immigrunts.

However, it may now be revealed that it was not Ring, Jr. (called Bill in those days) who made the trip with his parents, but his older brother John. This is one of the smallest literary hoaxes on record.

PREFACE

The person whose name is signed to this novel was born on the nineteenth day of August, 1915, and was therefore four years and three months old when the manuscript was found, late in November, 1919. The narrative is substantially true, with the following exceptions:

1. "My Father," the leading character in the work, is depicted as a man of short temper, whereas the person from whom the character was drawn is in reality as pleasant a fellow as one would care to meet and seldom has a cross word for any one, let alone women and children.

2. The witty speeches accredited to "My Father" have, possibly owing to the limitations of a child's memory, been so garbled and twisted that they do not look half so good in print as they sounded in the open air.

3. More stops for gas were made than are mentioned in the story.

As the original manuscript was written on a typewriter with a rather frayed ribbon, and as certain words were marked out and others handwritten in, I have taken the liberty of copying the entire work with a fresh ribbon and the inclusion of the changes which the author indicated in pencil in the first draft. Otherwise the story is presented to the reader exactly as it was first set down.

THE FATHER.

CHAPTER 1

MY PARENTS

My parents are both married and ½ of them are very good looking. The balance is tall and skiny and has a swarty complexion with moles but you hardly ever notice them on account of your gaze being rapped up in his feet which would be funny if brevvity wasnt the soul of wit. Everybody says I have his eyes and I am glad it didnt half to be something else tho Rollie Zeider the ball player calls him owl eyes for a nick name but if I was Rollie Zeider and his nose I wouldnt pick on somebodys else features.

He wears pretty shirts which he bought off of another old ball player Artie Hofman to attrack tension off of his feet and must of payed a big price for them I heard my ant tell my uncle when they thorght I was a sleep down to the lake tho I guess he pays even more for his shoes if they sell them by the frunt foot.

I was born in a hospittle in Chicago 4 years ago and liked it very much and had no idear we were going to move till 1 day last summer I heard my mother arsk our nurse did she think she could get along O. K. with myself and 3 brothers John Jimmie and David for 10 days wilst she and my old man went east to look for a costly home.

Well yes said our nurse barshfully.

I may as well exclaim to the reader that John is 7 and Jimmie is 5 and I am 4 and David is almost nothing as yet you might say and tho I was named for my father they call me Bill thank God.

The conversation amungst my mother and our nurse took place right after my father came back from Toledo where Jack Dempsey knocked Jessie Willard for a gool tho my father liked the big fellow and bet on him.

David was in his bath at the time and my mother and our nurse and myself and 2 elder brothers was standing around admireing him tho I notice that when the rest of the family takes their bath they dont make open house of the occassion.

Well my parents went east and dureing their absents myself and brothers razed hell with David on the night shift but when they come back my mother said to the nurse were they good boys.

Fine replid our nurse lamely and where are you going to live. Connecticut said my mother.

Our nurse forced a tired smile.

Here we will leave my parents to unpack and end this chapter.

CHAPTER 2

STARTING GAILY

We spent the rest of the summer on my granmother in Indiana and my father finley went to the worst series to write it up as he has followed sports of all sorts for years and is a expert so he bet on the wite sox and when he come home he acted rarther cross.

Well said my mother simperingly I suppose we can start east now.

We will start east when we get good and ready said my father with a lordly sneeze.

The next thing was how was we going to make the trip as my father had boughten a new car that the cheepest way to get it there was drive it besides carrying a grate deal of our costly bagage but if all of us went in it they would be no room left for our costly bagage and besides 2 of my brothers always acts like devils incarnite when they get in a car so my mother said to our nurse.

If you think you can manage the 2 older boys and David on the train myself and husband will take Bill in the car said my mother to our nurse.

Fine replid our nurse with a gastly look witch my mother did not see.

Myself and parents left Goshen Indiana on a fine Monday morning leaveing our nurse and brothers to come latter in the weak on the railway. Our plans was to reach Detroit that night and stop with my uncle and ant and the next evening take the boat to Buffalo and thence to Connecticut by motor so the first town we past through was Middlebury.

Elmer Flick the old ball player use to live here said my father modestly.

My mother forced a smile and soon we were acrost the Michigan line and my mother made the remark that she was thirsty.

We will stop at Coldwater for lunch said my father with a strate face as he pulls most of his lines without changeing expressions.

Sure enough we puled up to 1 side of the road just after leaveing Coldwater and had our costly viands of frid chicken and doughnuts and milk fernished by my grate ant and of witch I partook freely.

We will stop at Ypsilanti for supper said my father in calm tones that is where they have the state normal school.

I was glad to hear this and hoped we would get there before dark as I had always wanted to come in contack with normal peaple and see what they are like and just at dusk we entered a large size town and drove past a large size football field.

Heavens said my mother this must be a abnormal school to have such a large football field.

My father wore a qeer look.

This is not Ypsilanti this is Ann Arbor he crid.

But I thorght you said we would go south of Ann Arbor and direct to Ypsilanti said my mother with a smirk.

I did say that but I thorght I would surprise you by comeing into Ann Arbor replid my father with a corse jesture.

Personly I think the surprise was unanimous.

Well now we are here said my mother we might as well look up Bill.

Bill is my uncle Bill so we stoped at the Alfa Delt house and got him and took him down to the hotel for supper and my old man called up Mr. Yost the football coach of the Michigan football team and he come down and visited with us.

What kind of a team have you got coach said my father lamely.

I have got a determined team replid Mr. Yost they are determined to not play football.

At this junction my unlucky mother changed the subjeck to the league of nations and it was 10 o'clock before Mr. Yost come to a semi colon so we could resume our journey and by the time we past through Ypsilanti the peaple was not only subnormal but unconsius. It was nerly midnight when we puled up in frunt of my ants and uncles house in Detroit that had been seting up since 7 expecting us.

Were sorry to be so late said my mother bruskly.

Were awfully glad you could come at all replid my ant with a ill consealed yawn.

We will now leave my relitives to get some sleep and end this chapter.

CHAPTER 3

ERIE LAKE

The boat leaves Detroit every afternoon at 5 oclock and reachs Buffalo the next morning at 9 tho I would better exclaim to my readers that when it is 9 oclock in Buffalo it is only 8 oclock in Goshen for instants as Buffalo peaple are qeer.

Well said my father the next morning at brekfus I wander what time we half to get the car on the board of the boat.

I will find out down town and call up and let you know replid my uncle who is a engineer and digs soors or something.

Sure enough he called up dureing the fornoon and said the car must be on the board of the boat at 3 oclock so my father left the house at 2 oclock and drove down to the worf tho he had never drove a car in Detroit before but has nerves of steal. Latter my uncle come out to his home and took myself and mother and ant down to the worf where my old man was waiting for us haveing put the car on the board.

What have you been doing ever since 3 oclock arsked my mother as it was now nerly 5.

Haveing a high ball my father replid.

I thorght Detroit was dry said my mother shyly.

Did you said my father with a rye smile and as it was now nerly time for the boat to leave we said good by to my uncle and ant and went on the boat. A messenger took our costly bagage and put it away wilst myself and parents went out on the porch and set looking at the peaple on the worf. Suddenly they was a grate hub bub on the worf and a young man and lady started up the gangs plank wilst a big crowd throwed rice and old shoes at them and made a up roar.

Bride and glum going to Niagara Falls said my father who is well travelled and seams to know everything.

Instantly the boat give a blarst on the wistle and I started with suprise.

Did that scare you Bill said my father and seamed to enjoy it and I suppose he would of laughed out right had I fell overboard and been drowned in the narsty river water.

Soon we were steeming up the river on the city of Detroit 3.

That is Canada over there is it not said my mother.

What did you think it was the Austrian Tyrol replid my father explodeing a cough. Dureing our progress up the river I noticed sevral funny things flotting in the water with lanterns hanging on them and was wandering what they could be when my mother said they seam to have plenty of boys.

They have got nothing on us replid my father quick as a flarsh.

A little latter who should come out on the porch and set themselfs ner us but the bride and glum.

Oh I said to myself I hope they will talk so as I can hear them as I have always wandered what newlyweds talk about on their way to Niagara Falls and soon my wishs was realized.

Some night said the young glum are you warm enough.

I am perfectly comfertible replid the fare bride tho her looks belid her words what time do we arive in Buffalo.

9 oclock said the lordly glum are you warm enough.

I am perfectly comfertible replid the fare bride what time do we arrive in Buffalo.

9 oclock said the lordly glum I am afrade it is too cold for you out here.

Well maybe it is replid the fare bride and without farther adieu they went in the spacius parlers.

I wander will he be arsking her 8 years from now is she warm enough said my mother with a faint grimace.

The weather may change before then replid my father.

Are you warm enough said my father after a slite pause.

No was my mothers catchy reply.

Well said my father we arive in Buffalo at 9 oclock and with that we all went inside as it was now pitch dark and had our supper and retired and when we rose the next morning and drest and had brekfus we puled up to the worf in Buffalo and it was 9 oclock so I will leave the city of Detroit 3 tide to the worf and end this chapter.

CHAPTER 4

BUFFALO TO ROCHESTER 76.4

As we was leaveing the boat who should I see right along side of us but the fare bride and the lordly glum.

We are right on the dot said the glum looking at his costly watch it is just 9 oclock and so they past out of my life.

We had to wait qite a wile wilst the old man dug up his bill of loading and got the costly moter.

We will half to get some gas he said I wonder where they is a garage.

No sooner had the words fell from his lips when a man with a flagrant Adams apple handed him a card with the name of a garage on it.

Go up Genesee st 5 blks and turn to the left or something said the man with the apple.

Soon we reached the garage and had the gas tank filled with gas it was 27 cents in Buffalo and soon we was on our way to Rochester. Well these are certainly grate roads said my father barshfully.

They have lots better roads in the east than out west replid my mother with a knowing wink.

The roads all through the east are better than out west remarked my father at lenth.

These are wonderfull replid my mother smuggleing me vs her arm.

The time past quickly with my parents in so jocular a mood and all most before I knew it we was on the outer skirts of Batavia.

What town is this quired my mother in a tolerant voice.

Batavia husked my father sloughing down to 15 miles per hour.

Well maybe we would better stop and have lunch here said my mother coyly.

We will have lunch in Rochester replid my father with a loud cough.

My mother forced a smile and it was about ½ past 12 when we arived in Rochester and soon we was on Genesee st and finley stoped in front of a elegant hotel and shared a costly lunch.

CHAPTER 5

MY FATHER'S IDEAR

Wilst participateing in the lordly viands my father halled out his map and give it the up and down.

Look at here he said at lenth they seams to be a choice of 2 main roads between here and Syracuse but 1 of them gos way up north to Oswego wilst the other gos way south to Geneva where as Syracuse is strate east from here you might say so it looks to me like we would save both millage and time if we was to drive strate east through Lyons the way the railway gos.

Well I dont want to ride on the ties said my mother with a loud cough.

Well you dont half to because they seams to be a little road that gos strate through replid my father removeing a flys cadaver from the costly farina.

Well you would better stick to the main roads said my mother tacklessly.

Well you would better stick to your own business replid my father with a pungent glance.

Soon my father had payed the check and gave the waiter a lordly bribe and once more we sprang into the machine and was on our way. The lease said about the results of my fathers grate idear the soonest mended in a word it turned out to be a holycost of the first water as after we had covered miles and miles of ribald roads we suddenly come to a abrupt conclusion vs the side of a stagnant freight train that was stone deef to honks. My father set there for nerly ½ a hour reciteing the 4 Horses of the Apoplex in a under tone but finely my mother mustard up her curage and said affectedly why dont we turn around and go back somewheres. I cant spell what my father replid.

At lenth my old man decided that Lyons wouldnt never come to Mahomet if we set it out on the same lines all winter so we backed up and turned around and retraced 4 miles of shell holes and finely reached our objective by way of Detour.

Puling up in front of a garage my father beckoned to a dirty mechanic.

How do we get to Syracuse from her arsked my father blushing furiously.

Go strate south to Geneva and then east to Syracuse replid the dirty mechanic with a loud cough.

Isnt there no short cut arsked my father.

Go strate south to Geneva and then east to Synacuse replid the dirty mechanic.

You see daddy we go to Geneva after all I said brokenly but luckly for my piece of mind my father dont beleive in corporeal punishment a specially in front of Lyons peaple.

Soon we was on a fine road and nothing more happened till we puled into Syracuse at 7 that evening and as for the conversation that changed hands in the car between Lyons and Syracuse you could stick it in a day message and send it for 30 cents.

CHAPTER 6

SYRACUSE TO HUDSON 183.2

Soon we was on Genesee st in Syracuse but soon turned off a blk or 2 and puled up in front of a hotel that I cant ether spell or pronounce besides witch they must of been a convention of cheese sculpters or something stoping there and any way it took the old man a hour to weedle a parler bed room and bath out of the clerk and put up a cot for me.

Wilst we was enjoying a late and futile supper in the hotel dinning room a man named Duffy reckonized my father and came to our table and arsked him to go to some boxing matchs in Syracuse that night.

Thanks very much said my father with a slite sneeze but you see what I have got on my hands besides witch I have been driveing all day and half to start out again erly in the morning so I guess not.

Between you and I dear reader my old man has been opposed to pugilisms since the 4 of July holycost.

Who is that man arsked my mother when that man had gone away.

Mr. Duffy replid my father shove the ketchup over this way.

Yes I know he is Mr. Duffy but where did you meet him insisted my mother quaintly.

In Boston my father replid where would a person meet a man named Duffy.

When we got up the next morning it was 6 oclock and purring rain but we eat a costly brekfus and my father said we would save time if we would all walk down to the garage where he had horded the car witch he stated was only 2 short blks away from the hotel. Well if it was only 2 short blks why peaple that lives next door to each other in Syracuse are by no means neighbors and when we got there the entire party was soping wet and rarther rabid.

We will all catch our death of cold chuckled my mother.

What of it explained my old man with a dirty look at the sky.

Maybe we would better put up the curtains sugested my mother smirking.

Maybe we wouldnt too said my father cordialy.

Well maybe it will clear up said my mother convulsively.

Maybe it wont too replid my father as he capered into the drivers seat.

My father is charming company wilst driveing on strange roads through a purring rain and even when we past through Oneida and he pronounced it like it was a biscuit neither myself or my mother ventured to correct him but finely we reached Utica when we got to witch we puled up along side the kerb and got out and rang ourselfs out to a small extent when suddenly a closed car sored past us on the left.

Why that was Mrs. Heywood in that car explained my mother with a fierce jesture. By this time it was not raining and we got back into the car and presently over took the closed car witch stoped when they reckonized us.

And witch boy is this quired Mrs. Heywood when the usual compliments had been changed.

This is the third he is named for his father replid my mother forceing a smile.

He has his eyes was the comment.

Bill dont you remember Mrs. Heywood said my mother turning on me she use to live in Riverside and Dr. Heywood tended to you that time you had that slite atack of obesity.

Well yes I replid with a slite accent but did not add how rotten the medicine tasted that time and soon we was on Genesee st on our way out of Utica.

I wander why they dont name some of their sts Genesee in these eastren towns said my father for the sun was now shining but no sooner had we reached Herkimer when the clouds bersed with renude vigger and I think my old man was about to say we will stop here and have lunch when my mother sugested it herself.

No replid my father with a corse jesture we will go on to Little Falls.

It was raining cats and dogs when we arived at Little Falls and my father droped a quaint remark.

If Falls is a verb he said the man that baptized this town was a practicle joker.

We will half to change our close replid my mother steping into a mud peddle in front of the hotel with a informal look.

When we had done so we partook of a meger lunch and as it was now only drooling resumed our jurney.

They soked me 5 for that room said my father but what is a extra sokeing or 2 on a day like this.

I didnt mean for you to get a room said my mother violently.

Where did you want us to change our close on the register said my old man turning pail.

Wasnt it funny that we should happen to see Mrs. Heywood in Utica said my mother at lenth.

They live there dont they my father replid.

Why yes my mother replid.

Well then my father replid the real joke would of been if we had of happened to see her in Auburn.

A little wile latter we past a grate many signs reading dine at the Big Nose Mountain Inn.

Rollie Zeider never told me they had named a mountain after him crid my father and soon we past through Fonda.

Soon we past through Amsterdam and I guess I must of dosed off at lease I cant remember anything between there and Schenectady and I must apologize to my readers for my laps as I am unable to ether describe the scenery or report anything that may of been said between these 2 points but I recall that as we entered Albany a remark was adrest to me for the first time since lunch.

Bill said my mother with a ½ smirk this is Albany the capital of New York state.

So this is Albany I thorght to myself.

Who is governor of New York now arsked my mother to my
father.

Smith replid my father who seams to know everything.

Queer name said my mother sulkily.

Soon we puled up along side a policeman who my farther arsked
how do we get acrost the river to the New York road and if Albany
pays their policemans by the word I'll say we were in the presents
of a rich man and by the time he got through it was dark and still
drooling and my old man didnt know the road and under those
conditions I will not repete the conversation that transpired between Albany and Hudson but will end my chapter at the city
limits of the last named settlemunt.

CHAPTER 7

HUDSON

We were turing gaily down the main st of Hudson when a man
of 12 years capered out from the side walk and hoped on the
runing board.

Do you want a good garage he arksed with a dirty look.

Why yes my good man replid my father tenderly but first where
is the best hotel.

I will take you there said the man.

I must be a grate favorite in Hudson my father wispered at
my mother.

Soon folling the mans directions we puled up in front of a
hotel but when my father went at the register the clerk said I am
full tonight.

Where do you get it around here arsked my father tenderly.

We have no rooms replid the senile clerk paying no tension to
my old mans remark but there is a woman acrost the st that takes
loggers.

Not to excess I hope replid my father but soon we went acrost
the st and the woman agrede to hord us for the night so myself
and mother went to our apartmunts wilst my father and the 12 year
old besought the garage. When we finley got reunited and went back
to the hotel for supper it was past 8 oclock as a person could of
told from the viands. Latter in front of our loggings we again met

the young man who had welcomed us to Hudson and called my father to 1 side.

There is a sailer going to spend the night here he said in a horse wisper witch has walked all the way from his home Schenectady and he has got to report on his ship in New York tomorrow afternoon and has got no money so if he dont get a free ride he will be up vs it.

He can ride with us replid my father with a hiccup if tomorrow is anything like today a sailer will not feel out of place in my costly moter.

I will tell him replid the man with a corse jesture.

Will you call us at ½ past 5 my mother reqested to our lanlady as we entered our Hudson barracks.

I will if I am awake she replid useing her handkerchief to some extent.

Latter we wandered how anybody could help from being awake in that hot bed of mones and grones and cat calls and caterwauls and gulish screaks of all kinds and tho we had rose erly at Syracuse and had a day of retchedness we was all more than ready to get up when she wraped on our door long ere day brake.

Where is that sailer that stoped here last night quired my father as we was about to make a lordly outburst.

He wouldnt pay his bill and razed hell so I kicked him out replid the lanlady in her bear feet.

Without farther adieu my father payed his bill and we walked into the dismul st so I will end this chapter by leaveing the fare lanlady flaping in the door way in her sredded night gown.

Chapter 8

HUDSON TO YONKERS 106.5

It was raining a little so my father bad my mother and I stand in the st wilst he went to the garage and retained the costly moter. He returned ½ a hour latter with the story that the garage had been locked and he had to go to the props house and roust him out.

How did you know where he lived quired my mother barshfully.

I used the brains god gave me was my fathers posthumous reply.

Soon we rumpled into Rhinebeck and as it was now day light

and the rain had siezed we puled up in front of the Beekman arms for brekfus.

It says this is the oldest hotel in America said my mother reading the programme.

The eggs tastes all right replid my father with a corse jesture.

What is the next town quired my mother when we again set sale.

Pokippsie was my father's reply.

Thats where Vassar is said my mother as my old man stiffled a yawn I wonder if there is a store there that would have a koop for David.

I doubt it they ever heard of him said my father dryly how much do they cost.

Well I dont know.

We entered Pokippsie at lenth and turned to the left up the main st and puled up in front of a big store where myself and mother went in and purchased a koop for my little brother and a kap for me witch only took a ½ hour dureing witch my father lost his temper and when we finley immerged he was barking like a dog and giveing the Vassar yell. 2 men come out of the store with us and tost the koop with the rest of the junk in the back seat and away we went.

Doesnt this look cute on him said my mother in regards to my new kap.

What of it replid my father with a grimace and with that we puled into Garrison.

Isnt this right acrost the river from West Point said my mother with a gastly look.

What of it replid my father tenderly and soon we found ourselfs in Peekskill.

This is where that young girl cousin of mine gos to school said my father from Philadelphia.

What of it said my mother with a loud cough and presently we stoped and bought 15 gals of gas.

I have got a fund of usefull information about every town we come to said my father admireingly for instants this is Harmon where they take off the steem engines and put on the electric bullgines.

My mother looked at him with ill consealed admiration.

And what do you know about this town she arsked as we frisked into Ossining.

Why this is Ossining where they take off the hair and put on the stripes replid my father qick as a flarsh and the next place is Tarry-town where John D. Rockefeller has a estate.

What is the name of the estate quired my mother breathlessly.

Socony I supose was the sires reply.

With that we honked into Yonkers and up the funny looking main st.

What a funny looking st said my mother and I always thorght it was the home of well to do peaple.

Well yes replid my father it is the home of the ruling class at lease Bill Klem the umpire and Bill Langford the referee lives here.

I will end my chapter on that one.

CHAPTER 9

THE BUREAU OF MANHATTAN

Isn't it about time said my mother as we past Spuyten Duyvil and entered the Bureau of Manhattan that we made our plans.

What plans said my father all my plans is all ready made.

Well then you might make me your confident suggested my mother with a quaint smirk.

Well then heres the dope uttered my father in a vage tone I am going to drop you at the 125 st station where you will only half to wait 2 hours and a ½ for the rest of the family as the train from the west is do at 350 at 125 st in the meen wile I will drive out to Grenitch with Bill and see if the house is ready and etc and if the other peaples train is on time you can catch the 4 4 and I an Bill will meet you at the Grenitch station.

If you have time get a qt of milk for David said my mother with a pail look.

What kind of milk arsked my dad.

Oh sour milk my mother screened.

As she was now in a pretty bad temper we will leave her to cool off for 2 hours and a ½ in the 125 st station and end this chapter.

CHAPTER 10

N. Y. TO GRENITCH 500.0

The lease said about my and my fathers trip from the Bureau of Manhattan to our new home the soonest mended. In some way ether I or he got balled up on the grand concorpse and next thing you know we was thretning to swoop down on Pittsfield.

Are you lost daddy I arsked tenderly.

Shut up he explained.

At lenth we doubled on our tracks and done much better as we finley hit New Rochelle and puled up along side a policeman with falling archs.

What road do I take for Grenitch Conn quired my father with poping eyes.

Take the Boston post replid the policeman.

I have all ready subscribed to one out of town paper said my father and steped on the gas so we will leave the flat foot gaping after us like a prune fed calf and end this chapter.

CHAPTER 11

HOW IT ENDED

True to our promise we were at the station in Grenitch when the costly train puled in from 125 st. Myself and father hoped out of the lordly moter and helped the bulk of the famly off of the train and I aloud our nurse and my 3 brothers to kiss me tho Davids left me rarther moist.

Did you have a hard trip my father arsked to our nurse shyly.

Why no she replid with a slite stager.

She did too said my mother they all acted like little devils.

Did you get Davids milk she said turning on my father.

Why no does he like milk my father replid with a gastly smirk.

We got lost mudder I said brokenly.

We did not screened my father and accidently cracked me in the shins with a stray foot.

To change the subjeck I turned my tensions on my brother Jimmie who is nerest my age.

I've seen our house Jimmie I said brokenly I got here first.

Yes but I slept all night on a train and you didnt replid Jimmie with a dirty look.

Nether did you said my brother John to Jimmie you was awake all night.

Were awake said my mother.

Me and David was awake all night and crid said my brother John.

But I only crid once the whole time said my brother Jimmie.

But I didnt cry at all did I I arsked to my mother.

So she replid with a loud cough Bill was a very very good boy.

So now we will say fare well to the characters in this book.

The Big Town

Very few authors (present company excepted) write books today. They write outlines for movies, easily converted into musical comedies—sometimes about the musical comedy they wrote about the musical comedy they wrote from the book—and it is all sold to ladies' magazines or run in the newspapers as a serial simultaneous with four big book club deals.

Ring Lardner didn't know about this monkey business but in 1947 one of his stories was made into a movie anyway. Stanley Kramer produced "So This Is New York" from the piece which follows. He had in mind to capture the 'flavor' of Lardner. The locale was the easy money town of the early twenties, but Mr. Kramer thought it best not to explain this to the audience; they thought it was some kind of funny-costume picture.

The casting was a work of art. Rudy Vallee, Hugh Herbert and Virginia Grey were in it; and the male lead got the job because he had read a lot of Lardner. He certainly hadn't read any Stanislavsky. The dialogue was fixed up so as not to be too amusing and the plot was shelved in favor of a series of sight gags.

What had set out to be a charming, quietly amusing gem of a motion picture emerged as a quietly amusing tax loss.

Dauntless, Mr. Kramer went on to enormous success in the medium.

The male lead, having carefully saved his salary from the picture, waited fifteen years and then wrote an introduction to this story.

PREFACE

This book deals with the adventures of a man and his wife and his sister-in-law who move to New York from a small Middle Western city. Because the writer and she who jokingly married him moved to New York from the Middle West, and because the writer has almost as many sisters-in-law as Solomon, several Nordic blondes have inquired whether the hero and heroines of the book are not

31

actually us. Fortunately most of the inquirers made the inquiry of me, the possessor of a notoriously sweet disposition. Two of them, however, asked the madam herself and were both shot down.

In the first place, the ladies of the book are supposed to have inherited enough money to make them and the gent more or less independent. Nothing like that in our family.

In the second place, the sister-in-law of the book has a hard time getting a man. The sisters-in-law in real life acquired permanent men while still in their nonage, you might say, and didn't have to move out of the Middle West to do it. And though none of them, perhaps, can be said to have done as well as the madam herself, at least from an esthetic standpoint, still it is something to boast of that none of them was obliged to go Democratic.

The contents of "The Big Town" were written mostly in a furnished house in Greenwich, Connecticut, and the author wishes to thank the rats for staying out of the room while he worked. It was winter time and the furnished house was a summer cottage, but we didn't realize that when we rented it. Nor, apparently, did the rats.

R. W. L.

March 1925.

I. Quick Returns

This is just a clipping from one of the New York papers; a little kidding piece that they had in about me two years ago. It says:

Hoosier Cleans Up in Wall Street. Employees of the brokerage firm of H. L. Krause & Co. are authority for the statement that a wealthy Indiana speculator made one of the biggest killings of the year in the Street yesterday afternoon. No very definite information was obtainable, as the Westerner's name was known to only one of the firm's employees, Francis Griffin, and he was unable to recall it last night.

You'd think I was a millionaire and that I'd made a sucker out of Morgan or something, but it's only a kid, see? If they'd of printed the true story they wouldn't of had no room left for that day's selections at Pimlico, and God knows that would of been fatal.

But if you want to hear about it, I'll tell you.

Well, the War wound up in the fall of 1918. The only member of my family that was killed in it was my wife's stepfather. He died of grief when it ended with him two hundred thousand dollars ahead. I immediately had a black bandage sewed round my left funny bone, but when they read us the will I felt all right again and tore it off. Our share was seventy-five thousand dollars. This was after we had paid for the inheritance tax and the amusement stamps on a horseless funeral.

My young sister-in-law, Katie, dragged down another seventy-five thousand dollars and the rest went to the old bird that had been foreman in Papa's factory. This old geezer had been starving to death for twenty years on the wages my stepfather-in-law give him, and the rest of us didn't make no holler when his name was read off for a small chunk, especially as he didn't have no teeth to enjoy it with.

I could of had this old foreman's share, maybe, if I'd of took advantage of the offer "Father" made me just before his daughter and I was married. I was over in Niles, Michigan, where they lived, and he insisted on me seeing his factory, which meant smelling it too. At that time I was knocking out about eighteen hundred dollars per annum selling cigars out of South Bend, and the old man said he would start me in with him at only about a fifty per cent cut, but we would also have the privilege of living with him and my wife's kid sister.

"They's a lot to be learnt about this business," he says, "but if you would put your mind on it you might work up to manager. Who knows?"

"My nose knows," I said, and that ended it.

The old man had lost some jack and went into debt a good many years ago, and for a long wile before the war begin about all as he was able to do was support himself and the two gals and pay off a part of what he owed. When the war broke loose and leather went up to hell and gone I and my wife thought he would get prosperous, but before this country went in his business went on about the same as usual.

"I don't know how they do it," he would say. "Other leather men is getting rich on contracts with the Allies, but I can't land one."

I guess he was trying to sell razor strops to Russia.

Even after we got into it and he begin to clean up, with the factory running day and night, all as we knew was that he had contracts with the U. S. Government, but he never confided in us what special stuff he was turning out. For all as we knew, it may of been medals for the ground navy.

Anyway, he must of been hitting a fast clip when the armistice come and ended the war for everybody but Congress! It's a cinch he wasn't amongst those arrested for celebrating too loud on the night of November 11. On the contrary they tell me that when the big news hit Niles the old bird had a stroke that he didn't never recover from, and though my wife and Katie hung round the bedside day after day in the hopes he would tell how much he was going to leave he was keeping his fiscal secrets for Oliver Lodge or somebody, and it wasn't till we seen the will that we knew we wouldn't have to work no more, which is pretty fair consolation even for the loss of a stepfather-in-law that ran a perfume mill.

"Just think," said my wife, "after all his financial troubles, Papa died a rich man!"

"Yes," I said to myself, "and a patriot. His only regret was that he just had one year to sell leather to his country."

If the old codger had of only been half as fast a salesman as his two daughters this clipping would of been right when it called me a wealthy Hoosier. It wasn't two weeks after we seen the will when the gals had disposed of the odor factory and the old home in Niles, Michigan. Katie, it seemed, had to come over to South Bend and live with us. That was agreeable to me, as I figured that if two could live on eighteen hundred dollars a year three could struggle along some way on the income off one hundred and fifty thousand dollars.

Only for me, though, Ella and Sister Kate would of shot the whole wad into a checking account so as the bank could enjoy it wile it lasted. I argued and fought and finally persuaded them to keep five thousand apiece for pin money and stick the rest into bonds.

The next thing they done was run over to Chi and buy all the party dresses that was vacant. Then they come back to South Bend and wished somebody would give a party. But between you and I the people we'd always ran round with was birds that was ready for bed as soon as they got home from the first show, and even though it had been printed in the *News-Times* that we had fell heir to a lot of jack we didn't have to hire no extra clerical help to tend to invitations received from the demi-Monday.

Finally Ella said we would start something ourselves. So she got a lot of invitations printed and sent them to all our friends that could read and hired a cater and a three-piece orchestra and everything, and made me buy a dress suit.

Well, the big night arrived and everybody come that had somebody to leave their baby with. The hosts wore evening clothes and the rest of the merrymakers prepared for the occasion with a shine or a clean collar. At first the cat had everybody's tongue, but when we sat down to eat some of the men folks begun to get comical. For instance, they would say to my wife or Katie, "Ain't you afraid you'll catch cold?" And they'd say to me, "I didn't know you was a waiter at the Oliver." Before the fish course everybody was in a fair way to get the giggles.

After supper the musicians come and hid behind a geranium and played a jazz. The entire party set out the first dance. The second was a solo between Katie and I, and I had the third with my wife. Then Kate and the Mrs. had one together, wile I tried holds with a lady named Mrs. Eckhart, who seemed to think that somebody had ast her to stand for a time exposure. The men folks had all drifted over behind the plant to watch the drummer, but after the stalemate between Mrs. Eckhart and I, I grabbed her husband and took him out in the kitchen and showed him a bottle of bourbon that I'd been saving for myself, in the hopes it would loosen him up. I told him it was my last bottle, but he must of thought I said it was the last bottle in the world. Anyway, when he got through they was international prohibition.

We went back in the ballroom and sure enough he ast Katie to dance. But he hadn't no sooner than win one fall when his wife challenged him to take her home and that started the epidemic that emptied the house of everybody but the orchestra and us. The orchestra had been hired to stay till midnight, which was still two hours and a half distance, so I invited both of the gals to dance with me at once, but it seems like they was surfeited with that sport and wanted to cry a little. Well, the musicians had ran out of blues, so I chased them home.

"Some party!" I said, and the two girls give me a dirty look like it was my fault or something. So we all went to bed and the ladies beat me to it on account of being so near ready.

Well, they wasn't no return engagements even hinted at and the only other times all winter when the gals had a chance to dress up was when some secondhand company would come to town with a show and I'd have to buy a box. We couldn't ask nobody to go with us on account of not having no friends that you could depend on to not come in their stocking feet.

Finally it was summer and the Mrs. said she wanted to get out of town.

"We've got to be fair to Kate," she said.

"We don't know no young unmarried people in South Bend and it's no fun for a girl to run round with her sister and brother-in-law. Maybe if we'd go to some resort somewheres we might get acquainted with people that could show her a good time."

So I hired us rooms in a hotel down to Wawasee Lake and we stayed there from the last of June till the middle of September. During that time I caught a couple of bass and Kate caught a couple of carp from Fort Wayne. She was getting pretty friendly with one of them when along come a wife that he hadn't thought was worth mentioning. The other bird was making a fight against the gambling fever, but one night it got the best of him and he dropped forty-five cents in the nickel machine and had to go home and make a new start.

About a week before we was due to leave I made the remark that it would seem good to be back in South Bend and get some home cooking.

"Listen!" says my wife. "I been wanting for a long wile to have a serious talk with you and now's as good a time as any. Here are I and Sis and you with an income of over eight thousand dollars a year and having pretty near as good a time as a bird with habitual boils. What's more, we can't never have a good time in South Bend, but have got to move somewheres where we are unknown."

"South Bend is certainly all of that," I said.

"No, it isn't," said the Mrs. "We're acquainted there with the kind of people that makes it impossible for us to get acquainted with the other kind. Kate could live there twenty years and never meet a decent man. She's a mighty attractive girl, and if she had a chance they's nobody she couldn't marry. But she won't never have a chance in South Bend. And they's no use of you saying 'Let her move,' because I'm going to keep her under my eye till she's married and settled down. So in other words, I want us to pack up and leave

South Bend for good and all and move somewheres where we'll get
something for our money."

"For instance, where?" I ast her.

"They's only one place," she said; "New York City."

"I've heard of it," said I, "but I never heard that people who
couldn't enjoy themselves on eight thousand a year in South Bend
could go to New York and tear it wide open."

"I'm not planning to make no big splurge," she says. "I just want
to be where they's Life and fun; where we can meet real live people.
And as for not living there on eight thousand, think of the families
that's already living there on half of that and less!"

"And think of the Life and fun they're having!" I says.

"But when you talk about eight thousand a year," said the Mrs.,
"why do we have to hold ourselves to that? We can sell some of those
bonds and spend a little of our principal. It will just be taking
money out of one investment and putting it in another."

"What other?" I ast her.

"Kate," said the wife. "You let me take her to New York and
manage her and I'll get her a husband that'll think our eight
thousand a year fell out of his vest."

"Do you mean," I said, "that you'd let a sister of yours marry for
money?"

"Well," she says, "I know a sister of hers that wouldn't mind if
she had."

So I argued and tried to compromise on somewheres in America,
but it was New York or nothing with her. You see, she hadn't never
been here, and all as she knew about it she'd read in books and
magazines, and for some reason another when authors starts in on
that subject it ain't very long till they've got a weeping jag. Besides,
what chance did I have when she kept reminding me that it was her
stepfather, not mine, that had croaked and made us all rich?

When I had give up she called Kate in and told her, and Kate
squealed and kissed us both, though God knows I didn't deserve no
remuneration or ask for none.

Ella had things all planned out. We was to sell our furniture and
take a furnished apartment here, but we would stay in some hotel till
we found a furnished apartment that was within reason.

"Our stay in some hotel will be life-long," I said.

The furniture, when we come to sell it, wasn't worth nothing, and that's what we got. We didn't have nothing to ship, as Ella found room for our books in my collar box. I got two lowers and an upper in spite of the Government, and with two taxi drivers and the baggageman thronging the station platform we pulled out of South Bend and set forth to see Life.

The first four miles of the journey was marked by considerable sniveling on the part of the heiresses.

"If it's so painful to leave the Bend let's go back," I said.

"It isn't leaving the Bend," said the Mrs., "but it makes a person sad to leave any place."

"Then we're going to have a muggy trip," said I. "This train stops pretty near everywheres to either discharge passengers or employees."

They were still sobbing when we left Mishawaka and I had to pull some of my comical stuff to get their minds off. My wife's mighty easy to look at when she hasn't got those watery blues, but I never did see a gal that knocked you for a goal when her nose was in full bloom.

Katie had brought a flock of magazines and started in on one of them at Elkhart, but it's pretty tough trying to read with the Northern Indiana mountains to look out at, to say nothing about the birds of prey that kept prowling up and down the aisle in search of a little encouragement or a game of rhum.

I noticed a couple of them that would of give a lady an answer if she'd approached them in a nice way, but I've done some traveling myself and I know what kind of men it is that allows themselves to be drawed into a flirtation on trains. Most of them has made the mistake of getting married some time, but they don't tell you that. They tell you that you and a gal they use to be stuck on is as much alike as a pair of corsets, and if you ever come to Toledo to give them a ring, and they hand you a telephone number that's even harder to get than the ones there are; and they ask you your name and address and write it down, and the next time they're up at the Elks they show it to a couple of the brothers and tell what they'd of done if they'd only been going all the way through.

"Say, I hate to talk about myself! But say!"

Well, I didn't see no sense in letting Katie waste her time on those kind of guys, so every time one of them looked our way I give him the fish eye and the non-stop signal. But this was my first long trip since the Government started to play train, and I didn't know the new rules in regards to getting fed; otherwise I wouldn't of never cleaned up in Wall Street.

In the old days we use to wait till the boys come through and announced that dinner was now being served in the dining car forward; then we'd saunter into the washroom and wash our hands if necessary, and ramble into the diner and set right down and enjoy as big a meal as we could afford. But the Government wants to be economical, so they've cut down the number of trains, to say nothing about the victuals; and they's two or three times as many people traveling, because they can't throw their money away fast enough at home. So the result is that the wise guys keeps an eye on their watch and when it's about twenty minutes to dinner time they race to the diner and park against the door and get quick action; and after they've eat the first time they go out and stand in the vestibule and wait till it's their turn again, as one Federal meal don't do nothing to your appetite only whet it, you might say.

Well, anyway, I was playing the old rules and by the time I and the two gals started for the diner we run up against the outskirts of a crowd pretty near as big as the ones that waits outside restaurant windows to watch a pancake turn turtle. About eight o'clock we got to where we could see the wealthy dining car conductor in the distance, but it was only about once every quarter of an hour that he raised a hand, and then he seemed to of had all but one of his fingers shot off.

I have often heard it said that the way to a man's heart is through his stomach, but every time I ever seen men and women keep waiting for their eats it was always the frail sex that give the first yelp, and personally I've often wondered what would of happened in the trenches Over There if ladies had of been occupying them when the rations failed to show up. I guess the bombs bursting round would of sounded like Sweet and Low sang by a quextette of deef mutes.

Anyway, my two charges was like wild animals, and when the con finally held up two fingers I didn't have no more chance or desire to stop them than as if they was the Center College Football Club right after opening prayer.

The pair of them was ushered to a table for four where they

already was a couple of guys making the best of it, and it wasn't more than ten minutes later when one of these birds dipped his bill in the finger bowl and staggered out, but by the time I took his place the other gent and my two gals was talking like barbers.

The guy was Francis Griffin that's in the clipping. But when Ella introduced us all as she said was, "This is my husband," without mentioning his name, which she didn't know at that time, or mine, which had probably slipped her memory.

Griffin looked at me like I was a side dish that he hadn't ordered. Well, I don't mind snubs except when I get them, so I ast him if he wasn't from Sioux City—you could tell he was from New York by his blue collar.

"From Sioux City!" he says. "I should hope not!"

"I beg your pardon," I said. "You look just like a photographer I used to know out there."

"I'm a New Yorker," he said, "and I can't get home too soon."

"Not on this train, you can't," I said.

"I missed the Century," he says.

"Well," I says with a polite smile, "the Century's loss is our gain."

"Your wife's been telling me," he says, "that you're moving to the Big Town. Have you ever been there?"

"Only for a few hours," I says.

"Well," he said, "when you've been there a few weeks you'll wonder why you ever lived anywhere else. When I'm away from old Broadway I always feel like I'm only camping out."

Both the gals smiled their appreciation, so I says: "That certainly expresses it. You'd ought to remember that line and give it to Georgie Cohan."

"Old Georgie!" he says. "I'd give him anything I got and welcome. But listen! Your wife mentioned something about a good hotel to stop at wile you're looking for a home. Take my advice and pick out one that's near the center of things; you'll more than make up the difference in taxi bills. I lived up in the Hundreds one winter and it averaged me ten dollars a day in cab fares."

"You must of had a pleasant home life," I says.

"Me!" he said. "I'm an old bachelor."

"Old!" says Kate, and her and the Mrs. both giggled.

"But seriously," he says, "if I was you I would go right to the Baldwin, where you can get a room for twelve dollars a day for the three of you; and you're walking distance from the theaters or shops or cafés or anywheres you want to go."

"That sounds grand!" said Ella.

"As far as I'm concerned," I said, "I'd just as lief be overseas from any of the places you've mentioned. What I'm looking for is a home with a couple of beds and a cookstove in the kitchen, and maybe a bath."

"But we want to see New York first," said Katie, "and we can do that better without no household cares."

"That's the idear!" says Griffin. "Eat, drink and be merry; to-morrow we may die."

"I guess we won't drink ourselves to death," I said, "not if the Big Town's like where we been living."

"Oh, say!" says our new friend. "Do you think little old New York is going to stand for prohibition? Why, listen! I can take you to thirty places to-morrow night where you can get all you want in any one of them."

"Let's pass up the other twenty-nine," I says.

"But that isn't the idear," he said. "What makes we New Yorkers sore is to think they should try and wish a law like that on Us. Isn't this supposed to be a government of the people, for the people and by the people?"

"People!" I said. "Who and the hell voted for prohibition if it wasn't the people?"

"The people of where?" he says. "A lot of small-time hicks that couldn't buy a drink if they wanted it."

"Including the hicks," I says, "that's in the New York State legislature."

"But not the people of New York City," he said. "And you can't tell me it's fair to spring a thing like this without warning on men that's got their fortunes tied up in liquor that they can't never get rid of now, only at a sacrifice."

"You're right," I said. "They ought to give them some warning. Instead of that they was never even a hint of what was coming off till Maine went dry seventy years ago."

"Maine?" he said. "What the hell is Maine?"

"I don't know," I said. "Only they was a ship or a boat or something named after it once, and the Spaniards sunk it and we sued them for libel or something."

"You're a smart Aleck," he said. "But speaking about war, where was you?"

"In the shipyards at South Bend painting a duck boat," I says. "And where was you?"

"I'd of been in there in a few more weeks," he says. "They wasn't no slackers in the Big Town."

"No," said I, "and America will never forget New York for coming in on our side."

By this time the gals was both giving me dirty looks, and we'd eat all we could get, so we paid our checks and went back in our car and I felt kind of apologetic, so I dug down in the old grip and got out a bottle of bourbon that a South Bend pal of mine, George Hull, had give me the day before; and Griffin and I went in the washroom with it and before the evening was over we was pretty near ready to forget national boundaries and kiss.

The old bourb' helped me save money the next morning, as I didn't care for no breakfast. Ella and Kate went in with Griffin and you could of knocked me over with a coupling pin when the Mrs. come back and reported that he'd insisted on paying the check. "He told us all about himself," she said. "His name is Francis Griffin and he's in Wall Street. Last year he cleared twenty thousand dollars in commissions and everything."

"He's a piker," I says. "Most of them never even think under six figures."

"There you go!" said the Mrs. "You never believe nothing. Why shouldn't he be telling the truth? Didn't he buy our breakfast?"

"I been buying your breakfast for five years," I said, "but that don't prove that I'm knocking out twenty thousand per annum in Wall Street."

Francis and Katie was setting together four or five seats ahead of us.

"You ought to of seen the way he looked at her in the diner," said the Mrs. "He looked like he wanted to eat her up."

"Everybody gets desperate in a diner these days," I said. "Did you and Kate go fifty-fifty with him? Did you tell him how much money we got?"

"I should say not!" says Ella. "But I guess we did say that you wasn't doing nothing just now and that we was going to New York to see Life, after being cooped up in a small town all these years.

And Sis told him you'd made us put pretty near everything in bonds, so all we can spend is eight thousand a year. He said that wouldn't go very far in the Big Town."

"I doubt if it ever gets as far as the Big Town," I said. "It won't if he makes up his mind to take it away from us."

"Oh, shut up!" said the Mrs. "He's all right and I'm for him, and I hope Sis is too. They'd make a stunning couple. I wished I knew what they're talking about."

"Well," I said, "they're both so reserved that I suppose they're telling each other how they're affected by cucumbers."

When they come back and joined us Ella said: "We was just re-marking how well you two young things seemed to be getting along. We was wondering what you found to say to one another all this time."

"Well," said Francis, "just now I think we were discussing you. Your sister said you'd been married five years and I pretty near felt like calling her a fibber. I told her you looked like you was just out of high school."

"I've heard about you New Yorkers before," said the Mrs. "You're always trying to flatter somebody."

"Not me," said Francis. "I never say nothing without meaning it."

"But sometimes," says I, "you'd ought to go on and explain the meaning."

Along about Schenectady my appetite begin to come back. I'd made it a point this time to find out when the diner was going to open, and then when it did our party fell in with the door.

"The wife tells me you're on the stock exchange," I says to Francis when we'd give our order.

"Just in a small way," he said. "But they been pretty good to me down there. I knocked out twenty thousand last year."

"That's what he told us this morning," said Ella.

"Well," said I, "they's no reason for a man to forget that kind of money between Rochester and Albany, even if this is a slow train."

"Twenty thousand isn't a whole lot in the Big Town," said Francis, "but still and all, I manage to get along and enjoy myself a little on the side."

"I suppose it's enough to keep one person," I said.

"Well," says Francis, "they say two can live as cheap as one."

Then him and Kate and Ella all giggled, and the waiter brought in a part of what he thought we'd ordered and we eat what we could and ast for the check. Francis said he wanted it and I was going to give in to him after a long hard struggle, but the gals reminded him that he'd paid for breakfast, so he said all right, but we'd all have to take dinner with him some night.

I and Francis set a wile in the washroom and smoked, and then he went to entertain the gals, but I figured the wife would go right to sleep like she always does when they's any scenery to look out at, so I stuck where I was and listened to what a couple of toothpick salesmen from Omsk would of done with the League of Nations if Wilson had of had sense enough to leave it to them.

Pulling into the Grand Central Station, Francis apologized for not being able to steer us over to the Baldwin and see us settled, but said he had to rush right downtown and report on his Chicago trip before the office closed. To see him when he parted with the gals you'd of thought he was going clear to Siberia to compete in the Olympic Games, or whatever it is we're in over there.

Well, I took the heiresses to the Baldwin and got a regular Big Town welcome. Ella and Kate set against a pillar wile I tried different tricks to make an oil-haired clerk look at me. New York hotel clerks always seem to of just dropped something and can't take their eyes off the floor. Finally I started to pick up the register and the guy give me the fish eye and ast what he could do for me.

"Well," I said, "when I come to a hotel I don't usually want to buy a straw hat."

He ast me if I had a reservation and I told him no.

"Can't do nothing for you then," he says. "Not till to-morrow morning anyway."

So I went back to the ladies.

"We'll have to go somewheres else," I said. "This joint's a joint. They won't give us nothing till to-morrow."

"But we can't go nowheres else," said the Mrs. "What would Mr. Griffin think, after recommending us to come here?"

"Well," I said, "if you think I'm going to park myself in a four-post chair all night just because we got a tip on a hotel from Wall Street you're Queen of the Cuckoos."

"Are you sure they haven't anything at all?" she says.

"Go ask them yourself!" I told her.

Well, she did, and in about ten minutes she come back and said everything was fixed.

"They'll give us a single room with bath and a double room with bath for fifteen dollars a day," she said.

" 'Give us' is good!" said I.

"I told him we'd wired for reservations and it wasn't our fault if the wire didn't get here," she said. "He was awfully nice."

Our rooms was right close to each other on the twenty-first floor. On the way up we decided by two votes to one that we'd dress for dinner. I was still monkeying with my tie when Katie come in for Ella to look her over. She had on the riskiest dress she'd bought in Chi.

"It's a pretty dress," she said, "but I'm afraid maybe it's too daring for just a hotel dining room."

Say we hadn't no sooner than set down in the hotel dining room when two other gals come in that made my team look like they was dressed for a sleigh ride with Doc Cook.

"I guess you don't feel so daring now," I said. "Compared to that baby in black you're wearing Jess Willard's ulster."

"Do you know what that black gown cost?" said Ella. "Not a cent under seven hundred dollars."

"That would make the material twenty-one hundred dollars a yard," I says.

"I'd like to know where she got it," said Katie.

"Maybe she cut up an old stocking," said I.

"I wished now," said the Mrs., "that we'd waited till we got here before we bought our clothes."

"You can bet one thing," says Katie. "Before we're ast out anywheres on a real party we'll have something to wear that isn't a year old."

"First thing to-morrow morning," says the Mrs., "we'll go over on Fifth Avenue and see what we can see."

"They'll only be two on that excursion," I says.

"Oh, we don't want you along," said Ella. "But I do wished you'd go to some first-class men's store and get some ties and shirts and things that don't look like an embalmer."

Well, after a wile one of the waiters got it in his head that maybe we hadn't came in to take a bath, so he fetched over a couple of programs.

"Never mind them," I says. "What's ready? We're in a hurry."

"The Long Island Duckling's very nice," he said. "And how about some nice au gratin potatoes and some nice lettuce and tomato salad with Thousand Island dressing, and maybe some nice French pastry?"

"Everything seems to be nice here," I said. "But wait a minute. How about something to drink?"

He give me a mysterious smile.

"Well," he said, "they're watching us pretty close here, but we serve something we call a cup. It comes from the bar and we're not supposed to know what the bartender puts in it."

"We'll try and find out," I said. "And rush this order through, as we're starved."

So he frisked out and was back again in less than an hour with another guy to help carry the stuff, though Lord knows he could of parked the three ducklings on one eyelid and the whole meal on the back of his hand. As for the cup, when you tasted it they wasn't no big mystery about what the bartender had put in it—a bottle of seltzer and a prune and a cherry and an orange peel, and maybe his finger. The check come to eighteen dollars and Ella made me tip him the rest of a twenty.

Before dinner the gals had been all for staying up a wile and looking the crowd over, but when we was through they both owned up that they hadn't slept much on the train and was ready for bed.

Ella and Kate was up early in the morning. They had their breakfast without me and went over to stun Fifth Avenue. About ten o'clock Francis phoned to say he'd call round for us that evening and take us to dinner. The gals didn't get back till late in the afternoon, but from one o'clock on I was too busy signing for packages to get lonesome. Ella finally staggered in with some more and I told her about our invitation.

"Yes, I know," she said.

"How do you know?" I ast her.

"He told us," she said. "We had to call him up to get a check cashed."

"You got plenty nerve!" I said. "How does he know your checks is good?"

"Well, he likes us," she said. "You'll like us too when you see us in some of the gowns we bought."

"Some!" I said.

"Why, yes," said the Mrs. "You don't think a girl can go round in New York with one evening dress!"

"How much money did you spend to-day?" I ast her.

"Well," she said, "things are terribly high—that is, nice things. And then, of course, there's suits and hats and things besides the gowns. But remember, it's our money. And as I told you, it's an investment. When young Mister Wall Street sees Kate to-night it'll be all off."

"I didn't call on you for no speech," I says. "I ast you how much you spent."

"Not quite sixteen hundred dollars."

I was still out on my feet when the phone rung. Ella answered it and then told me it was all right about the tickets.

"What tickets?" I said.

"Why, you see," she says, "after young Griffin fixing us up with that check and inviting us to dinner and everything we thought it would be nice to take him to a show to-night. Kate wanted to see *Ups and Downs,* but the girl said she couldn't get us seats for it. So I ast that nice clerk that took care of us yesterday and he's fixed it."

"All right," I said, "but when young Griffin starts a party, why and the hell not let him finish it?"

"I suppose he would of took us somewheres after dinner," says the Mrs., "but I couldn't be sure. And between you and I, I'm positive that if he and Kate is throwed together a whole evening, and her looking like she'll look to-night, we'll get mighty quick returns on our investment."

Well, to make a short story out of it, the gals finally got what they called dressed, and I wished Niles, Michigan, or South Bend could of seen them. If boxers wore bathing skirts I'd of thought I was in the ring with a couple of bantams.

"Listen!" I said. "What did them two girdles cost?"

"Mine was three hundred and Kate's three hundred and fifty," said the Mrs.

"Well," I says, "don't you know that you could of went to any cut-rate drugstore and wrapped yourself up just as warm in thirty-two cents' worth of adhesive tape? Listen!" I said. "What's the use of me paying a burglar for tickets to a show like *Ups and Downs* when I could set round here and look at you for nothing?"

Then Griffin rung up to say that he was waiting and we went downstairs. Francis took us in the same dining room we'd been in the night before, but this time the waiters all fought each other to get to us first.

I don't know what we eat, as Francis had something on the hip that kind of dazed me for a wile, but afterwards I know we got a taxi and went to the theater. The tickets was there in my name and only cost me thirteen dollars and twenty cents.

Maybe you seen this show wile it was here. Some show! I didn't read the program to see who wrote it, but I guess the words was by Noah and the music took the highest awards at the St. Louis Fair. They had a good system on the gags. They didn't spring none but what you'd heard all your life and knew what was coming, so instead of just laughing at the point you laughed all the way through it.

I said to Ella, I said, "I bet the birds that run this don't want prohibition. If people paid $3.30 apiece and come in here sober they'd come back the next night with a machine gun."

"I think it's dandy," she says, "and you'll notice every seat is full. But listen! Will you do something for me? When this is over suggest that we go up to the Castle Roof for a wile."

"What for?" I said. "I'm sleepy."

"Just this once," she says. "You know what I told you about quick returns!"

Well, I give in and made the suggestion, and I never seen people so easy coaxed. I managed to get a ringside table for twenty-two bucks. Then I ast the boy how about getting a drink and he ast me if I knew any of the head waiters.

"I do," says Francis. "Tell Hector it's for Frank Griffin's party."

So we ordered four Scotch highballs and some chicken à la King, and then the dinge orchestra tore loose some jazz and I was expecting a dance with Ella, but before she could ask me Francis had ast her, and I had one with Kate.

"Your Wall Street friend's a fox," I says, "asking an old married lady to dance so's to stand in with the family."

"Old married lady!" said Kate. "Sis don't look a day over sixteen to-night."

"How are you and Francis coming?" I ast her.

"I don't know," she says. "He acts kind of shy. He hasn't hardly said a word to me all evening."

Well, they was another jazz and I danced it with Ella; then her and Francis had another one and I danced again with Kate. By this time our food and refreshments was served and the show was getting ready to start.

I could write a book on what I don't remember about that show. The first sip of their idear of a Scotch highball put me down for the count of eight and I was practic'lly unconscious till the waiter woke me up with a check for forty bucks.

Francis seen us home and said he would call up again soon, and when Ella and I was alone I made the remark that I didn't think he'd ever strain his larnix talking to Kate.

"He acts gun-shy when he's round her," I says. "You seem to be the one that draws him out."

"It's a good sign," she says. "A man's always embarrassed when he's with a girl he's stuck on. I'll bet you anything you want to bet that within a week something'll happen."

Well, she win. She'd of win if she'd of said three days instead of a week. It was a Wednesday night when we had that party, and on the Friday Francis called up and said he had tickets for the Palace. I'd been laid up mean wile with the Scotch influenza, so I told the gals to cut me out. I was still awake yet when Ella come in a little after midnight.

"Well," I asked, "are we going to have a brother-in-law?"

"Mighty soon," she says.

So I ast her what had come off.

"Nothing—to-night," she says, "except this: He wrote me a note. He wants me to go with him to-morrow afternoon and look at a little furnished apartment. And he ast me if I could come without Sis, as he wants to pull a surprise on her. So I wondered if you couldn't think of some way to fix it so's I can sneak off for a couple of hours."

"Sure!" I said. "Just tell her you didn't sleep all night and you're wore out and want to take a nap."

So she pulled this gag at lunch Saturday and Katie said she was tired too. She went up to her room and Ella snuck out to keep her date with Francis. In less than an hour she romped into our room again and throwed herself on the bed.

"Well," I says, "it must of been a little apartment if it didn't only take you this long to see it."

"Oh, shut up!" she said. "I didn't see no apartment. And don't say a word to me or I'll scream."

Well, I finally got her calmed down and she give me the details. It seems that she'd met Francis, and he'd got a taxi and they'd got in the taxi and they hadn't no sooner than got in the taxi when Francis give her a kiss.

"Quick returns," I says.

"I'll kill you if you say another word!" she says.

So I managed to keep still.

Well, I didn't know Francis' home address, and Wall Street don't run Sundays, so I spent the Sabbath training on a quart of rye that a bell hop picked up at a bargain sale somewheres for fifteen dollars. Mean wile Katie had been let in on the secret and staid in our room all day, moaning like a prune-fed calf.

"I'm afraid to leave her alone," says Ella. "I'm afraid she'll jump out the window."

"You're easily worried," I said. "What I'm afraid of is that she won't."

Monday morning finally come, as it generally always does, and I told the gals I was going to some first-class men's store and buy myself some ties and shirts that didn't look like a South Bend embalmer.

So the only store I knew about was H. L. Krause & Co. in Wall Street, but it turned out to be an office. I ast for Mr. Griffin and they ast me my name and I made one up, Sam Hall or something, and out he come.

If I told you the rest of it you'd think I was bragging. But I did bust a few records. Charley Brickley and Walter Eckersall both kicked five goals from field in one football game, and they was a bird named Robertson or something out at Purdue that kicked seven. Then they was one of the old-time ball players, Bobby Lowe or Ed Delehanty, that hit four or five home runs in one afternoon. And out to Toledo that time Dempsey made big Jess set down seven times in one round.

Well, listen! In a little less than three minutes I floored this bird nine times and I kicked him for eight goals from the field and I hit him over the fence for ten home runs. Don't talk records to me!

So that's what they meant in the clipping about a Hoosier cleaning up in Wall Street. But it's only a kid, see?

II. Ritchey

Well, I was just getting used to the Baldwin and making a few friends round there when Ella suddenly happened to remember that it was Griffin who had recommended it. So one day, wile Kate was down to the chiropodist's, Ella says it was time for us to move and she had made up her mind to find an apartment somewheres.

"We could get along with six rooms," she said. "All as I ask is for it to be a new building and on some good street, some street where the real people lives."

"You mean Fifth Avenue," said I.

"Oh, no," she says. "That's way over our head. But we'd ought to be able to find something, say, on Riverside Drive." "A six room apartment," I says, "in a new building on Riverside Drive? What was you expecting to pay?"

"Well," she said, "you remember that time I and Kate visited the Kitchells in Chi? They had a dandy apartment on Sheridan Road, six rooms and brand new. It cost them seventy-five dollars a month. And Sheridan Road is Chicago's Riverside Drive."

"Oh, no," I says. "Chicago's Riverside Drive is Canal Street. But listen: Didn't the Kitchells have their own furniture?"

"Sure they did," said Ella.

"And are you intending to furnish us all over complete?" I asked her.

"Of course not," she says. "I expect to get a furnished apartment. But that don't only make about twenty-five dollars a month difference."

"Listen," I said: "It was six years ago that you visited the Kitchells; beside which, that was Chi and this is the Big Town. If you find a six room furnished apartment for a hundred dollars in New York City to-day, we'll be on Pell Street in Chinatown, and maybe Katie can marry into a laundry or a joss house."

"Well," said the wife, "even if we have to go to $150 a month for a place on the Drive, remember half of it's my money and half of it's Kate's, and none of it's yours."

"You're certainly letter perfect in that speech," I says.

"And further and more," said Ella, "you remember what I told you the other day. Wile one reason we moved to New York was to see Life, the main idear was to give Kate a chance to meet real men. So every nickel we spend making ourself look good is just an investment."

"I'd rather feel good than look good," I says, "and I hate to see us spending so much money on a place to live that they won't be nothing left to live on. For three or four hundred a month you might get a joint on the Drive with a bed and two chairs, but I can't drink furniture."

"This trip wasn't planned as no spree for you," says Ella. "On the other hand, I believe Sis would stand a whole lot better show of landing the right kind of a man if the rumor was to get out that her brother-in-law stayed sober once in a wile."

"Well," I said, "I don't think my liberal attitude on the drink question affected the results of our deal in Wall Street. That investment would of turned out just as good whether I was a teetotaler or a lush."

"Listen," she says: "The next time you mention ancient history like that, I'll make a little investment in a lawyer. But what's the use of arguing? I and Kate has made up our mind to do things our own way with our own money, and to-day we're going up on the Drive with a real estate man. We won't pay no more than we can afford. All as we want is a place that's good enough and big enough for Sis to entertain her gentleman callers in it, and she certainly can't do that in this hotel."

"Well," I says, "all her gentleman callers that's been around here in the last month, she could entertain them in one bunch in a telephone booth."

"The reason she's been let alone so far," says the Mrs., "is because I won't allow her to meet the kind of men that stays at hotels. You never know who they are."

"Why not?" I said. "They've all got to register their name when they come in, which is more than you can say for people that lives in $100 apartments on Riverside Drive."

Well, my arguments went so good that for the next three days the two gals was on a home-seekers' excursion and I had to spend my time learning the eastern intercollegiate kelly pool rules up to Doyle's. I win about seventy-five dollars.

When the ladies come home the first two nights they was all wore out and singing the landlord blues, but on the third afternoon they busted in all smiles.

"We've found one," says Ella. "Six rooms, too."

"Where at?" I asked her.

"Just where we wanted it," she says. "On the Drive. And it fronts right on the Hudson."

"No!" I said. "I thought they built them all facing the other way."

"It almost seems," said Katie, "like you could reach out and touch New Jersey."

"It's what you might call a near beer apartment," I says.

"And it's almost across the street from Grant's Tomb," says Ella.

"How many rooms has he got?" I says.

"We was pretty lucky," said Ella. "The people that had it was forced to go south for the man's health. He's a kind of a cripple. And they decided to sublet it furnished. So we got a bargain."

"Come on," I says. "What price?"

"Well," she says, "they don't talk prices by the month in New York. They give you the price by the year. So it sounds a lot more than it really is. We got it for $4,000."

"Sweet patootie!" I said. "That's only half your income."

"Well, what of it?" says Ella. "It won't only be for about a year and it's in the nicest kind of a neighborhood and we can't meet nothing only the best kind of people. You know what I told you."

And she give me a sly wink.

Well, it seems like they had signed up a year's lease and paid a month's rent in advance, so what was they left for me to say? All I done was make the remark that I didn't see how we was going to come even close to a trial balance.

"Why not?" said Katie. "With our rent paid we can get along easy on $4,000 a year if we economize."

"Yes," I said. "You'll economize just like the rest of the Riverside Drivers, with a couple of servants and a car and four or five new evening dresses a month. By the end of six months the bank'll be figuring our account in marks."

"What do you mean 'our' account?" says Ella.

"But speaking about a car," said Katie, "do you suppose we could get a good one cheap?"

"Certainly," I said. "They're giving away the good ones for four double coupons."

"But I mean an inexpensive one," says Kate.

"You can't live on the River and ride in a flivver," I said. "Besides, the buses limp right by the door."

"Oh, I love the buses!" said Ella.

"Wait till you see the place," says Katie to me. "You'll go simply wild! They's a colored boy in uniform to open the door and they's two elevators."

"How high do we go?" I said.

"We're on the sixth floor," says Katie.

"I should think we could get that far in one elevator," I says.

"What was it the real estate man told us?" said Ella. "Oh, yes, he said the sixth floor was the floor everybody tried to get on."

"It's a wonder he didn't knock it," I said.

Well, we was to have immediate possession, so the next morning we checked out of this joint and swooped up on the Drive. The colored boy, who I nicknamed George, helped us up with the wardrobe. Ella had the key and inside of fifteen minutes she'd found it.

We hadn't no sooner than made our entree into our new home when I knew what ailed the previous tenant. He'd crippled himself stumbling over the furniture. The living room was big enough to stage the high hurdles, and that's what was in it, only they'd planted them every two feet apart. If a stew with the blind staggers had of walked in there in the dark, the folks on the floor below would of thought he'd knocked the head pin for a goal.

"Come across the room," said Ella, "and look at the view."

"I guess I can get there in four downs," I said, "but you better have a substitute warming up."

"Well," she says, when I'd finally fell acrost the last white chalk mark, "what do you think of it?"

"It's a damn pretty view," I says, "but I've often seen the same view from the top of a bus for a thin dime."

Well, they showed me over the whole joint and it did look O. K., but not $4,000 worth. The best thing in the place was a half full bottle of rye in the kitchen that the cripple hadn't gone south with. I did.

We got there at eleven o'clock in the morning, but at three p.m. the gals was still hanging up their Follies costumes, so I beat it out and over to Broadway and got myself a plate of pea soup. When I come back, Ella and Katie was laying down exhausted. Finally I told Ella that I was going to move back to the hotel unless they served meals in this dump, so her and Kate got up and went marketing. Well, when you move from Indiana to the Big Town, of course you can't be expected to do your own cooking, so what we had that night was from the delicatessen, and for the next four days we lived on dill pickles with dill pickles.

"Listen," I finally says: "The only reason I consented to leave the hotel was in the hopes I could get a real home cook meal once in a wile and if I don't get a real home cook meal once in a while, I leave this dive."

"Have a little bit of patience," says Ella. "I advertised in the paper for a cook the day before we come here, the day we rented this apartment. And I offered eight dollars a week."

"How many replies did you get?" I asked her.

"Well," she said, "I haven't got none so far, but it's probably too soon to expect any."

"What did you advertise in, the world almanac?" I says.

"No, sir," she says. "I advertised in the two biggest New York papers, the ones the real estate man recommended."

"Listen," I said: "Where do you think you're at, in Niles, Michigan? If you get a cook here for eight dollars a week, it'll be a one-armed leper that hasn't yet reached her teens."

"What would you do, then?" she asked me.

"I'd write to an employment agency," I says, "and I'd tell them we'll pay good wages."

So she done that and in three days the phone rung and the agency said they had one prospect on hand and did we want her to come out and see us. So Ella said we did and out come a colleen for an interview. She asked how much we was willing to pay.

"Well," said Ella, "I'd go as high as twelve dollars. Or I'd make it fifteen if you done the washing."

Kathleen Mavourneen turned her native color.

"Well," I said, "how much do you want?"

"I'll work for ninety dollars a month," she said, only I can't get the brogue. "That's for the cookin' only. No washin'. And I would have to have a room with a bath and all day Thursdays and Sunday evenin's off."

"Nothing doing," said Ella, and the colleen started for the door.

"Wait a minute," I says. "Listen: Is that what you gals is getting in New York?"

"We're a spalpeen if we ain't," says the colleen bawn.

Well, I was desperate, so I called the wife to one side and says: "For heaven's sakes, take her on a month's trial. I'll pay the most of it with a little piece of money I picked up last week down to Doyle's. I'd rather do that than get dill pickled for a goal."

"Could you come right away?" Ella asked her.

"Not for a couple days," says Kathleen.

"It's off, then," I said. "You cook our supper to-night or go back to Greece."

"Well," she says, "I guess I could make it if I hurried."

So she went away and come back with her suitcase, and she cooked our supper that night. And Oh darlint!

Well, Beautiful Katie still had the automobile bug and it wasn't none of my business to steer her off of it and pretty near every day she would go down to the "row" and look them over. But every night she'd come home whistling a dirge.

"I guess I've seen them all," she'd say, "but they're too expensive or else they look like they wasn't."

But one time we was all coming home in a taxi from a show and come up Broadway and all of a sudden she yelled for the driver to stop.

"That's a new one in that window," she says, "and one I never see before."

Well, the dive was closed at the time and we couldn't get in, but she insisted on going down there the first thing in the morning and I and Ella must go along. The car was a brand new model Bam Eight.

"How much?" I asked him.

"Four thousand," he says.

"When could I get one?" says Katie.

"I don't know," said the salesman.

"What do you mean?" I asked him. "Haven't they made none of them?"

"I don't know," says the salesman. "This is the only one we got."

"Has anybody ever rode in one?" I says.

"I don't know," said the guy.

So I asked him what made it worth four thousand.

"Well," he says, "what made this lady want one?"

"I don't know," I said.

"Could I have this one that's on the floor?" says Katie.

"I don't know," said the salesman.

"Well, when do you think I could get one?" says Katie.

"We can't promise no deliveries," says the salesman.

Well, that kind of fretted me, so I asked him if they wasn't a salesman we could talk to.

"You're talking to one," he said.

"Yes, I know," said I. "But I used to be a kind of a salesman myself, and when I was trying to sell things, I didn't try and not sell them."

"Yes," he says, "but you wasn't selling automobiles in New York in 1920. Listen," he says: "I'll be frank with you. We got the New York agency for this car and was glad to get it because it sells for four thousand and anything that sells that high, why the people will eat up, even if it's a pearl-handle ketchup bottle. If we ever do happen to get a consignment of these cars, they'll sell like oil stock. The last word we got from the factory was that they'd send us three cars next September. So that means we'll get two cars a year from next October and if we can spare either of them, you can have one."

So then he begin to yawn and I said, "Come on, girls," and we got a taxi and beat it home. And I wouldn't of said nothing about it, only if Katie had of been able to buy her Bam, what come off might of never came off.

It wasn't only two nights later when Ella come in from shopping all excited. "Well," she said, "talk about experiences! I just had a ride home and it wasn't in a street car and it wasn't in a taxi and it wasn't on the subway and it wasn't on a bus."

"Let's play charades," said I.

"Tell us, Sis," says Katie.

"Well," said the wife, "I was down on Fifth Avenue, waiting for a bus, and all of a sudden a big limousine drew up to the curb with a livery chauffeur, and a man got out of the back seat and took off his hat and asked if he couldn't see me home. And of course I didn't pay no attention to him."

"Of course not," I said.

"But," says Ella, "he says, 'Don't take no offense. I think we're next door neighbors. Don't you live acrost the hall on the sixth floor of the Lucius?' So of course I had to tell him I did."

"Of course," I said.

"And then he said," says Ella, " 'Is that your sister living with you?' 'Yes,' I said, 'she lives with my husband and I.' 'Well,' he says, 'if you'll get in and let me take you home, I'll tell you what a beautiful girl I think she is.' So I seen then that he was all right, so I got in and come home with him. And honestly, Sis, he's just wild about you!"

"What is he like?" says Katie.

"He's stunning," says the wife. "Tall and wears dandy clothes and got a cute mustache that turns up."

"How old?" says Kate, and the Mrs. kind of stalled.

"Well," she said, "he's the kind of a man that you can't tell how old they are, but he's not old. I'd say he was, well, maybe he's not even that old."

"What's his name?" asked Kate.

"Trumbull," said the Mrs. "He said he was keeping bachelor quarters, but I don't know if he's really a bachelor or a widower. Anyway, he's a dandy fella and must have lots of money. Just imagine living alone in one of these apartments!"

"Imagine living in one of them whether you're a bachelor or a Mormon," I says.

"Who said he lived alone?" asked Katie.

"He did," says the Mrs. "He told me that him and his servants had the whole apartment to themselves. And that's what makes it so nice, because he's asked the three of us over there to dinner to-morrow night."

"What makes it so nice?" I asked her.

"Because it does," said Ella, and you can't ever beat an argument like that.

So the next night the two girls donned their undress uniforms and made me put on the oysters and horse radish and we went acrost the hall to meet our hero. The door was opened by a rug peddler and he showed us into a twin brother to our own living room, only you could get around it without being Houdini.

"Mr. Trumbull will be right out," said Omar.

The ladies was shaking like an aspirin leaf, but in a few minutes, in come mine host. However old Ella had thought he wasn't, she was wrong. He'd seen baseball when the second bounce was out. If he'd of started his career as a barber in Washington, he'd of tried to wish a face massage on Zachary Taylor. The only thing young about him was his teeth and his clothes. His dinner suit made me feel like I was walking along the station platform at Toledo, looking for hot boxes.

"Ah, here you are!" he says. "It's mighty nice of you to be neighborly. And so this is the young sister. Well," he says to me, "you had your choice, and as far as I can see, it was heads you win and tails you win. You're lucky."

So when he'd spread all the salve, he rung the bell and in come Allah with cocktails. I don't know what was in them, but when Ella and Katie had had two apiece, they both begin to trill.

Finally we was called in to dinner and every other course was hootch. After the solid and liquid diet, he turned on the steam piano and we all danced. I had one with Beautiful Katie and the rest of them was with my wife, or, as I have nicknamed them, quarrels. Well, the steam run out of three of us at the same time, the piano inclusive, and Ella sat down in a chair that was made for Eddie Foy's family and said how comfortable it was.

"Yes," says Methuselah, "that's my favorite chair. And I bet you wouldn't believe me if I told you how much it cost."

"Oh, I'd like to know," says Ella.

"Two hundred dollars," says mine host.

"Do you still feel comfortable?" I asked her.

"Speaking about furniture," said the old bird, "I've got a few bits that I'm proud of. Would you like to take a look at them?"

So the gals said they would and we had to go through the entire apartment, looking at bits. The best bits I seen was tastefully wrapped up in kegs and cases. It seemed like every time he opened a drawer, a cork popped up. He was a hundred per cent proofer than the governor of New Jersey. But he was giving us a lecture on the furniture itself, not the polish.

"I picked up this dining room suit for eighteen hundred," he says.

"Do you mean the one you've got on?" I asked him, and the gals give me a dirty look.

"And this rug," he says, stomping on an old rag carpet. "How much do you suppose that cost?"

It was my first guess, so I said fifty dollars.

"That's a laugh," he said. "I paid two thousand for that rug."

"The guy that sold it had the laugh," I says.

Finally he steered us into his bedroom.

"Do you see that bed?" he says. "That's Marie Antoinette's bed. Just a cool thousand."

"What time does she usually get in?" I asked him.

"Here's my hobby," he said, opening up a closet, "dressing gowns and bathrobes."

Well, they was at least a dozen of them hanging on hangers. They was all colors of the rainbow including the Scandinavian. He dragged one down that was redder than Ella's and Katie's cheeks.

"This is my favorite bathrobe," he said. "It's Rose D. Barry."

So I asked him if he had all his household goods and garments named after some dame.

"This bathrobe cost me an even two hundred," he says.

"I always take baths bare," I said. "It's a whole lot cheaper."

"Let's go back in the living room," says Katie.

"Come on," said Ella, tugging me by the sleeve.

"Wait a minute," I says to her. "I don't know how much he paid for his toothbrush."

Well, when we got back in the living room, the two gals acted kind of drowsy and snuggled up together on the davenport and I and the old bird was left to ourself.

"Here's another thing I didn't show you," he says, and pulls a pair of African golf balls out of a drawer in his desk. "These dice is real ivory and they cost me twelve and a half berries."

"You mean up to now," I said.

"All right," he said. "We'll make it a twenty-five dollar limit."

Well, I didn't have no business in a game with him, but you know how a guy gets sometimes. So he took them first and rolled a four.

"Listen," I says: "Do you know how many times Willard set down in the first round?"

And sure enough he sevened.

"Now solid ivory dice," I said, "how many days in the week?"

So out come a natural. And as sure as I'm setting here, I made four straight passes with the whole roll riding each time and with all that wad parked on the two thousand dollar rug, I shot a five and a three. "Ivory," I said, "we was invited here to-night, so don't make me pay for the entertainment. Show me eighter from Decatur."

And the lady from Decatur showed.

Just then they was a stir on the davenport, and Ella woke up long enough to make the remark that we ought to go home. It was the first time she ever said it in the right place.

"Oh," I says, "I've got to give Mr. Trumbull a chance to get even."

But I wasn't in earnest.

"Don't bother about that," said Old Noah. "You can accommodate me some other time."

"You're certainly a sport," I says.

"And thanks for a wonderful time," said Ella. "I hope we'll see you again soon."

"Soon is to-morrow night," said mine host. "I'm going to take you all up the river to a place I know."

"Well," I says to Katie, when we was acrost the hall and the door shut, "how do you like him?"

"Oh, shut up!" says Katie.

So the next night he come over and rung our bell and said Ritchey was waiting with the car and would we come down when we was ready. Well, the gals had only had all day to prepare for the trip, so in another half hour they had their wraps on and we went downstairs. They wasn't nothing in front but a Rools-Royce with a livery chauffeur that looked like he'd been put there by a rubber stamp.

"What a stunning driver!" said Katie when we'd parked ourself in the back seat.

"Ritchey?" says mine host. "He is a nice looking boy, but better than that, he's a boy I can trust."

Well, anyway, the boy he could trust took us out to a joint called the Indian Inn where you wouldn't of never knew they was an eighteenth amendment only that the proprietor was asking twenty berries a quart for stuff that used to cost four. But that didn't seem to bother Methuselah and he ordered two of them. Not only that but he got us a table so close to the orchestra that the cornet player thought we was his mute.

"Now, what'll we eat?" he says.

So I looked at the program and the first item I seen was "Guinea Hen, $4.50."

"That's what Katie'll want," I says to myself, and sure enough that's what she got.

Well, we eat and then we danced and we danced and we danced, and finally along about eleven I and Ella was out on the floor pretending like we was enjoying ourself, and we happened to look over to the table and there was Katie and Trumbull setting one out and to look at either you could tell that something was wrong.

"Dance the next one with her," says Ella, "and find out what's the matter."

So I danced the next one with Katie and asked her.

"He squeezed my hand," she says. "I don't like him."

"Well," said I, "if you'd of ordered guinea hen on me I wouldn't of stopped at your hand. I'd of went at your throat."

"I've got a headache," she says. "Take me out to the car."

So they was nothing to it but I had to take her out to the car and come back and tell Ella and Trumbull that she wasn't feeling any too good and wanted to go home.

"She don't like me," says the old guy. "That's the whole trouble."

"Give her time," says Ella. "Remember she's just a kid."

"Yes, but what a kid!" he says.

So then he paid the check without no competition and we went out and clumb in the big limmie. Katie was pretending like she was asleep and neither Ella or Trumbull acted like they wanted to talk, so the conversation on the way home was mostly one-sided, with me in the title role. Katie went in the apartment without even thanking mine host for the guinea hen, but he kept Ella and I outside long enough to say that Ritchey and the car was at our service any time we wanted them.

So Ella told her that the next noon at breakfast. "And you'd ought to be ashamed of yourself," says Ella, "for treating a man like that like that."

"He's too fresh," says Katie.

"Well," said Ella, "if he was a little younger, you wouldn't mind him being fresh."

"No," said Katie, "if he was fresh, I wouldn't care if he was fresh. But what's the number of the garage?"

And she didn't lose no time taking advantage of the old bird. That same afternoon it seemed she had to go shopping and the bus wasn't good enough no more. She was out in Trumbull's limmie from two o'clock till pretty near seven. The old guy himself come to our place long about five and wanted to know if we knew where she was at. "I haven't no idear," said Ella. "I expected her home long ago. Did you want to use the car?"

"What's the difference," I said, "if he wanted to use the car or not? He's only the owner."

"Well," says Trumbull, "when I make an offer I mean it, and that little girl is welcome to use my machine whenever she feels like it."

So Ella asked him to stay to dinner and he said he would if we'd allow him to bring in some of his hootch, and of course I kicked on that proposition, but he insisted. And when Katie finally did get home, we was all feeling good and so was she and you'd never of thought they'd been any bad feelings the night before.

Trumbull asked her what she'd been buying.

"Nothing," she says. "I was looking at dresses, but they want too much money."

"You don't need no dresses," he says.

"No, of course not," said Katie. "But lots of girls is wearing them."

"Where did you go?" said Ella.

"I forget," says Katie. "What do you say if we play cards?"

So we played rummy till we was all blear-eyed and the old guy left, saying we'd all go somewheres next day. After he'd gone Ella begin to talk serious.

"Sis," she says, "here's the chance of a lifetime. Mr. Trumbull's head over heels in love with you and all as you have to do is encourage him a little. Can't you try and like him?"

"They's nobody I have more respect for," said Katie, "unless it's George Washington."

And then she give a funny laugh and run off to bed.

"I can't understand Sis no more," said Ella, when we was alone.

"Why not?" I asked her.

"Why, look at this opportunity staring her in the face," says the Mrs.

"Listen," I said: "The first time I stared you in the face, was you thinking about opportunity?"

Well, to make a short story out of it, I was the only one up in the house the next morning when Kathleen said we had a caller. It was the old boy.

"I'm sorry to be so early," he says, "but I just got a telegram and it means I got to run down to Washington for few days. And I wanted to tell you that wile I'm gone Ritchey and the car is at your service."

So I thanked him and he said good-by and give his regards to the Mrs. and especially Katie, so when they got up I told them about it and I never seen a piece of bad news received so calm as Katie took it.

"But now he's gone," I said at the breakfast table, "why not the three of us run out to Bridgeport and call on the Wilmots?"

They're cousins of mine.

"Oh, fine!" said Ella.

"Wait a minute," says Katie. "I made a kind of an engagement with a dressmaker for to-day."

Well, as I say, to make a short story out of it, it seems like she'd made engagements with the dressmaker every day, but they wasn't no dresses ever come home.

In about a week Trumbull come back from Washington and the first thing he done was look us up and we had him in to dinner and I don't remember how the conversation started, but all of a sudden we was on the subject of his driver, Ritchey.

"A great boy," says Trumbull, "and a boy you can trust. If I didn't like him for nothing else, I'd like him for how he treats his family."

"What family?" says Kate.

"Why," says Trumbull, "his own family: his wife and two kids."

"My heavens!" says Katie, and kind of fell in a swoon.

So it seems like we didn't want to live there no more and we moved back to the Baldwin, having sublet the place on the Drive for three thousand a year.

So from then on, we was paying a thousand per annum for an apartment we didn't live in two weeks. But as I told the gals, we was getting pretty near as much for our money as the people that rented New York apartments and lived in them, too.

III. Lady Perkins

Along the first week in May they was a couple hot days, and Katie can't stand the heat. Or the cold, or the medium. Anyway, when it's hot she always says: "I'm simply stifling." And when it's cold: "I'm simply frozen." And when it ain't neither one: "I wished the weather would do one thing another." I don't s'pose she knows what she's saying when she says any one of them things, but she's one of these here gals that can't bear to see a conversation die out and thinks it's her place to come through with a wise crack whenever they's a vacuum.

So during this hot spell we was having dinner with a bird named Gene Buck that knowed New York like a book, only he hadn't never read a book, and Katie made the remark that she was simply stifling.

"If you think this is hot," says our friend, "just wait till the summer comes. The Old Town certainly steams up in the Old Summer Time."

So Kate asked him how people could stand it.

"They don't," he says. "All the ones that's got a piece of change ducks out somewheres where they can get the air."

"Where do they go?" Katie asked him.

"Well," he says, "the most of my pals goes to Newport or Maine or up in the Adirondacks. But of course them places is out of most people's reach. If I was you folks I'd go over on Long Island somewheres and either take a cottage or live in one of them good hotels."

"Where, for instance?" says my Mrs.

"Well," he said, "some people takes cottages, but the rents is something fierce, and besides, the desirable ones is probably all eat up by this time. But they's plenty good hotels where you get good service and swell meals and meet good people; they won't take in no riffraff. And they give you a pretty fair rate if they know you're going to make a stay."

So Ella asked him if they was any special one he could recommend.

"Let's think a minute," he says.

"Let's not strain ourself," I said.

"Don't get cute!" said the Mrs. "We want to get some real information and Mr. Buck can give it to us."

"How much would you be willing to pay?" said Buck.

It was Ella's turn to make a wise crack.

"Not no more than we have to," she says.

"I and my sister has got about eight thousand dollars per annum between us," said Katie, "though a thousand of it has got to go this year to a man that cheated us up on Riverside Drive.

"It was about a lease. But Papa left us pretty well off; over a hundred and fifty thousand dollars."

"Don't be so secret with Mr. Buck," I says. "We've knew him pretty near a week now. Tell him about them four-dollar stockings you bought over on Fifth Avenue and the first time you put them on they got as many runs as George Sisler."

"Well," said Buck, "I don't think you'd have no trouble getting comfortable rooms in a good hotel on seven thousand dollars. If I was you I'd try the Hotel Decker. It's owned by a man named Decker."

"Why don't they call it the Griffith?" I says.

"It's located at Tracy Estates," says Buck. "That's one of the garden spots of Long Island. It's a great big place, right up to the minute, and they give you everything the best. And they's three good golf courses within a mile of the hotel."

The gals told him they didn't play no golf.

"You don't know what you've missed," he says.

"Well," I said, "I played a game once myself and missed a whole lot."

"Do they have dances?" asked Kate.

"Plenty of them," says Buck, "and the guests is the nicest people you'd want to meet. Besides all that, the meals is included in the rates, and they certainly set a nasty table."

"I think it sounds grand," said the Mrs. "How do you get there?"

"Go over to the Pennsylvania Station," says Buck, "and take the

Long Island Railroad to Jamaica. Then you change to the Haverton branch. It don't only take a half hour altogether."

"Let's go over to-morrow morning and see can we get rooms," said Katie.

So Ella asked how that suited me.

"Go just as early as you want to," I says. "I got a date to run down to the Aquarium and see the rest of the fish."

"You won't make no mistake stopping at the Decker," says Buck.

So the gals thanked him and I paid the check so as he would have more to spend when he joined his pals up to Newport.

Well, when Ella and Kate come back the next afternoon, I could see without them telling me that it was all settled. They was both grinning like they always do when they've pulled something nutty.

"It's a good thing we met Mr. Buck," said the Mrs., "or we mightn't never of heard of this place. It's simply wonderful. A double room with a bath for you and I and a room with a bath for Katie. The meals is throwed in, and we can have it all summer."

"How much?" I asked her.

"Two hundred a week," she said. "But you must remember that's for all three of us and we get our meals free."

"And I s'pose they also furnish knobs for the bedroom doors," says I.

"We was awful lucky," said the wife. "These was the last two rooms they had, and they wouldn't of had those only the lady that had engaged them canceled her reservation."

"I wished I'd met her when I was single," I says.

"So do I," says Ella.

"But listen," I said. "Do you know what two hundred a week amounts to? It amounts to over ten thousand a year, and our income is seven thousand."

"Yes," says Katie, "but we aren't only going to be there twenty weeks, and that's only four thousand."

"Yes," I said, "and that leaves us three thousand for the other thirty-two weeks, to pay for board and room and clothes and show tickets and a permanent wave every other day."

"You forget," said Kate, "that we still got our principal, which we can spend some of it and not miss it."

"And you also forget," said the Mrs., "that the money belongs to Sis and I, not you."

"I've got a sweet chance of forgetting that," I said. "It's hammered into me three times a day. I hear about it pretty near as often as I hear that one of you's lost their new silk bag."

"Well, anyway," says Ella, "it's all fixed up and we move out there early tomorrow morning, so you'll have to do your packing to-night."

I'm not liable to celebrate the anniversary of the next day's trip. Besides the trunks, the gals had a suitcase and a grip apiece and I had a suitcase. So that give me five pieces of baggage to wrestle, because of course the gals had to carry their parasol in one hand and their wrist watch in the other. A redcap helped load us on over to the station, but oh you change at Jamaica! And when we got to Tracy Estates we seen that the hotel wasn't only a couple of blocks away, so the ladies said we might as well walk and save taxi fare.

I don't know how I covered them two blocks, but I do know that when I reeled into the Decker my hands and arms was paralyzed and Ella had to do the registering.

Was you ever out there? Well, I s'pose it's what you might call a family hotel, and a good many of the guests belongs to the caynine family. A few of the couples that can't afford dogs has got children, and you're always tripping over one or the other. They's a dining room for the grown-ups and another for the kids, wile the dogs and their nurses eats in the grillroom à la carte. One part of the joint is bachelor quarters. It's located right next to the dogs' dormitories, and they's a good deal of rivalry between the dogs and the souses to see who can make the most noise nights. They's also a ballroom and a couple card rooms and a kind of a summer parlor where the folks sets round in the evening and listen to a three-piece orchestra that don't know they's been any music wrote since Poets and Peasants. The men get up about eight o'clock and go down to New York to Business. They don't never go to work. About nine the women begins limping downstairs and either goes to call on their dogs or take them for a walk in the front yard. This is a great big yard with a whole lot of benches strewed round it, but you can't set on them in the daytime because the women or the nurses uses them for a place to read to the dogs or kids, and in the evenings you would have to share them with the waitresses, which you have already had enough of them during the day.

When the women has prepared themselves for the long day's grind with a four-course breakfast, they set round on the front porch and discuss the big questions of the hour, like for instance the last trunk murder or whether an Airedale is more loving than a Golden Bantam. Once in a wile one of them cracks that it looks like they was bound to be a panic pretty soon and a big drop in prices, and so forth. This shows they're broad-minded and are giving a good deal of thought to up-to-date topics. Every so often one of them'll say: "The present situation can't keep up." The hell it can't!

By one o'clock their appetites is whetted so keen from brain exercise that they make a bum out of a plate of soup and an order of Long Island duckling, which they figure is caught fresh every day, and they wind up with salad and apple pie à la mode and a stein of coffee. Then they totter up to their rooms to sleep it off before Dear gets home from Business.

Saturday nights everybody puts on their evening clothes like something was going to happen. But it don't. Sunday mornings the husbands and bachelors gets up earlier than usual to go to their real business, which is golf. The womenfolks are in full possession of the hotel till Sunday night supper and wives and husbands don't see one another all day long, but it don't seem as long as if they did. Most of them's approaching their golden-wedding jubilee and haven't nothing more to say to each other that you could call a novelty. The husband may make the remark, Sunday night, that he would of broke one hundred and twenty in the afternoon round if the caddy hadn't of handed him a spoon when he asked for a nut pick, and the wife'll probably reply that she's got to go in Town some day soon and see a chiropodist. The rest of the Sabbath evening is spent in bridge or listening to the latest song hit from *The Bohemian Girl*.

The hotel's got all the modern conveniences like artificial light and a stopper in the bathtubs. They even got a barber and a valet, but you can't get a shave wile he's pressing your clothes, so it's pretty near impossible for a man to look their best at the same time.

Well, the second day we was there I bought me a deck of cards and got so good at solitary that pretty soon I could play fifty games between breakfast and lunch and a hundred from then till supper-time. During the first week Ella and Kate got on friendly terms with over a half dozen people—the head waiter, our waitress, some of the clerks and the manager and the two telephone gals. It wasn't from lack of trying that they didn't meet even more people. Every day one or the other of them would try and swap a little small talk with one of the other squatters, but it generally always wound up as a short monologue.

Ella said to me one day, she says: "I don't know if we can stick it out here or not. Every hotel I was ever at before, it was easy enough to make a lot of friends, but you could stick a bottle of cream alongside one of these people and it'd stay sweet a week. Unless they looked at it. I'm sick of talking to you and Sis and the hired help, and Kate's so lonesome that she cries herself to sleep nights."

Well, if I'd of only had sense enough to insist on staying we'd of probably packed up and took the next train to Town. But instead of that I said: "What's to prevent us from going back to New York?"

"Don't be silly!" says the Mrs. "We come out here to spend the summer and here is where we're going to spend the summer."

"All right," I says, "and by September I'll be all set to write a book on one-handed card games."

"You'd think," says Ella, "that some of these women was titled royalties the way they snap at you when you try and be friends with them. But they's only one in the bunch that's got any handle to her name; that's Lady Perkins."

I asked her which one was that.

"You know," says Ella. "I pointed her out to you in the dining room. She's a nice-looking woman, about thirty-five, that sets near our table and walks with a cane."

"If she eats like some of the rest of them," I says, "she's lucky they don't have to w'eel her."

"She's English," says Ella. "They just come over and her husband's in Texas on some business and left her here. She's the one that's got that dog."

"That dog!" I said. "You might just as well tell me she's the one that don't play the mouth organ. They've all got a dog."

"She's got two," said the wife. "But the one I meant is that big German police dog that I'm scared to death of him. Haven't you saw her out walking with him and the little chow?"

"Yes," I said, "if that's what it is. I always wondered what the boys in the Army was talking about when they said they eat chow."

"They probably meant chowchow," says the Mrs. "They wouldn't of had these kind of chows, because in the first place, who would eat a dog, and besides these kind costs too much."

"Well," I says, "I'm not interested in the price of chows, but if you want to get acquainted with Lady Perkins, why I can probably fix it for you."

"Yes, you'll fix it!" said Ella. "I'm beginning to think that if we'd of put you in storage for the summer the folks round here wouldn't shy away from us like we was leopards that had broke out of a pest-house. I wished you would try and dress up once in a wile and not always look like you was just going to do the chores. Then maybe I and Sis might get somewheres."

Well, of course when I told her I could probably fix it up with Lady Perkins, I didn't mean nothing. But it wasn't only the next morning when I started making good. I was up and dressed and downstairs about half past eight, and as the gals wasn't ready for their breakfast yet I went out on the porch and set down. They wasn't nobody else there, but pretty soon I seen Lady Perkins come up the path with her two whelps. When she got to the porch steps their nurse popped out of the servants' quarters and took them round to the grillroom for their breakfast. I s'pose the big one ordered sauerkraut and kalter Aufschnitt, wile the chow had tea and eggs fo yung. Anyway, the Perkins dame come up on the porch and flopped into the chair next to mine.

In a few minutes Ed Wurz, the manager of the hotel, showed, with a bag of golf instruments and a trick suit. He spotted me and asked me if I didn't want to go along with him and play.

"No," I said. "I only played once in my life."

"That don't make no difference," he says. "I'm a bum myself. I just play shinny, you might say."

"Well," I says, "I can't anyway, on account of my dogs. They been giving me a lot of trouble."

Of course I was referring to my feet, but he hadn't no sooner than went on his way when Lady Perkins swung round on me and says: "I didn't know you had dogs. Where do you keep them?"

At first I was going to tell her "In my shoes," but I thought I might as well enjoy myself, so I said: "They're in the dog hospital over to Haverton."

"What ails them?" she asked me.

Well, I didn't know nothing about cay-nine diseases outside of hydrophobia, which don't come till August, so I had to make one up.

"They got blanny," I told her.

"Blanny!" she says. "I never heard of it before."

"No," I said. "It hasn't only been discovered in this country just this year. It got carried up here from Peru some way another."

"Oh, it's contagious, then!" says Lady Perkins.

"Worse than measles or lockjaw," says I. "You take a dog that's been in the same house with a dog that's got blanny, and it's a miracle if they don't all get it."

She asked me if I'd had my dogs in the hotel.

"Only one day," I says, "the first day we come, about a week ago. As soon as I seen what was the matter with them, I took them over to Haverton in a sanitary truck."

"Was they mingling with the other dogs here?" she says.

"Just that one day," I said.

"Heavens!" said Lady Perkins. "And what's the symptoms?"

"Well," I said, "first you'll notice that they keep their tongue stuck out a lot and they're hungry a good deal of the time, and finally they show up with a rash."

"Then what happens?" she says.

"Well," said I, "unless they get the best of treatment, they kind of dismember."

Then she asked me how long it took for the symptoms to show after a dog had been exposed. I told her any time between a week and four months.

"My dogs has been awful hungry lately," she says, "and they most always keeps their tongue stuck out. But they haven't no rash."

"You're all right, then," I says. "If you give them treatments before the rash shows up, they's no danger."

"What's the treatment?" she asked me.

"You rub the back of their neck with some kind of dope," I told her. "I forget what it is, but if you say the word, I can get you a bottle of it when I go over to the hospital this afternoon."

"I'd be ever so much obliged," she says, "and I hope you'll find your dear ones a whole lot better."

"Dear ones is right," I said. "They cost a pile of jack, and the bird I bought them off of told me I should ought to get them insured, but I didn't. So if anything happens to them now, I'm just that much out."

Next she asked me what kind of dogs they was.

"Well," I said, "you might maybe never of heard of them, as they don't breed them nowheres only way down in Dakota. They call them yaphounds—I don't know why; maybe on account of the noise they make. But they're certainly a grand-looking dog and they bring a big price."

She set there a wile longer and then got up and went inside, probably to the nursery to look for signs of rash.

Of course I didn't tell the Mrs. and Kate nothing about this incidence. They wouldn't of believed it if I had of, and besides, it would be a knock-out if things broke right and Lady Perkins come up and spoke to me wile they was present, which is just what happened.

During the afternoon I strolled over to the drugstore and got me an empty pint bottle. I took it up in the room and filled it with water and shaving soap. Then I laid low till evening, so as Perk would think I had went to Haverton.

I and Ella and Kate breezed in the dining room kind of late and we hadn't no more than ordered when I seen the Lady get up and start out. She had to pass right past us, and when I looked at her and smiled she stopped.

"Well," she said, "how's your dogs?"

I got up from the table.

"A whole lot better, thank you," says I, and then I done the honors. "Lady Perkins," I said, "meet the wife and sister-in-law."

The two gals staggered from their chairs, both popeyed. Lady Perkins bowed to them and told them to set down. If she hadn't the floor would of bounced up and hit them in the chin.

"I got a bottle for you," I said. "I left it upstairs and I'll fetch it down after supper."

"I'll be in the red card room," says Perk, and away she went.

I wished you could of see the two gals. They couldn't talk for a minute, for the first time in their life. They just set there with their mouth open like a baby blackbird. Then they both broke out with a rash of questions that come so fast I couldn't understand none of them, but the general idear was, What the hell!

"They's no mystery about it," I said. "Lady Perkins was setting out on the porch this morning and you two was late getting down to breakfast, so I took a walk, and when I come back she noticed that I kind of limped and asked me what ailed my feet. I told her they always swoll up in warm weather and she said she was troubled the same way and did I know any medicine that shrank them. So I told her I had a preparation and would bring her a bottle of it."

"But," says Kate, "I can't understand a woman like she speaking to a man she don't know."

"She's been eying me all week," I said. "I guess she didn't have the nerve to break the ice up to this morning; then she got desperate."

"She must of," said Ella.

"I wished," said Kate, "that when you introduce me to people you'd give them my name."

"I'm sorry," I said, "but I couldn't recall it for a minute, though your face is familiar."

"But listen," says the wife. "What ails your dogs is a corn. You haven't got no swelled feet and you haven't got no medicine for them."

"Well," I says, "what I give her won't hurt her. It's just a bottle of soap and water that I mixed up, and pretty near everybody uses that once in a wile without no bad after effects."

Now, the whole three of us had been eating pretty good ever since we'd came to the Decker. After living à la carte at Big Town prices for six months, the American plan was sweet patootie. But this night the gals not only skrimped themselves but they was in such a hurry for me to get through that my molars didn't hardly have time to identify what all was scampering past them. Ella finally got so nervous that I had to take off the feed bag without dipping my bill into the stewed rhubarb.

"Lady Perkins will get tired waiting for you," she says. "And besides, she won't want us horning in there and interrupting them after their game's started."

"Us!" said I. "How many do you think it's going to take to carry this bottle?"

"You don't mean to say we can't go with you!" said Kate.

"You certainly can't," I says. "I and the nobility won't have our little romance knocked for a gool by a couple of country gals that can't get on speaking terms with nobody but the chambermaid."

"But they'll be other people there," says Kate. "She can't play cards alone."

"Who told you she was going to play cards?" I says. "She picked the red card room because we ain't liable to be interrupted there. As for playing cards alone, what else have I done all week? But when I get there she won't have to play solitary. It'll be two-handed hearts; where if you was to crowd in, it couldn't be nothing but rummy."

Well, they finally dragged me from the table, and the gals took a seat in the lobby wile I went upstairs after the medicine. But I hadn't no sooner than got a hold of the bottle when Ella come in the room.

"Listen," she says. "They's a catch in this somewheres. You needn't to try and tell me that a woman like Lady Perkins is trying to start a flirtation with a yahoo. Let's hear what really come off."

"I already told you," I said. "The woman's nuts over me and you should ought to be the last one to find fault with her judgment."

Ella didn't speak for a wile. Then she says: "Well, if you're going to forget your marriage vows and flirt with an old hag like she, I guess two can play at that little game. They's several men round this hotel that I like their looks and all as they need is a little encouragement."

"More than a little, I guess," says I, "or else they'd of already been satisfied with what you and Kate has give them. They can't neither one of you pretend that you been fighting on the defense all week, and the reason you haven't copped nobody is because this place is a hotel, not a home for the blind."

I wrapped a piece of newspaper round the bottle and started for the door. But all of a sudden I heard snuffles and stopped.

"Look here," I said. "I been kidding you. They's no need for you to get sore and turn on the tear ducks. I'll tell you how this thing happened if you think you can see a joke."

So I give her the truth, and afterwards I says: "They'll be plenty of time for you and Kate to get acquainted with the dame, but I don't want you tagging in there with me to-night. She'd think we was too cordial. Tomorrow morning, if you can manage to get up, we'll all three of us go out on the porch and lay for her when she brings the whelps back from their hike. She's sure to stop and inquire about my kennel. And don't forget, wile she's talking, that we got a couple of yaphounds that's suffering from blanny, and if she asks any questions let me do the answering, as I can think a lot quicker. You better tell Kate the secret, too, before she messes everything up, according to custom."

Then I and the Mrs. come downstairs and her and Katie went out to listen to the music wile I beat it to the red card room. I give Perkie the bottle of rash poison and she thanked me and said she would have the dogs' governess slap some of it onto them in the morning. She was playing bridge w'ist with another gal and two dudes. To look at their faces they wasn't playing for just pins. I had sense enough to not talk, but I stood there watching them a few minutes. Between hands Perk introduced me to the rest of the party. She had to ask my name first. The other skirt at the table was a Mrs. Snell and one of the dudes was a Doctor Platt. I didn't get the name of Lady Perkins' partner.

"Mr. Finch," says Perk, "is also a dog fancier. But his dogs is sick with a disease called blanny and he's got them over to the dog hospital at Haverton."

"What kind of dogs?" asked Platt.

"I never heard of the breed before," says Perk. "They're yaphounds."

"They raise them in South Dakota," I says.

Platt gives me a funny look and said: "I been in South Dakota several times and I never heard of a yaphound neither; or I never heard of a disease named blanny."

"I s'pose not," says I. "You ain't the only old-fashioned doctor that left themself go to seed when they got out of school. I bet you won't admit they's such a thing as appendicitis."

Well, this got a laugh from Lady Perkins and the other dude, but it didn't go very big with Doc or Mrs. Snell. Wile Doc was trying to figure a come-back I said I must go and look after my women-folks. So I told the party I was glad to of met them and walked out.

I found Ella and Katie in the summer parlor, and they wasn't alone. A nice-looking young fella named Codd was setting alongside of them, and after we was introduced Ella leaned over and w'ispered to me that he was Bob Codd, the famous aviator. It come out that he had invented some new kind of an aeroplane and had came to demonstrate it to the Williams Company. The company—Palmer Williams and his brother, you know—they've got their flying field a couple miles from the hotel. Well, a guy with nerve enough to go up in one of them things certainly ain't going to hesitate about speaking to a strange gal when he likes their looks. So this Codd baby had give himself an introduction to my Mrs. and Kate, and I guess they hadn't sprained an ankle running away from him.

Of course Ella wanted to know how I'd came out with Lady Perkins. I told her that we hadn't had much chance to talk because she was in a bridge game with three other people, but I'd met them and they'd all seemed to fall for me strong. Ella wanted to know who they was and I told her their names, all but the one I didn't get. She squealed when I mentioned Mrs. Snell.

"Did you hear that, Sis?" she says to Kate. "Tom's met Mrs. Snell. That's the woman, you know, that wears them funny clothes and has the two dogs."

"You're describing every woman in the hotel," I said.

"But this is *the* Mrs. Snell," said the wife. "Her husband's the sugar man and she's the daughter of George Henkel, the banker. They say she's a wonderful bridgeplayer and don't never play only for great big stakes. I'm wild to meet her."

"Yes," I said, "if they's one person you should ought to meet, it's a wonderful bridge player that plays for great big stakes, especially when our expenses is making a bum out of our income and you don't know a grand slam from no dice."

"I don't expect to gamble with her," says Ella. "But she's just the kind of people we want to know."

Well, the four of us set there and talked about this and that, and Codd said he hadn't had time to get his machine put together yet, but when he had her fixed and tested her a few times he would take me up for a ride.

"You got the wrong number," I says. "I don't feel flighty."

"Oh, I'd just love it!" said Kate.

"Well," says Codd, "you ain't barred. But I don't want to have no passengers along till I'm sure she's working O. K."

When I and Ella was upstairs she said that Codd had told them he expected to sell his invention to the Williamses for a cold million. And he had took a big fancy to Kate.

"Well," I said, "they say that the reckless aviators makes the best ones, so if him and Kate gets married he'll be better than ever. He won't give a damn after that."

"You're always saying something nasty about Sis," said the Mrs.; "but I know you just talk to hear yourself talk. If I thought you meant it I'd walk out on you."

"I'd hate to lose you," I says, "but if you took her along I wouldn't write it down as a total loss."

The following morning I and the two gals was down on the porch bright and early and in a few minutes, sure enough, along came Lady Perkins, bringing the menagerie back from the parade. She turned them over to the nurse and joined us. She said that Martha, the nurse, had used the rash poison and it had made a kind of a lather on the dogs' necks and she didn't know whether to wash it off or not, but it had dried up in the sun. She asked me how many times a day the dope should ought to be put on, and I told her before every meal and at bedtime.

"But," I says, "it's best to not take the dogs right out in the sun where the lather'll dry. The blanny germ can't live in that kind of lather, so the longer it says moist, why, so much the better."

Then she asked me was I going to Haverton to see my pets that day and I said yes, and she said she hoped I'd find them much improved. Then Ella cut in and said she understood that Lady Perkins was very fond of bridge.

"Yes, I am," says Perk. "Do you people play?"

"No, we don't," says Ella, "but we'd like to learn."

"It takes a long wile to learn to play good," said Perk. "But I do wished they was another real player in the hotel so as we wouldn't have to take Doctor Platt in. He knows the game, but he don't know enough to keep still. I don't mind people talking wile the cards is being dealt, but once the hands is picked up they ought to be absolute silence. Last night I lost about three hundred and seventy dollars just because he talked at the wrong time."

"Three hundred and seventy dollars!" said Kate. "My, you must play for big stakes!"

"Yes, we do," says Lady Perkins; "and when a person is playing for sums like that it ain't no time to trifle, especially when you're playing against an expert like Mrs. Snell."

"The game must be awfully exciting," said Ella. "I wished we could watch it sometimes."

"I guess it wouldn't hurt nothing," says Perkie; "not if you kept still. Maybe you'd bring me luck."

"Was you going to play to-night?" asked Kate.

"No," says the Lady. "They's going to be a little dance here to-night and Mr. Snell's dance mad, so he insists on borrowing his wife for the occasion. Doctor Platt likes to dance too."

"We're all wild about it," says Kate. "Is this an invitation affair?"

"Oh, no," says Perk. "It's for the guests of the hotel."

Then she said good-by to us and went in the dining room. The rest of our conversation all day was about the dance and what should we wear, and how nice and democratic Lady Perkins was, and to hear her talk you wouldn't never know she had a title. I s'pose the gals thought she ought to stop every three or four steps and declare herself.

I made the announcement about noon that I wasn't going to partake in the grand ball. My corn was the alibi. But they wasn't no way to escape from dressing up and escorting the two gals into the grand ballroom and then setting there with them.

The dance was a knock-out. Outside of Ella and Kate and the aviator and myself, they was three couple. The Snells was there and so was Doctor Platt. He had a gal with him that looked like she might be his mother with his kid sister's clothes on. Then they was a pair of young shimmy shakers that ought to of been give their bottle and tucked in the hay at six p.m. A corn wouldn't of bothered them the way they danced; their feet wasn't involved in the transaction.

I and the Mrs. and Kate was the only ones there in evening clothes. The others had attended these functions before and knew that they wouldn't be enough suckers on hand to make any difference whether you wore a monkey suit or rompers. Besides, it wasn't Saturday night.

The music was furnished by the three-piece orchestra that usually done their murder in the summer parlor.

Ella was expecting me to introduce her and Kate to the Snell gal, but her and her husband was so keen for dancing that they called it off in the middle of the second innings and beat it upstairs. Then Ella said she wouldn't mind meeting Platt, but when he come past us and I spoke to him he give me a look like you would expect from a flounder that's been wronged.

So poor Codd danced one with Kate and one with Ella, and so on, and so on, till finally it got pretty late, a quarter to ten, and our party was the only merry-makers left in the joint. The orchestra looked over at us to see if we could stand some more punishment. The Mrs. told me to go and ask them to play a couple more dances before they quit. They done what I asked them, but maybe I got my orders mixed up.

The next morning I asked Wurz, the manager, how often the hotel give them dances.

"Oh," he says, "once or twice a month."

I told him I didn't see how they could afford it.

Kate went out after supper this next evening to take an automobile ride with Codd. So when I and Ella had set in the summer parlor a little wile, she proposed that we should go in and watch the bridge game. Well, I wasn't keen for it, but when you tell wife you don't want to do something she always says, "Why not?" and even if you've got a reason she'll make a monkey out of it. So we rapped at the door of the red card room and Lady Perkins said, "Come in," and in we went.

The two dudes and Mrs. Snell was playing with her again, but Perk was the only one that spoke.

"Set down," she said, "and let's see if you can bring me some luck."

So we drawed up a couple of chairs and set a little ways behind her. Her and the anonymous dude was partners against Doc and Mrs. Snell, and they didn't change all evening. I haven't played only a few games of bridge, but I know a little about it, and I never see such hands as Perkie held. It was a misdeal when she didn't have the ace, king and four or five others of one suit and a few picture cards and aces on the side. When she couldn't get the bid herself she doubled the other pair and made a sucker out of them. I don't know what they was playing a point, but when they broke up Lady Perkins and her dude was something like seven hundred berries to the good.

I and Ella went to bed wile they was settling up, but we seen her on the porch in the morning. She smiled at us and says: "You two are certainly grand mascots! I hope you can come in and set behind me again to-night. I ain't even yet, but one more run of luck like last night's and I'll be a winner. Then," she says, "I s'pose I'll have to give my mascots some kind of a treat."

Ella was tickled to death and couldn't hardly wait to slip Sis the good news. Kate had been out late and overslept herself and we was half through breakfast when she showed up. The Mrs. told her about the big game and how it looked like we was in strong with the nobility, and Kate said she had some good news of her own; that Codd had as good as told her he was stuck on her.

"And he's going to sell his invention for a million," says Ella. "So I guess we wasn't as crazy coming out to this place as some people thought we was."

"Wait till the machine's made good," I said.

"It has already," says Kate. "He was up in it yesterday and everything worked perfect and he says the Williamses was wild over it. And what do you think's going to come off to-morrow morning? He's going to take me up with him."

"Oh, no, Sis!" said Ella. "S'pose something should happen!"

"No hope," says I.

"But even if something should happen," said Katie, "what would I care as long as it happened to Bob and I together!"

I told the waitress to bring me another order of fried mush.

"To-night," said Kate, "Bob's going in Town to a theater party with some boys he went to college with. So I can help you bring Lady Perkins good luck."

Something told me to crab this proposition and I tried, but it was passed over my veto. So the best I could do was to remind Sis, just before we went in the gambling den, to keep her mouth shut while the play was going on.

Perk give us a smile of welcome and her partner smiled too.

For an hour the game went along about even. Kate acted like she was bored, and she didn't have nothing to say after she'd told them, wile somebody was dealing, that she was going to have an aeroplane ride in the morning. Finally our side began to lose, and lose by big scores. They was one time when this was about sixteen hundred points to the bad. Lady Perkins didn't seem to be enjoying herself and when Ella addressed a couple of remarks to her the cat had her tongue.

But the luck switched round again and Lady Perk had all but caught up when the blow-off come.

It was the rubber game, with the score nothing and nothing. The Doc dealt the cards. I was setting where I could see his hand and Perk's both. Platt had the king, jack and ten and five other hearts. Lady Perkins held the ace and queen of hearts, the other three aces and everything else in the deck.

The Doc bid two hearts. The other dude and Mrs. Snell passed.

"Two without," says Lady Perkins.

"Three hearts," says Platt.

The other two passed again and Perk says: "Three without."

Katie had come strolling up and was pretty near behind Perk's chair.

"Well," says Platt, "it looks like——"

But we didn't find out what it looked like, as just then Katie says: "Heavens! Four aces! Don't you wished you was playing penny ante?" It didn't take Lady Perkins no time at all to forget her title.

"You fool!" she screams, w'eeling round on Kate. "Get out of here, and get out of here quick, and don't never come near me again! I hope your aeroplane falls a million feet. You little fool!"

I don't know how the hand come out. We wasn't there to see it played.

Lady Perkins got part of her hope. The aeroplane fell all right, but only a couple of miles instead of a million feet. They say that they was a defect or something in poor Codd's engine. Anyway, he done an involuntary nose dive. Him and his invention was spilled all over Long Island. But Katie had been awake all night with the hysterics and Ella hadn't managed to get her to sleep till nine a.m. So when Codd had called for her Ella'd told him that Sis would go some other day. Can you beat it?

Wile I and Ella was getting ready for supper I made the remark that I s'posed we'd live in a vale of tears for the next few days.

"No," said Ella. "Sis is taking it pretty calm. She's sensible. She says if that could of happened, why the invention couldn't of been no good after all. And the Williamses probably wouldn't of give him a plugged dime for it."

Lady Perkins didn't only speak to me once afterwards. I seen her setting on the porch one day, reading a book. I went up to her and said: "Hello." They wasn't no answer, so I thought I'd appeal to her sympathies.

"Maybe you're still interested in my dogs," I said. "They was too far gone and the veter'nary had to order them shot."

"That's good," said Perk, and went on reading.

IV. Only One

About a week after this, the Mrs. made the remark that the Decker wasn't big enough to hold both she and Perkins.

"She treats us like garbage," says the Mrs., "and if I stay here much longer I'll forget myself and do her nose in a braid."

But Perk left first and saved us the trouble. Her husband was down in Texas looking after some oil gag and he wired her a telegram one day to come and join him as it looked like he would have to stay there all summer. If I'd of been him I'd of figured that Texas was a sweet enough summer resort without adding your wife to it.

We was out on the porch when her ladyship and two dogs shoved off.

"Three of a kind," said the Mrs.

And she stuck her tongue out at Perk and felt like that made it all even. A woman won't stop at nothing to revenge insults. I've saw them stagger home in a new pair of 3 double A shoes because some fresh clerk told them the 7 Ds they tried on was too small. So anyway we decided to stay on at the Decker and the two gals prettied themselves up every night for dinner in the hopes that somebody besides the head waiter would look at them twice, but we attracted about as much attention as a dirty finger nail in the third grade.

That is, up till Herbert Daley come on the scene.

Him and Katie spotted each other at the same time. It was the night he come to the Decker. We was pretty near through dinner when the head waiter showed him to a table a little ways from us. The majority of the guests out there belongs to the silly sex and a new man is always a riot, even with the married ones. But Daley would of knocked them dead anywheres. He looked like he was born and raised in Shubert's chorus and the minute he danced in all the women folks forgot the feed bag and feasted their eyes on him. As for Daley, after he'd glanced at the bill of fare, he let his peepers roll over towards our table and then they quit rolling. A cold stare from Kate might have scared him off, but if they was ever a gal with "Welcome" embroidered on her pan, she's it.

It was all I could do to tear Ella and Sis from the dining room, though they was usually in a hurry to romp out to the summer parlor and enjoy a few snubs. I'd just as soon of set one place as another, only for the waitress, who couldn't quit till we did and she generally always had a date with the big ski jumper the hotel hires to destroy trunks.

Well, we went out and listened a wile to the orchestra, which had brought a lot of new jazz from the Prince of Pilsen, and we waited for the new dude to show up, but he didn't, and finally I went in to the desk to buy a couple of cigars and there he was, talking to Wurz, the manager. Wurz introduced us and after we'd shook hands Daley excused himself and said he was going upstairs to write a letter. Then Wurz told me he was Daley the horseman.

"He just came up from the South," says Wurz. "He's going to be with us till the meetings is over at Jamaica and Belmont. He's got a whale of a stable and he expects to clean up round New York with Only One, which he claims can beat any horse in the world outside of Man o' War. They's some other good ones in the bunch, too, and he says he'll tell me when he's going to bet on them. I don't only bet once in a long wile and then never more than $25 at a crack, but I'll take this baby's tips as often as he comes through with them. I guess a man won't make no mistake following a bird that bets five and ten thousand at a clip, though of course it don't mean much to him if he win or lose. He's dirty with it."

I asked Wurz if Daley was married and he said no.

"And listen," he says: "It looks like your little sister-in-law had hit him for a couple of bases. He described where she was setting in the dining room and asked who she was."

"Yes," I said, "I noticed he was admiring somebody at our table, but I thought maybe it was me."

"He didn't mention you," says Wurz, "only to make sure you wasn't Miss Kate's husband."

"If he was smart he'd know that without asking," I said. "If she was my wife I'd be wearing weeds."

I went back to the gals and told them I'd met the guy. They was all steamed up.

"Who is he?" says Kate.

"His name is Herbert Daley," I told her. "He's got a stable over to Jamaica."

"A stable!" says Ella, dropping her jaw. "A man couldn't dress like he and run a livery."

So I had to explain that he didn't run no livery, but owned a string of race horses.

"How thrilling!" says Katie. "I love races! I went to the Grand Circuit once, the time I was in Columbus."

"These is different," I says. "These is thurlbreds."

"So was they thurlbreds!" she says. "You always think a thing can't be no good if you wasn't there."

I let her win that one.

"We must find out when the race is and go," said the Mrs.

"They's six of them every day," I said, "but it costs about five smackers apiece to get in, to say nothing about what you lose betting."

"Betting!" says Katie. "I just love to bet and I never lose. Don't you remember the bet I made with Sammy Pass on the baseball that time? I took him for a five-pound box of candy. I just felt that Cincinnati was going to win."

"So did the White Sox," I says. "But if you bet with the boys over to Jamaica, the only candy they'll take you for is an all-day sucker."

"What did Mr. Daley have to say?" asked Ella.

"He had to say he was pleased to meet me," I told her. "He proved it by chasing upstairs to write a letter."

"Probably to his wife," said Kate.

"No," I said. "Wurz tells me he ain't got no wife. But he's got plenty of jack, so Wurz says."

"Well, Sis," says the Mrs., "that's no objection to him, is it?"

"Don't be silly!" said Katie. "He wouldn't look at me."

"I guess not!" I says. "He was so busy doing it in the dining room, that half his soup never got past his chin. And listen: I don't like to get you excited, but Wurz told me he asked who you was."

"O Sis!" said the Mrs. "It looks like a Romance."

"Wurz didn't say nothing about a Romance," said I. "He may be interested like the rubes who stare with their mouth open at Ringling's 'Strange People.'"

"Oh, you can't tease Sis like that," said Ella. "She's as pretty as a picture to-night and nobody could blame a man from admiring her."

"Especially when we don't know nothing about him," I says. "He may be a snow-eater or his upstairs rooms is unfurnished or something."

"Well," says Ella, "if he shows up again to-night, don't you forget to introduce us."

"Better not be in no hurry," I said.

"Why not?" said Ella. "If him and Sis likes each other's looks, why, the sooner they get acquainted, it won't hurt nothing."

"I don't know," I says. "I've noticed that most of the birds you chose for a brother-in-law only stayed in the family as long as they was strangers."

"Nobody said nothing about Mr. Daley as a brother-in-law," says Ella.

"Oh!" I said. "Then I suppose you want Katie to meet him so as she can land a hostler's job."

Well, in about a half hour, the gals got their wish and Daley showed up. I didn't have to pull no strategy to land him. He headed right to where we was setting like him and I was old pals. I made the introductions and he drawed up a chair and parked. The rest of the guests stared at us goggle-eyed.

"Some hotel!" says Daley.

"We like it," says the Mrs. "They's so many nice people lives here."

"We know by hearsay," I said, but she stepped on my foot.

"It's handy for me," said Daley. "I have a few horses over to the Jamaica race track and it's a whole lot easier to come here than go in Town every night."

"Do you attend the races every day?" says Katie.

"Sure," he says. "It's my business. And they's very few afternoons when one of my nags ain't entered."

"My! You must have a lot of them!" said Kate.

"Not many," says Daley. "About a hundred. And I only shipped thirty."

"Imagine!" said Kate.

"The army's got that many," I said.

"The army ain't got none like mine," says Daley. "I guess they wished they had of had. I'd of been glad to of helped them out, too, if they'd asked me."

"That's why I didn't enlist," I said. "Pershing never even suggested it."

"Oh, I done my bit all right," says Daley. "Two hundred thousand in Liberty Bonds is all."

"Just like throwing it away!" I says.

"Two hundred thousand!" says Ella. "And you've still got money left?"

She said this in a joking way, but she kept the receiver to her ear.

"I ain't broke yet," says Daley, "and I don't expect to be."

"You don't half know this hotel," I says.

"The Decker does charge good prices," said Daley, "but still and all, a person is willing to pay big for the opportunity of meeting young ladies like the present company."

"O Mr. Daley!" said Kate. "I'm afraid you're a flatterer."

"I bet he makes them pretty speeches to every woman he meets," says Ella.

"I haven't met none before who I felt like making them," says Daley.

Wile they was still talking along these lines, the orchestra began to drool a Perfect Day, so I ducked out on the porch for air. The gals worked fast wile I was gone and when I come back it was arranged that Daley was to take us to the track next afternoon in his small car.

His small car was a toy that only had enough room for the people that finds fault with Wilson. I supposed he had to leave his big car in New York on account of the Fifty-ninth Street bridge being so frail.

Before we started I asked our host if they was a chance to get anything to drink over to the track and he says no, but pretty near everybody brought something along on the hip, so I said for them to wait a minute wile I went up to the room and filled a flask. When we was all in the car, the Mrs. wanted to know if it wasn't risky, me taking the hootch along.

"It's against the prohibition law," she says.

"So am I," I said.

"They's no danger," says Daley. "They ain't began to force prohibition yet. I only wished they had. It would save me a little worry about my boy."

"Your boy!" said Katie, dropping her jaw a foot.

"Well, I call him my boy," says Daley. "I mean little Sid Mercer, that rides for me. He's the duke of them all when he lays off the liquor. He's gave me his word that he won't touch nothing as long as he's under contract to me, and he's kept straight so far, but I can't help from worr'ing about him. He ought to be good, though, when I pay him $20,000 for first call, and leave him make all he can on the side. But he ain't got much stren'th of character, you might say, and if something upsets him, he's liable to bust things wide open.

"I remember once he was stuck on a gal down in Louisville and he was supposed to ride Great Scott for Bradley in the Derby. He was the only one that could handle Scott right, and with him up Scott would of win as far as from here to Dallas. But him and the gal had a brawl the day before the race and that night the kid got stiff. When it come time for the race he couldn't of kept a seat on a saw horse. Bradley had to hustle round and dig up another boy and Carney was the only one left that could ride at all and him and Great Scott was strangers. So Bradley lose the race and canned Mercer."

"Whisky's a terrible thing," says Ella. A woman'll sometimes pretend for a long wile like she's stupid and all of a sudden pull a wise crack that proves she's a thinker.

"Well," says Daley, "when Bradley give him the air, I took him, and he's been all right. I guess maybe I know how to handle men."

"Men only?" says Katie smiling.

"Men and horses," said Daley. "I ain't never tried to handle the fair sex and I don't know if I could or not. But I've just met one that I think could handle me." And he give her a look that you could pour on a waffle.

Daley had a table saved for him in the clubhouse and we eat our lunch. The gals had clubhouse sandwiches, probably figuring they was caught fresh there. They was just one of Daley's horses entered that day and he told us he wasn't going to bet on it, as it hadn't never showed nothing and this was just a try-out. He said, though, that they was other horses on the card that looked good and maybe he would play them after he'd been round and talked to the boys.

"Yes," says Kate, "but the men you'll talk to knows all about the different horses and they'll tell you what horses to bet on and how can I win?"

"Why," says Daley, "if I decide to make a little bet on So-and-So I'll tell you about it and you can bet on the same horse."

"But if I'm betting with you," says Kate, "how can we bet on the same horse?"

"You're betting with me, but you ain't betting against me," said Daley. "This ain't a bet like you was betting with your sister on a football game or something. We place our bets with the bookmakers, that makes their living taking bets. Whatever horses we want to bet on, they take the bet."

"They must be crazy!" says Katie. "Your friends tell you what horse is going to win and you bet on them and the bookbinders is stung."

"My friends makes mistakes," says Daley, "and besides, I ain't the only guy out here that bets. Pretty near everybody at the track bets and the most of them don't know a race horse from a corn plaster. A bookmaker that don't finish ahead on the season's a cuckoo. Now," he says, "if you'll excuse me for a few minutes, I'll go down to the paddock and see what's new."

So wile he was gone we had a chance to look round and they was plenty to see. It was a Saturday and a big crowd out. Lots of them was gals that you'd have to have a pick to break through to their regular face. Since they had their last divorce, about the only excitement they could enjoy was playing a long shot. Which reminds me that they's an old saying that nobody loves a fat man, but you go out to a race track or down to Atlantic City or any place where the former wifes hangs out and if you'll notice the birds with them, the gents that broke up their home, you'll find out that the most of them is guys with chins that runs into five and six figures and once round their waist is a sleeper jump.

Besides the Janes and the fat rascals with them, you seen a flock of ham actors that looked like they'd spent the night in a Chinese snowstorm, and maybe a half a dozen losers'-end boxers that'd used the bridge of their nose to block with and always got up in the morning just after the clock had struck ten, thinking they'd been counted out.

Pretty near everybody wore a pair of field glasses on a strap and when the race was going on they'd look through them and tell the world that the horse they'd bet on was three len'ths in front and just as good as in, but I never heard of a bookie paying off on that dope; and personally when someone would insist on lending me a pair to look through I couldn't tell if the things out there racing was horses or gnats.

Daley was back with us in a few minutes and says to Kate: "I guess you'll have to bet on yourself in the first race."

So she asked him what did he mean and he said: "I had a tip on a filly named Sweet and Pretty."

"O Mr. Daley!" says Kate.

"They don't expect her to win," says Daley, "but she's six, two and even, and I'm going to play her place and show."

Then he explained what that was and he said he was going to bet a thousand each way and finally the gals decided to go in for $10 apiece to show. It tickled them to death to find out that they didn't have to put up nothing. We found seats down in front wile Daley went to place the bets. Pretty soon the horses come out and Kate and Ella both screamed when they seen how cute the jockeys was dressed. Sweet and Pretty was No. 10 and had a combination of colors that would knock your eye out. Daley come back and explained that every owner had their own colors and of course the gals wanted to know what his was and he told them Navy blue and orange sleeves with black whoops on them and a blue cap.

"How beautiful!" says Ella. "I can't hardly wait to see them!"

"You must have wonderful taste in colors!" says Kate.

"Not only in colors," he says.

"O Mr. Daley!" she says again.

Well, the race was ran and No. 10 was a Sweet and Pretty last.

"Now," I says, "you O Mr. Daley."

The gals had yelped themself hoarse and didn't have nothing to say, but I could tell from their face that it would take something more than a few pretty speeches to make up for that twenty men.

"Never mind that!" said Daley. "She got a rotten ride. We'll get that back on the next one."

His hunch in the next one was Sena Day and he was betting a thousand on her to place at 4 to 1. He made the gals go in for $20 apiece, though they didn't do it with no pep. I went along with him to place the bets and he introduced me to a bookie so as I could bet a few smackers of my own when I felt like it. You know they's a law against betting unless it's a little bet between friends and in order to be a bookie's friend he's got to know your name. A quick friendship sprung up between I and a guy named

Joe Meyer, and he not only give me his card but a whole deck of them. You see the law also says that when you make one of these bets with your pals he can't give you no writing to show for it, but he's generally always a man that makes a lot of friends and it seems like they all want to make friendly bets with him, and he can't remember where all his buddies lives, so he makes them write their names and address on the cards and how much the friendly wager is for and who on, and so forth, and the next day he mails them the bad news and they mail him back a check for same. Once in a wile, of course, you get the bad news and forget to mail him the check and he feels blue over it as they's nothing as sad as breaking up an old friendship.

I laid off Sena Day and she win. Daley smiled at the gals.

"There!" he says. "I'm sorry we didn't play her on the nose, but I was advised to play safe."

"Fine advice!" said Kate. "It's cost Sis and I $60 so far."

"What do you mean?" says Daley.

"We lose $20 on the first race," she says, "and you tell us we'll get it back on the next one and we bet the horse'll come second and it don't."

So we had to explain that if a horse win, why it placed, too, and her and Ella had grabbed $160 on that race and was $140 ahead. He was $2,000 winners himself.

"We'll have a drink on Sena," he says. "I don't believe they was six people out here that bet a nickel on her."

So Katie told him he was wonderful and him and the gals had a sarsaparilla or something and I poured my own. He'd been touting Cleopatra in the third race, but her and everybody else was scratched out of it except Captain Alcock and On Watch. On Watch was 9 to 10 and Alcock even money and Daley wouldn't let us bet.

"On Watch is best," he says, "but he's giving away twenty pounds and you can't tell. Anyway, it ain't worth it at that price."

"Only two horses in the race?" asked Ella.

"That's all," he says.

"Well, then, listen," she says, all excited: "Why not bet on one of them for place?"

Daley laughed and said it was a grand idear only he didn't think the bookbinders would stand for it.

"But maybe they don't know," she says.

"I guess they do," said Daley. "It's almost impossible to keep a secret like that round a race track."

"Besides," I said, "the bookworms owes you and Kate $70 apiece and if you put something like that over on them and they find it out, they'll probably get even by making you a check on the West Bank of the Hudson River."

So we decided to play fair and lay off the race entirely. On Watch come through and the gals felt pretty bad about it till we showed them that they'd of only grabbed off nine smackers apiece if they'd of plunged on him for $20 straight.

Along toward time for the next race, Daley steered us down by the paddock and we seen some of the nags close up. Daley and the gals raved over this one and that one, and wasn't this one a beauty, and so forth. Personally they was all just a horse to me and I never seen one yet that wasn't homelier than the City Hall. If they left it up to me to name the world's champion eyesore, I'd award the elegant barb' wire wash rag to a horse rode by a woman in a derby hat. People goes to the Horse Show to see the Count de Fault; they don't know a case of withers from an off hand hock. And if the Sport of Kings was patronized by just birds that admires equine charms, you could park the Derby Day crowd in a phone booth.

A filly named Tamarisk was the favorite in the fourth race and Daley played her for eight hundred smackers at 4 to 5. The gals trailed along with $8 apiece and she win from here to Worcester. The fifth was the one that Daley had an entry in—a dog named Fly-by-Night. It was different in the daytime. Mercer had the mount and done the best he could, which was finish before supper. Nobody bet, so nobody was hurt.

"He's just a green colt," Daley told us. "I wanted to see how he'd behave."

"Well," I said, "I thought he behaved like a born caboose."

Daley liked the Waterbury entry in the last and him and the gals played it and win. All told, Daley was $4,000 ahead on the day and Ella and Kate had picked up $160 between them. They wanted to kiss everybody on the way out. Daley sent us to the car to wait for him. He wanted to see Mercer a minute. After a wile he come out and brought Mercer along and introduced him. He's a good-looking kid only for a couple of blotches on his pan and got an under lip and chin that kind of lags behind. He was about Kate's

height, and take away his Adams apple and you could mail him to
Duluth for six cents. Him and Kate got personal right away and
she told him how different he looked now than in his riding make-
up. He said he had a new outfit that he'd of wore if he'd knew
she was looking on. So I said I hoped he didn't expect to ride Fly-
by-Night round the track and keep a suit new, and he laughed, and
Daley didn't seem to enjoy the conversation and said we we'd have
to be going, but when we started off, Kate and Mercer give each
other a smile with a future in it. She's one of these gals that can't
help from looking open house, even if the guy takes after a pelican.

Daley moved to our table that night and after that we eat breakfast and supper with him pretty near every day. After breakfast the
gals would go down to New York to spend what they had win the
day before, and I'll admit that Daley give us many a winner. I
begin betting a little of my own jack, but I stuck the proceeds in
the old sock. I ain't superstitious about living off a woman's money
as long as you're legally married, but at the clip the two gals was
going, it looked like their old man's war profits was on the way to
join their maker, and the more jack I laid by, the less sooner I
would have to go to work.

We'd meet every afternoon at the track and after the races Daley'd
bring us back to the hotel. After supper we'd set round and chin or
play rummy or once in a wile we'd go in Town to a show or visit
one of the road houses near the Decker. The mail service on Long
Island's kind of rotten and they's a bunch of road houses that hasn't
heard of prohibition.

During the time we'd lived in Town Katie had got acquainted
with three or four birds that liked her well enough to take her
places where they wasn't no cover charge, but since we'd moved to
the Decker we hadn't heard from none of them. That is, till a few
days after we'd met Daley, when she told us that one of the New
York boys, a guy named Goldberg, had called up and wanted her
to come in and see a show with him. He's a golf champion or something. Well, Daley offered to drive her in, but she said no, she'd
rather go on the train and Goldberg was going to meet her. So she
went, and Daley tried to play cards with Ella and I, but he was too
restless and finally snuck up to his room.

They wasn't no question about his feelings toward Kate. He was
always trying to fix it to be alone with her, but I guess it was the

first time in her life when she didn't have to do most of the leading and she kept him at arm's len'th. Her and Ella had many a battle. Ella told her that the first thing she knowed he'd get discouraged and walk out on her; that she'd ought to quit monking and give him to understand that she was ready to yes him when he spoke up. But Katie said she guessed she could run her own love affairs as she'd had a few more of them than Ella.

So Ella says: "Maybe you have, but which one of us has got the husband?"

"You, thank the Lord!" says Katie.

"Thank him twice," I said.

Kate didn't come home from her New York party till two o'clock and she overslept herself till it was too late to go down again and shop. So we all drove over to the track with Daley and most of the way over he acted like a child. Katie kept talking about what a good show she seen and had a grand time, and so forth, and he pretended he wasn't listening. Finally she cut it out and give him the old oil and by the time we got to the clubhouse he'd tossed in the sponge.

That was the last day at Jamaica and a couple of his horses was in. We was all down on them and they both copped, though Mercer had to give one of them a dude ride to pull us through. Daley got maudlin about what a grand rider the kid was and a grand little fella besides, and he had half a notion to bring him along with us back to the hotel and show him a good time. But Kate said what was the use of an extra man, as it would kind of spoil things and she was satisfied with just Daley. So of course that tickled him and everybody was feeling good and after supper him and Kate snuck out alone for the first time. Ella made me set up till they come back, so as she could get the news. Well, Daley had asked her all right, but she told him she wanted a little wile to think.

"Think!" says Ella. "What does she want to think for?"

"The novelty, I suppose," said I.

Only One was in the big stake race the next day, when we shifted over to Belmont. They was five or six others in with him, all of them pretty good, and the price on him was 3 to 1. He hadn't started yet since Daley'd brought him here, but they'd been nursing him along and Mercer and the trainer said he was right.

I suppose of course you've been out to Belmont. At that time they run the wrong way of the track, like you deal cards. Daley's table was in a corner of the clubhouse porch and when you looked up the track, the horses was coming right at you. Even the boys with the trick glasses didn't dast pretend they could tell who's ahead.

The Belmont national hymn is Whispering. The joint's so big and scattered round that a German could sing without disturbing the party at the next table. But they seems to be a rule that when they's anything to be said, you got to murmur it with the lips stuck to the opponent's earlobe. They shush you if you ask out loud for a toothpick. Everywheres you'll see two or three guys with their heads together in a whispering scene. One of them has generally always just been down to the horses' dining room and had lunch with Man o' War or somebody and they told him to play Sea Mint in the next race as Cleopatra had walked the stall all night with her foal. A little ways off they'll be another pair of shushers and one of them's had a phone call from Cleopatra's old dam to put a bet on Cleo as Captain Alcock had got a hold of some wild oats and they couldn't make him do nothing but shimmy.

If they's ten horses in a race you can walk from one end of the clubhouse to the other and get a whisper on all ten of them. I remember the second time Man o' War run there. They was only one horse that wanted to watch him from the track and the War horse was 1 to 100. So just before the race, if you want to call it that, I seen a wise cracker that I'd got acquainted with, that had always been out last night with Madden or Waterbury, so just kidding I walked up to him and asked him who he liked. So he motioned me to come over against the wall where they wasn't nobody near us and whispered, "Man o' War's unbeatable." You see if that remark had of been overheard and the news allowed to spread round, it might of forced the price to, say, 1 to a lump of coal, and spoiled the killing.

Well, wile the Jamaica meeting was on, the gals had spent some of their spare time figuring out how much they'd of been ahead if Daley had of let them bet more than ten to twenty smackers a race. So this day at Belmont, they said that if he liked Only One so much, he should ought to leave them raise the ante just once and play fifty apiece.

But he says: "No, not this time. I'm pretty sure he'll win, but he's in against a sweet field and he ain't raced for a month. I'll bet forty on the nose for the two of you, and if he looks good you can gamble some real money the next time he runs."

So Ella and Kate had to be satisfied with $20 apiece. Daley himself bet $2,000 and I piked along with $200 that I didn't tell the gals nothing about. We all got 3 to 1. A horse named Streak of Lightning was favorite at 6 to 5. It was a battle. Only One caught the Streak in the last step and win by a flea's jaw. Everybody was in hysterics and the gals got all messed up clawing each other.

"Nobody but Mercer could of did it!" says Daley, as soon as he could talk.

"He's some jockey!" yelled Kate. "O you Sid!"

Pretty soon the time was give out and Only One had broke the track record for the distance, whatever it was.

"He's a race horse!" said Daley. "But it's too bad he had to extend himself. We won't get no price the next time out."

Well, altogether the race meant $14,000 to Daley, and he said we'd all go to Town that night and celebrate. But when we got back to the Decker, they was a telegram for him and he had to pack up and beat it for Kentucky.

Daley being away didn't stop us from going to the track. He'd left orders with Ernest, his driver, to take us wherever we wanted to go and the gals had it so bad now that they couldn't hardly wait till afternoon. They kept on trimming the books, too. Kate got a phone call every morning that she said was from this Goldberg and he was giving her tips. Her and Ella played them and I wished I had. I would of if I'd knew who they was from. They was from Mercer, Daley's boy. That's who they was from.

I and Ella didn't wise up till about the third night after Daley'd went. That night, Kate took the train to Town right after supper, saying she had a date with Goldberg. It was a swell night and along about eight, I and Ella decided we might as well have a ride. So we got a hold of Ernest and it wound up by us going to New York too. We seen a picture and batted round till midnight and then Ella says why not go down to the Pennsylvania Station and pick Kate up when she come to take the train, and bring her home. So we done it. But when Katie showed up for the train, it was Mercer that was with her, not Goldberg.

Well, Mercer was pretty near out to the car with us when he happened to think that Daley's driver mustn't see him. So he said good night and left us. But he didn't do it quick enough. Daley's

driver had saw him and I seen that he'd saw him and I knowed
that he wasn't liable to be stuck on another of Daley's employs that
was getting ten times as much money as him and all the cheers, and
never had to dirty himself up changing a tire. And I bet it was
all Ernest could do was wait till Daley come back so as he could
explode the boom.

Kate and Ella didn't know Ernest was hep and I didn't tell them
for fear of spoiling the show, so the women done their brawling
on the way home in a regular race track whisper. The Mrs. told
Kate she was a hick to be monking round with a jockey when Daley
was ready and willing to give her a modern home with a platinum
stopper in the washbowl. Kate told Ella that she wasn't going to
marry nobody for their money, and besides, Mercer was making
more than enough to support a wife, and how that boy can dance!

"But listen," she says: "I ain't married to neither of them yet
and don't know if I want to be."

"Well," says Ella, "you won't have no chance to marry Daley if
he finds out about you and Mercer."

"He won't find out unless you tell him," said Kate.

"Well, I'll tell him," says Ella, "unless you cut this monkey
business out."

"I'll cut it out when I get good and ready," says Kate. "You can
tell Daley anything you please."

She knew they wasn't no chance of Ella making good.

"Daley'll be back in a couple of days," says the Mrs. "When he
comes he'll want his answer and what are you going to say?"

"Yes or no, according to which way I make up my mind," said
Kate. "I don't know yet which one I like best."

"That's ridic'lous!" Ella says. "When a girl says she can't make
up her mind, it shows they's nothing to make up. Did you ever
see me when I couldn't make up my mind?"

"No," said Katie, "but you never had even one whole man to
choose between."

The last half of the ride neither of them were talking. That's
a world's record in itself. They kind of made up the next morning
after I'd told Ella that the surest way to knock Daley's chances for
a gool was to paste Mercer.

"Just lay off of it," I told her. "The best man'll win in fair competition, which it won't be if you keep plugging for Daley."

We had two more pretty fair days at the track on Kate's tips that

Mercer give her. We also went on a party with him down Town, but we used the train, not Daley's car.

Daley showed up on a Wednesday morning and had Ernest take him right over to the track. I suppose it was on this trip that Ernest squealed. Daley didn't act no different when we joined him on the clubhouse porch, but that night him and Kate took a ride alone and come back engaged.

They'd been pointing Only One for the Merrick Handicap, the fourth race on Saturday. It was worth about $7,000 to the winner. The distance was seven furlongs and Only One had top weight, 126 pounds. But Thursday he done a trial over the distance in 1.22, carrying 130 pounds, so it looked like a set-up.

Thursday morning I and Ella happened to be in Katie's room when the telephone rung. It was Mercer on the other end. He asked her something and she says: "I told you why in my note."

So he said something else and she says: "Not with no jailbird."

And she hung up.

Well, Ella wanted to know what all the pleasantries was about, but Kate told her to mind her own business.

"You got your wish and I'm engaged to Daley," she says, "and that's all you need to know."

For a gal that was going to marry a dude that was supposed to have all the money in the world, she didn't act just right, but she wouldn't been Kate if she had of, so I didn't think much about it.

Friday morning I got a wire from one of the South Bend boys, Goat Anderson, sent from Buffalo, saying he'd be in New York that night and would I meet him at the Belmont at seven o'clock. So I went in Town from the track and waited round till pretty near nine, but he didn't show up. I started to walk across to the Pennsylvania Station and on the way I dropped in at a place where they was still taking a chance. I had one up at the bar and was throwing it into me when a guy in the back part yelled "Hey! Come here!" It was Mercer yelling and it was me he wanted.

He was setting at a table all alone with a highball. It didn't take no Craig Kennedy to figure out that it wasn't his first one.

"Set down before I bat you down!" he says.

"Listen," I says: "I wished you was champion of the world. You'd hold onto the title just long enough for me to reach over and sock you where most guys has a chin."

"Set down!" he says. "It's your wife I'm going to beat up, not you."

"You ain't going to beat up nobody's wife or nobody's husband," I says, "and if you don't cut out that line of gab you'll soon be asking the nurse how you got there."

"Set down and come clean with me," he says. "Was your wife the one that told Daley about your sister-in-law and I?"

"If she did, what of it?" I says.

"I'm asking you, did she?" he says.

"No, she didn't," I said. "If somebody told him his driver told him. He seen you the other night."

"Ernest!" he says. "Frank and Ernest! I'll Ernest him right in the jaw!"

"You're a fine matchmaker!" I says. "He could knock you for a row of flat tires. Why don't you try and get mad at Dempsey?"

"Set down and have a drink," says Mercer.

"I didn't mean that about your wife. You and her has treated me all right. And your sister-in-law, too, even if she did give me the air. And called me a jailbird. But that's all right. It's Daley I'm after and it's Daley I'm going to get."

"Sweet chance!" I says. "What could you do to him?"

"Wait and see!" said Mercer, and smiled kind of silly.

"Listen," I says. "Have you forgot that you're supposed to ride Only One to-morrow?"

"Supposed to ride is right," he says, and smiled again.

"Ain't you going to ride him?" I said.

"You bet I am!" he says.

"Well, then," I said, "you better call it a day and go home."

"I'm over twenty-one," he says, "and I'm going to set here and enjoy myself. But remember, I ain't keeping you up."

Well, they wasn't nothing I could do only set there and wait for him to get stiff and then see him to his hotel. We had a drink and we had another and a couple more. Finally he opened up. I wished you could of heard him. It took him two hours to tell his story, and everything he said, he said it over and over and repeated it four and five times. And part of the time he talked so thick that I couldn't hardly get him.

"Listen," he says. "Can you keep a secret? Listen," he says. "I'm going to take a chance with you on account of your sister-in-law. I loved that little gal. She's give me the air, but that don't make

no difference; I loved that little gal and I don't want her to lose
no money. So I'm going to tell you a secret and if you don't keep
your clam shut I'll roll you for a natural. In the first place," he says,
"how do you and Daley stack up?"

"That ain't no secret," I said. "I think he's all right. He's been
a good friend of mine."

"Oh," says Mercer, "so he's been a good friend of yours, has he?
All right, then. I'm going to tell you a secret. Do you remember
the day I met you and the gals in the car? Well, a couple of days
later, Daley was feeling pretty good about something and he asked
me how I liked his gal? So I told him she looked good. So he says,
'I'm going to marry that gal,' he says. He says, 'She likes me and
her sister and brother-in-law is encouraging it along,' he says. 'They
know I've got a little money and they're making a play for me.
They're a couple of rats and I'm the cheese. They're going to make
a meal off of me. They think they are,' he says. 'But the brother-
in-law's a smart Aleck that thinks he's a wise cracker. He'd be a
clown in a circus, only that's work. And his wife's fishing for a
sucker with her sister for bait. Well, the gal's a pip and I'm going
to marry her,' he says, 'but as soon as we're married, it's good-by,
family-in-law! Me and them is going to be perfect strangers. They
think they'll have free board and lodging at my house,' he says,
'but they won't get no meal unless they come to the back door for it,
and when they feel sleepy they can make up a lower for themself on
my cement porch.' That's the kind of a friend of yours this baby
is," says Mercer.

I didn't say nothing and he went on.

"He's your friend as long as he can use you," he says. "He's been
my friend since I signed to ride for him, that is, up till he found
out I was stealing his gal. Then he shot my chances for a bull's-eye
by telling her about a little trouble I had, five or six years ago.
I and a girl went to a party down in Louisville and I seen another
guy wink at her and I asked him what he meant by it and he said
he had St. Vitus' dance. So I pulled the iron and knocked off a
couple of his toes, to cure him. I was in eleven months and that's
what Daley told Kate about. And of course he made her promise
to not tell, but she wrote me a good-by note and spilled it. That's
the kind of a pal he is.

"After I got out I worked for Bradley, and when Bradley turned
me loose, he give me a $10,000 contract."

"He told us twenty," I said.

"Sure he did," says Mercer. "He always talks double. When he gets up after a tough night, both his heads aches. And if he ever has a baby he'll invite you over to see the twins. But anyway, what he pays me ain't enough and after to-morrow I'm through riding. What's ten or fifteen thousand a year when you can't drink nothing and you starve to death for the fear you'll pick up an ounce! Listen," he says. "I got a brother down in Oklahoma that's in the oil lease game. He cleaned up $25,000 last year and he wants me to go in with him. And with what I've saved up and what I'm going to win to-morrow, I should worry if we don't make nothing in the next two years."

"How are you going to win to-morrow?" I said. "The price'll be a joke."

"The price on who?" says Mercer.

"Only One," I said.

He give a silly laugh and didn't say nothing for a minute. Then he asked if Daley done the betting for I and the two gals. I told him he had did it at first, but now I was doing it.

"Well," he says, "you do it to-morrow, see? That little lady called me a jailbird, but I don't want her to lose her money."

So I asked him what he meant and he asked me for the tenth or eleventh time if I could keep a secret. He made me hold up my hand and swear I wouldn't crack what he was going to tell me.

"Now," he says, "what's the name of the horse I'm riding to-morrow?"

"Only One," I said.

"That ain't all of it," said Mercer. "His name to-morrow is Only One Left. See? Only One Left."

"Do you mean he's going to get left at the post?" I says.

"You're a Ouija board!" says Mercer. "Your name is Ouija and the horse's name is Only One Left. And listen," he says. "Everything but three horses is going to be scratched out of this race and we'll open at about 1 to 3 and back up to 1 to 5. And Daley's going to bet his right eye. But they's a horse in the race named Sap and that's the horse my two thousand smackers is going down on. And you're a sap, too, if you don't string along with me."

"Suppose you can't hold Only One?"

"Get the name right," said Mercer. "Only One Left. And don't worry about me not handling him. He thinks I'm Billy Sunday and everything I say he believes. Do you remember the other day when I beat Streak of Lightning? Well, the way I done that was whispering in One's ear, coming down the stretch. I says to him, 'One,' I says, 'this Lightning hoss has been spilling it round that your father's grandmother was a zebra. Make a bum out of him!' That's what I whispered to him and he got sore and went past Lightning like he was standing still. And to-morrow, just before we're supposed to go, I'll say to him, 'One, we're back at Jamaica. You're facing the wrong way.' And when Sap and the other dog starts, we'll be headed towards Rhode Island and in no hurry to get there."

"Mercer," I said, "I don't suppose they's any use talking to you, but after all, you're under contract to give Daley the best you've got and it don't look to me just like you was treating him square."

"Listen!" he says. "Him and square don't rhyme. And besides, I won't be under contract to nobody by this time to-morrow. So you save your sermon for your own parish."

I don't know if you'll think I done right or not. Or I don't care. But what was the sense of me tipping off a guy that had said them sweet things about I and Ella? And even if I don't want a sister-in-law of mine running round with a guy that's got a jail record, still Daley squealing on him was rotten dope. And besides, I don't never like to break a promise, especially to a guy that shoots a man's toes off just for having St. Vitus' dance.

Well, anyway, the third race was over and the Merrick Handicap was next, and just like Mercer had said, they all quit but our horse and Sap and a ten-ton truck named Honor Bright. He was 20 to 1 and Sap was 6. Only One was 1 to 3 and Daley hopped on him with fifteen thousand men. Before post time the price was 1 to 5 and 1 to 6.

Daley was off his nut all afternoon and didn't object when I said I'd place the gals' money and save him the trouble. Kate and Ella had figured out what they had win up to date. It was about $1,200 and Daley told them to bet it all.

"You'll only make $400 between you," he says, "but it's a cinch."

"And four hundred's pretty good interest on $1,200," says Kate. "About ten per cent, ain't it?"

I left them and went downstairs. I wrote out a card for a hundred smackers on Sap. Then my feet caught cold and I didn't turn it in. I walked down towards the paddock and got there just as the boys

was getting ready to parade. I seen Mercer and you wouldn't of
never knew he'd fell off the wagon.

Daley was down there, too, and I heard him say: "Well, Sid, how
about you?"

"Never better," says Mercer. "If I don't win this one I'll quit
riding."

Then he seen me and smiled.

I chased back to the clubhouse, making up my mind on the way.
I decided to not bet a nickel for the gals on anything. If Mercer was
crossing me, I'd give Ella and Kate their $400 like they had win it,
and say nothing. Personally, I was going to turn in the card I'd
wrote on Sap. That was my idear when I got to Joe Meyer. But all
of a sudden I had the hunch that Mercer was going through; they
wasn't a chance in the world for him to weaken. I left Meyer's stand
and went to a bookie named Haynes, who I'd bet with before.

Sap had went up to 8 to 1, and instead of a hundred smackers
I bet a thousand.

He finished ahead by thee len'ths, probably the most surprised
horse in history. Honor Bright got the place, but only by a hair.
Only One, after being detained for some reason another, come
faster at the end than any horse ever run before. And Mercer give
him an unmerciful walloping, pretending to himself, probably, that
the hoss was its master.

We come back to our table. The gals sunk down in their chairs.
Ella was blubbering and Kate was as white as a ghost. Daley finally
joined us, looking like he'd had a stroke. He asked for a drink and
I give him my flask.

"I can't understand it!" he says. "I don't know what happened!"

"You don't!" hollered Kate. "I'll tell you what happened. You
stole our money! Twelve hundred dollars! You cheat!"

"Oh, shut your fool mouth!" says Daley.

And another Romance was knocked for a row of sour apple
trees.

Kate brought the mail in the dining room Monday morning.
They was a letter for her and one for me. She read hers and they
was a couple of tears in her eyes.

"Mercer's quit riding," she says. "This is a farewell note. He's
going to Oklahoma."

Ella picked up my envelope.

"Who's this from?" she says.

"Give it here," I said, and took it away from her. "It's just the statement from Haynes, the bookie."

"Well, open it up," she said.

"What for?" said I. "You know how much you lose, don't you?"

"He might of made a mistake, mightn't he?" she says.

So I opened up the envelope and there was the check for $8,000.

"Gosh!" I said. "It looks like it was me that made the mistake!" And I laid the check down where her and Kate could see it. They screamed and I caught Ella just as she was falling off the chair.

"What does this mean?" says Kate.

"Well," I said, "I guess I was kind of rattled Saturday, and when I come to make my bet I got balled up and wrote down Sap. And I must of went crazy and played him for a thousand men."

"But where's our statement, mine and Sis'?" says Ella.

"That my mistake again," I said. "I wrote out your ticket, but I must of forgot to turn it in."

They jumped up and come at me, and before I could duck I was kissed from both sides at once.

"O Sis!" yelps the Mrs. "Just think! We didn't lose our twelve hundred! We didn't lose nothing at all. We win eight thousand dollars!"

"Try and get it!" I says.

V. Katie Wins a Home

Oh yes, we been back here quite a wile. And we're liable to be here quite a wile. This town's good enough for me and it suits the Mrs. too, though they didn't neither one of us appreciate it till we'd give New York a try. If I was running the South Bend Boosters' club, I'd make everybody spend a year on the Gay White Way. They'd be so tickled when they got to South Bend that you'd never hear them razz the old burg again. Just yesterday we had a letter from Katie, asking us would we come and pay her a visit. She's a regular New Yorker now. Well, I didn't have to put up no fight with my Mrs. Before I could open my pan she says, "I'll write and tell her we can't come; that you're looking for a job and don't want to go nowhere just now."

Well, they's some truth in that. I don't want to go nowheres and

I'll take a job if it's the right kind. We could get along on the interest from Ella's money, but I'm tired of laying round. I didn't
do a tap of work all the time I was east and I'm out of the habit,
but the days certainly do drag when a man ain't got nothing to do
and if I can find something where I don't have to travel, I'll try
it out.

But the Mrs. has still got most of what the old man left her and
all and all, I'm glad we made the trip. I more than broke even by
winning pretty close to $10,000 on the ponies down there. And we
got Katie off our hands, which was one of the objects of us going in
the first place—that and because the two gals wanted to see Life.
So I don't grudge the time we spent, and we had some funny experiences when you look back at them. Anybody does that goes on
a tour like that with a cuckoo like Katie. You hear a lot of songs and
gags about mother-in-laws. But I could write a book of them about
sister-in-laws that's twenty years old and pretty and full of peace
and good will towards Men.

Well, after the blow-off with Daley, Long Island got too slow,
besides costing us more than we could afford. So the gals suggested
moving back in Town, to a hotel called the Graham on Sixty-
seventh Street that somebody had told them was reasonable.

They called it a family hotel, but as far as I could see, Ella and
I was the only ones there that had ever forced two dollars on the
clergy. Outside of the transients, they was two song writers and a
couple of gals that had their hair pruned and wrote for the papers,
and the rest of the lodgers was boys that had got penned into a
sixteen-foot ring with Benny Leonard by mistake. They looked like
they'd spent many an evening hanging onto the ropes during the
rush hour.

When we'd staid there two days, Ella and Katie was ready to
pack up again.

"This is just a joint," said Ella. "The gals may be all right, but
they're never in, only to sleep. And the men's impossible; a bunch
of low prize-fighters."

I was for sticking, on account of the place being cheap, so I said:

"Second prize ain't so low. And you're overlooking the two handsome tune thiefs. Besides, what's the difference who else lives here
as long as the rooms is clean and they got a good restaurant? What
did our dude cellmates out on Long Island get us? Just trouble!"

But I'd of lose the argument as usual only for Kate oversleeping herself. It was our third morning at the Graham and her and Ella had it planned to go and look for a better place. But Katie didn't get up till pretty near noon and Ella went without her. So it broke so's Sis had just came downstairs and turned in her key when the two bellhops reeled in the front door bulging with baggage and escorting Mr. Jimmy Ralston. Yes, Jimmy Ralston the comedian. Or comic, as he calls it.

Well, he ain't F. X. Bushman, as you know. But no one that seen him could make the mistake of thinking he wasn't somebody. And he looked good enough to Kate so as she waited till the clerk had him fixed up, and then ast who he was. The clerk told her and she told us when the Mrs. come back from her hunt. Ella begin to name a few joints where we might move, but it seemed like Sis had changed her mind.

"Oh," she says, "let's stay here a wile longer, a week anyway."

"What's came over you!" ast Ella. "You just said last night that you was bored to death here."

"Maybe we won't be so bored now," said Kate, smiling. "The Graham's looking up. We're entertaining a celebrity—Jimmy Ralston of the Follies."

Well, they hadn't none of us ever seen him on the stage, but of course we'd heard of him. He'd only just started with the Follies, but he'd made a name for himself at the Winter Garden, where he broke in two or three years ago. And Kate said that a chorus gal she'd met—Jane Abbott—had told her about Ralston and what a scream he was on a party.

"He's terribly funny when he gets just the right number of drinks," says Kate.

"Well, let's stay then," says Ella. "It'll be exciting to know a real actor."

"I would like to know him," says Katie, "not just because he's on the stage, but I think it'd be fun to set and listen to him talk. He must say the screamingest things! If we had him round we wouldn't have to play cards or nothing for entertainment. Only they say it makes people fat to laugh."

"If I was you, I'd want to get fat," I said. "Looking like an E string hasn't started no landslide your way."

"Is he attractive?" ast the Mrs.

"Well," said Kate, "he isn't handsome, but he's striking looking. You wouldn't never think he was a comedian. But then, ain't it generally always true that the driest people have sad faces?"

"That's a joke!" I said. "Did you ever see Bryan when he didn't look like somebody was tickling his feet?"

"We'll have to think up some scheme to get introduced to him," says Ella.

"It'll be tough," I says. "I don't suppose they's anybody in the world harder to meet than a member of the Follies, unless it's an Elk in a Pullman washroom."

"But listen," says Kate: "We don't want to meet him till we've saw the show. It'd be awfully embarrassing to have him ask us how we liked the Follies and we'd have to say we hadn't been to it."

"Yes," said the Mrs., "but still if we tell him we haven't been to it, he may give us free passes."

"Easy!" I said. "And it'd take a big load off his mind. They say it worries the Follies people half sick wondering what to do with all their free passes."

"Suppose we go to-night!" says Kate. "We can drop in a hotel somewhere and get seats. The longer we don't go, the longer we won't meet him."

"And the longer we don't meet him," I says, "the longer till he gives you the air."

"I'm not thinking of Mr. Ralston as a possible suitor," says Katie, swelling up. "But I do want to get acquainted with a man that don't bore a person to death."

"Well," I says, "if this baby's anything like the rest of your gentlemen friends, he won't hardly be round long enough for that."

I didn't make no kick about going to the show. We hadn't spent no money since we'd moved back to Town and I was as tired as the gals of setting up in the room, playing rummy. They said we'd have to dress, and I kicked just from habit, but I'd got past minding that end of it. They was one advantage in dolling up every time you went anywheres. It meant an hour when they was no chance to do something even sillier.

We couldn't stop to put on the nose bag at the Graham because the women was scared we'd be too late to get tickets. Besides, when you're dressed for dinner, you at least want the waiter to be the same. So we took a taxi down to the Spencer, bought Follies seats in the ninth row, and went in to eat. It's been in all the papers that the price of food has came down, but the hotel man can't read. They fined us eleven smackers for a two-course banquet that if the Woman's Guild, here, would dast soak you four bits a plate for it, somebody'd write a nasty letter to the *News-Times*.

We got in the theater a half hour before the show begin. I put in the time finding out what the men will wear, and the gals looked up what scenes Ralston'd be in. He was only on once in each act. They don't waste much time on a comedian in the Follies. It don't take long to spring the two gags they can think up for him in a year, and besides, he just interferes with the big gal numbers, where Bunny Granville or somebody dreams of the different flappers he danced with at the prom, and the souvenirs they give him; and one by one the different gals writhes in, dressed like the stage director thinks they dress at the female colleges—a Wesley gal in pink tights, a Vassar dame in hula-hula, and a Smith gal with a sombrero and a tailor suit. He does a couple of steps with them and they each hand him a flower or a vegetable to remember them by. The song winds up:

> But my most exclusive token
> Is a little hangnail broken
> Off the gal from Gussie's School for Manicures.

And his real sweet patootie comes on made up as a scissors.

You've saw Ralston? He's a good comedian; no getting away from that. The way he fixes up his face, you laugh just to look at him. I yelled when I first seen him. He was supposed to be an office boy and he got back late from lunch and the boss ast him what made him late and he said he stopped to buy the extra. So the boss ast him what extra and he says the extra about the New York society couple getting married. So the boss said, "Why, they wouldn't print an extra about that. They's a New York society couple married most every day." So Ralston said, "Yes, but this couple is both doing it for the first time."

I don't remember what other gags he had, and they're old anyway by now. But he was a hit, especially with Ella and Kate. They screamed so loud I thought we'd get the air. If he didn't say a word, he'd be funny with that fool make-up and that voice.

I guess if it wasn't for me the gals would of insisted on going back to the stage door after the show and waiting for him to come out. I've saw Katie bad a lot of times, but never as cuckoo as this. It wasn't no case of love at first or second sight. You couldn't be stuck on this guy from seeing him. But she'd always been kind of stage-struck and was crazy over the idear of getting acquainted with a celebrity, maybe going round to places with him, and having people see her with Jimmy Ralston, the comedian. And then, of course, most anybody wants to meet a person that can make you laugh.

I managed to persuade them that the best dope would be to go back to the Graham and wait for him to come home; maybe we could fix it up with the night clerk to introduce us. I told them that irregardless of what you read in books, they's some members of the theatrical profession that occasionally visits the place where they sleep. So we went to the hotel and set in the lobby for an hour and a half, me trying to keep awake wile the gals played Ralston's part of the show over again a couple thousand times. They's nothing goes so big with me as listening to people repeat gags out of a show that I just seen.

The clerk had been tipped off and when Ralston finally come in and went to get his key, I strolled up to the desk like I was after mine. The clerk introduced us.

"I want you to meet my wife and sister-in-law," I said.

"Some other time," says Ralston. "They's a matinee to-morrow and I got to run off to bed."

So off he went and I got bawled out for Ziegfeld having matinees. But I squared myself two days afterwards when we went in the restaurant for lunch. He was just having breakfast and the three of us stopped by his table. I don't think he remembered ever seeing me before, but anyway he got up and shook hands with the women. Well, you couldn't never accuse Ella of having a faint heart, and she says:

"Can't we set down with you, Mr. Ralston? We want to tell you how much we enjoyed the Follies."

So he says, sure, set down, but I guess we would of anyway.

"We thought it was a dandy show," says Katie.

"It ain't a bad troupe," says Ralston.

"If you'll pardon me getting personal," said Ella, "we thought you was the best thing in it."

He looked like he'd strain a point and forgive her.

"We all just yelled!" says Katie. "I was afraid they'd put us out, you made us laugh so hard."

"Well," says Ralston, "I guess if they begin putting people out for that, I'd have to leave the troupe."

"It wouldn't be much of a show without you," says Ella.

"Well, all that keeps me in it is friendship for Ziggy," says Ralston. "I said to him last night, I says, 'Ziggy, I'm going to quit the troupe. I'm tired and I want to rest a wile.' So he says, 'Jim, don't quit or I'll have to close the troupe. I'll give you fifteen hundred a week to stay.' I'm getting a thousand now. But I says to him, I said, 'Ziggy, it ain't a question of money. What I want is a troupe of my own, where I get a chance to do serious work. I'm sick of making a monkey of myself in front of a bunch of saps from Nyack that don't appreciate no art but what's wrapped up in a stocking.' So he's promised that if I'll stick it out this year, he'll star me next season in a serious piece."

"Is he giving you the five hundred raise?" I ast him.

"I wouldn't take it," said Ralston. "I don't need money."

"At that, a person can live pretty cheap at this hotel," I says.

"I didn't move here because it was cheap," he said. "I moved here to get away from the pests—women that wants my autograph or my picture. And all they could say was how much they enjoyed my work and how did I think up all them gags, and so forth. No real artist likes to talk about himself, especially to people that don't understand. So that's the reason why I left the Ritz, so's I'd be left alone, not to save money. And I don't save no money, neither. I've got the best suite in the house—bedroom, bath, and study."

"What do you study?" ast Kate.

"The parts I want to play," he says; "Hamlet and Macbeth and Richard."

"But you're a comedian," says Kate.

"It's just a stepping stone," said Ralston.

He'd finished his breakfast and got up.

"I must go to my study and work," he says. "We'll meet again."

"Yes, indeed," says Ella. "Do you always come right back here nights after the show?"

"When I can get away from the pests," he says.

"Well," says Ella, "suppose you come up to our rooms to-night and we'll have a bite to eat. And I think the husband can give you a little liquid refreshments if you ever indulge."

"Very little," he says. "What is your room number?"

So the Mrs. told him and he said he'd see us after the show that night, and walked out.

"Well," said Ella, "how do you like him?"

"I think he's wonderful!" says Katie. "I didn't have no idear he was so deep, wanting to play Hamlet."

"Pretty near all comedians has got that bug," I says.

"Maybe he's different when you know him better," said Ella.

"I don't want him to be different," says Kate.

"But he was so serious," said the Mrs. "He didn't say nothing funny."

"Sure he did," I says. "Didn't he say artists hate to talk about themselfs?"

Pretty soon the waiter come in with our lunch. He ast us if the other gentleman was coming back.

"No," said Ella. "He's through."

"He forgot his check," says the dish smasher.

"Oh, never mind!" says Ella. "We'll take care of that."

"Well," I says, "I guess the bird was telling the truth when he said he didn't need no money."

I and the gals spent the evening at a picture show and stopped at a delicatessen on the way home to stock up for the banquet. I had a quart and a pint of yearling rye, and a couple of bottles of McAllister that they'd fined me fifteen smackers apiece for and I wanted to save them, so I told Kate that I hoped her friend would get comical enough on the rye.

"He said he drunk very little," she reminded me.

"Remember, don't make him talk about himself," said the Mrs. "What we want is to have him feel at home, like he was with old friends, and then maybe he'll warm up. I hope we don't wake the whole hotel, laughing."

Well, Ralston showed up about midnight. He'd remembered his date and apologized for not getting there before.

"I like to walk home from the theater," he says. "I get some of my funniest idears wile I walk."

I come to the conclusion later that he spent practically his whole life riding.

Ella's and my room wasn't no gymnasium for size and after the third drink, Ralston tried to get to the dresser to look at himself in the glass, and knocked a $30 vase for a corpse. This didn't go very big with the Mrs., but she forced a smile and would of accepted his apology if he'd made any. All he done was mumble something about cramped quarters. They was even more cramped when we set the table for the big feed, and it was my tough luck to have our guest park himself in the chair nearest the clothes closet, where my two bottles of Scotch had been put to bed. The fourth snifter finished the pint of rye and I said I'd get the other quart, but before I could stop her, Ella says:

"Let Mr. Ralston get it. It's right there by him."

So the next thing you know, James has found the good stuff and he comes out with both bottles of it.

"McAllister!" he says. "That's my favorite. If I'd knew you had that, I wouldn't of drank up all your rye."

"You haven't drank it all up," I says. "They's another bottle of it in there."

"It can stay there as long as we got this," he says, and helped himself to the corkscrew.

Well, amongst the knickknacks the gals had picked up at the delicatessen was a roast chicken and a bottle of olives, and at the time I thought Ralston was swallowing bones, stones, and all. It wasn't till the next day that we found all these keepsakes on the floor, along with a couple dozen assorted cigarette butts.

Katie's chorus gal friend had told her how funny the guy was when he'd had just the right number of shots, but I'd counted eight and begin to get discouraged before he started talking.

"My mother could certainly cook a chicken," he says.

"Is your mother living?" Kate ast him.

"No," he says. "She was killed in a railroad wreck. I'll never forget when I had to go and identify her. You wouldn't believe a person could get that mangled! No," he says, "my family's all gone. I never seen my father. He was in the pesthouse with smallpox when I was born and he died there. And my only sister died of jaundice. I can still——"

But Kate was scared we'd wake up the hotel, laughing, so she says: "Do you ever give imitations?"

"You mustn't make Mr. Ralston talk about himself," says Ella.

"Imitations of who?" said Ralston.

"Oh, other actors," said Katie.

"No," he says. "I leave it to the other actors to give imitations of me."

"I never seen none of them do it," says Kate.

"They all do it, but they don't advertise it," he says. "Every comic in New York is using my stuff."

"Oh!" said Ella. "You mean they steal your idears."

"Can't you go after them for it?" ast Katie.

"You could charge them with petit larceny," I said.

"I wouldn't be mean," said Ralston. "But they ain't a comic on the stage to-day that I didn't give him every laugh he's got."

"You ain't only been on the stage three or four years," I says. "How did Hitchcock and Ed Wynn and them fellas get by before they seen you?"

"They wasn't getting by," he says. "I'm the baby that put them on their feet. Take Hitchy. Hitchy come to me last spring and says, 'Jim, I've ran out of stuff. Have you got any notions I could use?' So I says, 'Hitchy, you're welcome to anything I got.' So I give him a couple of idears and they're the only laughs in his troupe. And you take Wynn. He opened up with a troupe that looked like a flop and one day I seen him on Broadway, wearing a long pan, and I says, 'What's the matter, Eddie?' And he brightened up and says, 'Hello, there, Jim! You're just the boy I want to see.' So I says, 'Well, Eddie, I'm only too glad to do anything I can.' So he says, 'I got a flop on my hands unlest I can get a couple of idears, and you're the baby that can give them to me.' So I said, 'All right, Eddie.' And I give him a couple of notions to work on and they made his show. And look at Stone! And Errol! And Jolson and Tinney! Every one of them come to me at one time another, hollering for help. 'Jim, give me a couple of notions!' 'Jim, give me a couple of gags!' And not a one of them went away empty-handed."

"Did they pay you?" ast Ella.

Ralston smiled.

"I wouldn't take no actor's money," he says. "They're all brothers to me. They can have anything I got, and I can have anything they got, only they haven't got nothing."

Well, I can't tell you all he said, as I was asleep part of the time. But I do remember that he was the one that had give Bert Williams the notion of playing coon parts, and learnt Sarah Bernhardt to talk French.

Along about four o'clock, when they was less than a pint left in the second McAllister bottle, he defied all the theater managers in New York.

"I ain't going to monkey with them much longer!" he says. "I'll let you folks in on something that'll cause a sensation on Broadway. I'm going to quit the Follies!"

We was all speechless.

"That's the big secret!" he says. "I'm coming out as a star under my own management and in a troupe wrote and produced by myself!"

"When?" ast Kate.

"Just as soon as I decide who I'm going to let in as part owner," said Ralston. "I've worked for other guys long enough! Why should I be satisfied with $800 a week when Ziegfeld's getting rich off me!"

"When did he cut you $200?" I says. "You was getting $1,000 last time I seen you."

He didn't pay no attention.

"And why should I let some manager produce my play," he says, "and pay me maybe $1,200 a week when I ought to be making six or seven thousand!"

"Are you working on your play now?" Kate ast him.

"It's done," he says. "I'm just trying to make up my mind who's the right party to let in on it. Whoever it is, I'll make him rich."

"I've got some money to invest," says Katie. "Suppose you tell us about the play."

"I'll give you the notion, if you'll keep it to yourself," says Ralston. "It's a serious play with a novelty idear that'll be a sensation. Suppose I go down to my suite and get the script and read it to you."

"Oh, if you would!" says Kate.

"It'll knock you dead!" he says.

And just the thought of it was fatal to the author. He got up from his chair, done a nose dive acrost the table and laid there with his head in the chili sauce.

I called up the clerk and had him send up the night bellhop with our guest's key. I and the boy acted as pall bearers and got him to his "suite," where we performed the last sad rites. Before I come away I noticed that the "suite" was a ringer for Ella's and mine—a dinky little room with a bath. The "study" was prettily furnished with coat hangers.

When I got back to my room Katie'd ducked and the Mrs. was asleep, so I didn't get a chance to talk to them till we was in the restaurant at noon. Then I ast Kate if she'd figured out just what number drink it was that had started him being comical.

"Now listen," she says: "I don't think that Abbott girl ever met him in her life. Anyway, she had him all wrong. We expected he'd do stunts, like she said, but he ain't that kind that shows off or acts smart. He's too much of a man for that. He's a bigger man than I thought."

"I and the bellhop remarked that same thing," I says.

"And you needn't make fun of him for getting faint," says Katie. "I called him up a wile ago to find out how he was and he apologized and said they must of been something in that second bottle of Scotch."

So I says:

"You tell him they was, but they ain't."

Well, it couldn't of been the Scotch or no other brew that ruined me. Or if it was, it worked mighty slow. I didn't even look at a drink for three days after the party in our room. But the third day I felt rotten, and that night I come down with a fever. Ella got scared and called a doctor and he said it was flu, and if I didn't watch my step it'd be something worse. He advised taking me to a hospital and I didn't have pep enough to say no.

So they took me and I was pretty sick for a couple of weeks— too sick for the Mrs. to give me the news. And it's a wonder I didn't have a relapse when she finally did.

"You'll probably yelp when you hear this," she says. "I ain't crazy about it myself, but it didn't do me no good to argue at first and it's too late for argument now. Well, to begin with, Sis is in love with Ralston."

"What of it!" I said. "She's going through the city directory and she's just got to the R's."

"No, it's the real thing this time," said the Mrs. "Wait till you hear the rest of it. She's going on the stage!"

"I've got nothing against that," I says. "She's pretty enough to get by in the Follies chorus, and if she can earn money that way, I'm for it."

"She ain't going into no chorus," said Ella. "Ralston's quit the Follies and she's going in his show."

"The one he wrote?" I ast.

"Yes," said the Mrs.

"And who's going to put it on?" I ast her.

"That's it," she says. "They're going to put it on themself, Ralston and Sis. With Sis's money. She sold her bonds, fifty thousand dollars' worth."

"But listen," I says. "Fifty thousand dollars! What's the name of the play, Ringling Circus?"

"It won't cost all that," said Ella. "They figure it'll take less than ten thousand to get started. But she insisted on having the whole thing in a checking account, where she can get at it. If the show's a big success in New York they're going to have a company in Chicago and another on the road. And Ralston says her half of the profits in New York ought to run round $5,000 a week. But anyway, she's sure of $200 a week salary for acting in it."

"Where did she get the idear she can act?" I says.

"She's always had it," said the Mrs., "and I think she made him promise to put her in the show before she agreed to back it. Though she says it's a wonderful investment! She won't be the leading woman, of course. But they's only two woman's parts and she's got one of them."

"Well," I said, "if she's going to play a sap and just acts normal, she'll be a sensation."

"I don't know what she'll be," says Ella. "All I know is that she's mad over Ralston and believes everything he says. And even if you hadn't of been sick we couldn't of stopped her."

So I ast what the play was like, but Ella couldn't tell me.

Ralston had read it out loud to she and Kate, but she couldn't judge from just hearing it that way. But Kate was tickled to death with it. And they'd already been rehearsing a week, but Sis hadn't let Ella see the rehearsals. She said it made her nervous.

"Ralston thinks the main trouble will be finding a theater," said the Mrs. "He says they's a shortage of them and the men that owns them won't want to let him have one on account of jealousy."

"Has the Follies flopped?" I ast her.

"No," she says, "but they've left town."

"They always do, this time of year," I said.

"That's what I thought," says the Mrs., "but Ralston says they'd intended to stay here all the year round, but when the news come out that he'd left, they didn't dast. He's certainly got faith in himself. He must have, to give up a $600 a week salary. That's what he says he was really getting."

"You say Katie's in love," I says. "How about him?"

"I don't know and she don't know," says Ella. "He calls her dearie and everything and holds her hands, but when they're alone together, he won't talk nothing but business. Still, as I say, he calls her dearie."

"Actors calls every gal that," I says. "It's because they can't remember names."

Well, to make a short story out of it, they had another couple weeks' rehearsals that we wasn't allowed to see, and they finally got a theater—the Olney. They had to guarantee a $10,000 business to get it. They didn't go to Atlantic City or nowheres for a tryout. They opened cold. And Ralston didn't tell nobody what kind of a show it was.

Of course he done what they generally always do on a first night. He sent out free passes to everybody that's got a dress suit, and they's enough of them in New York to pretty near fill up a theater. These invited guests is supposed to be for the performance wile it's going on. After it's through, they can go out and ride it all over the island.

Well, the rules wasn't exactly lived up to at "Bridget Sees a Ghost." On account of Ralston writing the play and starring in it, the gang thought it would be comical and they come prepared to laugh. It was comical all right, and they laughed. They didn't only laugh; they yelled. But they yelled in the wrong place.

The programme said it was "a Daring Drama in Three Acts." The three acts was what made it daring. It took nerve to even have one. In the first place, this was two years after the armistice and the play was about the war, and I don't know which the public was most interested in by this time—the war or Judge Parker.

Act 1 was in July, 1917. Ralston played the part of Francis Shaw, a captain in the American army. He's been married a year, and when the curtain goes up, his wife's in their New York home, waiting for him to come in from camp on his weekly leave. She sets reading the war news in the evening paper, and she reads it out loud, like people always do when they're alone, waiting for somebody. Pretty soon in comes Bridget, the Irish maid—our own dear Katie. And I wished you could of heard her brogue. And seen her gestures. What she reminded me most like was a gal in a home talent minstrels giving an imitation of Lew Fields playing the part of the block system on the New York Central. Her first line was, "Ain't der Captain home yed?" But I won't try and give you her dialect.

"No," says Mrs. Shaw. "He's late." So Katie says better late than never, and the wife says, yes, but she's got a feeling that some day it'll be never; something tells her that if he ever goes to France, he won't come back. So Bridget says, "You been reading the war news again and it always makes you sad." "I hate wars!" says Mrs. Shaw, and that line got one of the biggest laughs.

After this they was a couple of minutes when neither of them could think of nothing to add, and then the phone rung and Bridget answered it. It was Capt. Shaw, saying he'd be there pretty soon; so Bridget goes right back to the kitchen to finish getting dinner, but she ain't no sooner than left the stage when Capt. Shaw struts in. He must of called up from the public booth on his front porch.

The audience had a tough time recognizing him without his comic make-up, but when they did they give him a good hand. Mrs. Shaw got up to greet him, but he brushed by her and come down to the footlights to bow. Then he turned and went back to his Mrs., saying "Maizie!" like this was the last place he expected to run acrost her. They kissed and then he ast her "Where is Bobbie, our dear little one?"—for fear she wouldn't know whose little one he meant. So she rung the bell and back come Bridget, and he says "Well, Bridget!" and Bridget says, "Well, it's the master!" This line was another riot. "Bring the little one, Bridget," says Mrs. Shaw, and the audience hollered again.

Wile Bridget was after the little one, the Captain celebrated the reunion by walking round the room, looking at the pictures. Bridget brings the baby in and the Captain uncovers its face and says, "Well, Bobbie!" Then he turns to his wife and says. "Let's see, Maizie. How old is he?" "Two weeks," says Maizie. "Two weeks!" says Captain Shaw, surprised. "Well," he says. "I hope by the time he's old enough to fight for the Stars and Stripes, they won't be no such a thing as war." So Mrs. Shaw says, "And I hope his father won't be called on to make the supreme sacrifice for him and we others that must stay home and wait. I sometimes think that in wartime, it's the women and children that suffers most. Take him back to his cozy cradle, Bridget. We mothers must be careful of our little ones. Who knows when the kiddies will be our only comfort!" So Bridget beat it out with the little one and I bet he hated to leave all the gaiety.

"Well," says Shaw to his wife, "and what's the little woman been doing?"

"Just reading," she says, "reading the news of this horrible war. I don't never pick up the paper but what I think that some day I'll see your name amongst the dead."

"Well," says the Captain bravely, "they's no danger wile I stay on U. S. soil. But only for you and the little one, I would welcome the call to go Over There and take my place in the battle line. The call will come soon, I believe, for they say France needs men." This rumor pretty near caused a riot in the audience and Ralston turned and give us all a dirty look.

Then Bridget come in again and said dinner was ready, and Shaw says, "It'll seem funny to set down wile I eat." Which was the first time I ever knew that army captains took their meals off the mantelpiece.

Wile the Shaws was out eating, their maid stayed in the living room, where she'd be out of their way. It seems that Ralston had wrote a swell speech for her to make in this spot, about what a tough thing war is, to come along and separate a happy young couple like the Shaws that hadn't only been married a year. But the speech started "This is terrible!" and when Bridget got that much of it out, some egg in the gallery hollered "You said a mouthful, kid!" and stopped the show.

The house finally quieted down, but Katie was dumb for the first time in her life. She couldn't say the line that was the cue for the phone to ring, and she had to go over and answer a silent call. It was for the Captain, and him and his wife both come back on the stage.

"Maizie," he says, after he'd hung up, "it's came! That was my general! We sail for France in half an hour!"

"O husband!" says Maizie. "This is the end!"

"Nonsense!" says Shaw with a brave smile. "This war means death for only a small per cent of our men."

"And almost no captains," yells the guy in the gallery.

Shaw gets ready to go, but she tells him to wait till she puts on her wraps; she'll go down to the dock and see him off.

"No, darling," he says. "Our orders is secret. I can't give you the name of our ship or where we're sailing from."

So he goes and she flops on the couch w'ining because he wouldn't tell her whether his ship left from Times Square or Grand Central.

They rung the curtain down here to make you think six days has passed. When it goes up again, Maizie's setting on the couch, holding the little one. Pretty soon Bridget comes in with the evening paper.

"They's a big headline, mum," she says. "A troopship has been torpedoed."

Well, when she handed her the paper, I could see the big headline. It said, "Phillies Hit Grimes Hard." But Maizie may of had a bet on Brooklyn. Anyway, she begin trembling and finally fell over stiff. So Bridget picked up the paper and read it out loud:

"Amongst the men lost was Capt. F. Shaw of New York."

Down went the curtain again and the first act was over, and some jokesmith in the audience yelled "Author! Author!"

"He's sunk!" said the egg in the gallery.

Well, Maizie was the only one in the whole theater that thought Shaw was dead. The rest of us just wished it. Still you couldn't blame her much for getting a wrong idear, as it was Nov. 11, 1918— over a year later—when the second act begins, and she hadn't heard from him in all that time. It wasn't never brought out why. Maybe he'd forgot her name or maybe it was Burleson's fault, like everything else.

The scene was the same old living room and Maizie was setting on the same old couch, but she was all dressed up like Elsie Ferguson. It comes out that she's expecting a gentleman friend, a Mr. Thornton, to dinner. She asks Bridget if she thinks it would be wrong of her to accept the guy the next time he proposed. He's ast her every evening for the last six months and she can't stall him much longer. So Bridget says it's all right if she loves him, but Maizie don't know if she loves him or not, but he looks so much like her late relic that she can't hardly tell the difference and besides, she has got to either

marry or go to work, or her and the little one will starve. They's a
knock at the door and Thornton comes in. Him and the absent
Captain looks as much alike as two brothers, yours and mine.
Bridget ducks and Thornton proposes. Maizie says, "Before I an-
swer, I must tell you a secret. Captain Shaw didn't leave me all alone.
I have a little one, a boy." "Oh, I love kiddies," says Thornton. "Can
I see him?" So she says it's seven o'clock and the little one's sup-
posed to of been put to bed, but she has Bridget go get him.

The little one's entrance was the sensation of this act. In act 1
he was just three or four towels, but now Bridget can't even carry
him acrost the stage, and when she put him on his feet, he comes
up pretty near to her shoulder. And when Thornton ast him would
he like to have a new papa, he says, "Yes, because my other papa's
never coming back."

Well, they say a woman can't keep a secret, but if Thornton had
been nosing round for six months and didn't know till now that they
was a spanker like Bobbie in the family circle, I wouldn't hardly call
Maizie the town gossip.

After the baby'd went back to read himself to sleep and Mrs.
Shaw had yessed her new admirer, Bridget dashed in yelling that the
armistice was signed and held up the evening paper for Maizie and
Thornton to see. The great news was announced in code. It said:
"Phillies Hit Grimes Hard." And it seemed kind of silly to not come
right out and say "Armistice Signed!" Because as I recall, even we
saps out here in South Bend had knew it since three o'clock that
morning.

The last act was in the same place, on Christmas Eve, 1918.
Maizie and her second husband had just finished doing up presents for the little one. We couldn't see the presents, but I suppose
they was giving him a cocktail shaker and a shaving set. Though
when he come on the stage you could see he hadn't aged much since
Act 2. He hadn't even begin to get bald.

Thornton and the Mrs. went off somewheres and left the kid alone,
but all of a sudden the front door opened and in come old Cap
Shaw, on crutches. He seen the kid and called to him. "Who are
you?" says the little one. "I'm Santa Claus," says the Cap, "and I've
broughten you a papa for Christmas." "I don't want no papa," says
Bobbie. "I've just got a new one." Then Bridget popped in and seen
"the master" and hollered, "A ghost!" So he got her calmed down

and she tells him what's came off. "It was in the paper that Capt. F. Shaw of New York was lost," she says. "It must of been another Capt. F. Shaw!" he says.

"It's an odd name," hollered the guy in the gallery.

The Captain thinks it all over and decides it's his move. He makes Bridget promise to never tell that she seen him and he says good-by to she and the kid and goes out into the night.

Maizie comes in, saying she heard a noise and what was it? Was somebody here? "Just the boy with the evening paper," says Bridget. And the cat's got Bobbie's tongue. And Maizie don't even ask for the paper. She probably figured to herself it was the old story; that Grimes was still getting his bumps.

Well, I wished you could of read what the papers wrote up about the show. One of them said that Bridget seen a ghost at the Olney theater last night and if anybody else wanted to see it, they better go quick because it wouldn't be walking after this week. Not even on crutches. The mildest thing they said about Ralston was that he was even funnier than when he was in the Follies and tried to be. And they said the part of Bridget was played by a young actress that they hoped would make a name for herself, because Ralston had probably called her all he could think of.

We waited at the stage door that night and when Kate come out, she was crying. Ralston had canned her from the show.

"That's nothing to cry about," I says. "You're lucky! It's just like as if a conductor had put you off a train a couple of minutes before a big smash-up."

The programme had been to all go somewheres for supper and celebrate the play's success. But all Katie wanted now was to get in a taxi and go home and hide.

On the way, I ast her how much she was in so far.

"Just ten thousand," she says.

"Ten thousand!" I said. "Why, they was only one piece of scenery and that looked like they'd bought it secondhand from the choir boys' minstrels. They couldn't of spent one thousand, let alone ten."

"We had to pay the theater a week's rent in advance," she says. "And Jimmy give five thousand to a man for the idear."

"The idear for what?" I ast.

"The idear for the play," she said.

"That stops me!" I says. "This baby furnishes idears for all the good actors in the world, but when he wants one for himself, he goes out and pays $5,000 for it. And if he got a bargain, you're Mrs. Fiske."

"Who sold him the idear?" ast Ella.

"He wouldn't tell me," says Kate.

"Ponzi," I said.

Ralston called Kate up the next noon and made a date with her at the theater. He said that he was sorry he'd been rough. Before she went I ast her to give me a check for the forty thousand she had left so's I could buy back some of her bonds.

"I haven't got only $25,000," she says. "I advanced Jimmy fifteen thousand for his own account, so's he wouldn't have to bother me every time they was bills to meet."

So I said: "Listen: I'll go see him with you and if he don't come clean with that money, I'll knock him deader'n his play."

"Thank you!" she says. "I'll tend to my own affairs alone."

She come back late in the afternoon, all smiles.

"Everything's all right," she said. "I give him his choice of letting me be in the play or giving me my money."

"And which did he choose?" I ast her.

"Neither one," she says. "We're going to get married."

"Bridget" went into the ashcan Saturday night and the wedding come off Monday. Monday night they left for Boston, where the Follies was playing. Kate told us they'd took Ralston back at the same salary he was getting before.

"How much is that?" I ast her.

"Four hundred a week," she says.

Well, two or three days after they'd left, I got up my nerve and says to the Mrs.:

"Do you remember what we moved to the Big Town for? We done it to see Life and get Katie a husband. Well, we got her a kind of a husband and I'll tell the world we seen Life. How about moseying back to South Bend?"

"But we haven't no home there now."

"Nor we ain't had none since we left there," I says. "I'm going down and see what's the first day we can get a couple of lowers."

"Get uppers if it's quicker," says the Mrs.

So here we are, really enjoying ourselfs for the first time in pretty near two years. And Katie's in New York, enjoying herself, too, I suppose. She ought to be, married to a comedian. It must be such fun to just set and listen to him talk.

The Tridget of Greva
Translated from the Squinch

"The Tridget of Greva" was the first of the famous nonsense plays. It has never been published before, but was presented in a revue called "The Forty-Niners" given by some members of the Round Table at the Algonquin. Parts of it have been used in the other plays (which have been in and out of print) but here is the whole Tridget, slightly edited and cut by Ring Lardner, Jr.

CHARACTERS

Louis Barhooter, *the Tridget*
Desire Corby, *a Corn Vitter*
Basil Laffler, *a Wham Salesman*

(*At the rise of the curtain,* BARHOOTER, CORBY *and* LAFFLER *are seated in three small flat-bottomed boats. They are fishing.*)

LAFFLER: Well, boys, any luck?

(*He looks from one to the other. Neither pays any attention*)

CORBY: (*After a pause, to* BARHOOTER) How's your wife, Louis?

BARHOOTER: She in pretty bad shape.

CORBY: (*Who has paid no attention to the reply*) That's fine.

BARHOOTER: By the way, what was *your* mother's name before she was married?

CORBY: I didn't know her then.

LAFFLER: Do they allow people to fish at the Aquarium?

(BARHOOTER *and* CORBY *ignore him*)

BARHOOTER: You must know her first name.

CORBY: I don't. I always called her Mother.

BARHOOTER: But your father must have called her something.

CORBY: Everything he could think of.

(LAFFLER'S *and* BARHOOTER'S *fishlines become entangled.* BARHOOTER *gets out of his boat, untangles the lines, and resumes his place in the boat*)

BARHOOTER: (*To* CORBY) I wanted to ask you something about your sister, too.

CORBY: What about her?

BARHOOTER: Just anything. For instance, what's the matter with her?

CORBY: Who?

BARHOOTER: Your sister.

CORBY: I'm not married.

(*After a pause,* BARHOOTER *and* CORBY *both laugh.*)

BARHOOTER: (*To* LAFFLER) Do you know what we were laughing at?

LAFFLER: I have no idea.

BARHOOTER: I wish I knew who to ask.

CORBY: (*To* BARHOOTER) Which way is the wind from?

BARHOOTER: (*Moistens his finger and holds it up*) It's from off-stage. (*He draws in his line, discovers the bait is gone*) That fellow got my bait. (*He throws his line out again without rebaiting it.*)

CORBY: (*To* BARHOOTER) I understand you're an uncle.

BARHOOTER: Yes, but do you want to know what happened?

CORBY: No.

BARHOOTER: Well, two days before the baby was born, Bertha and her husband were out driving.

LAFFLER: Who's Bertha?

BARHOOTER: (*Paying no attention*) They were going up a steep hill and Harry tried to change into second speed.

LAFFLER: Who's Harry?

BARHOOTER: But he made a mistake and shifted into reverse and the car went clear to the bottom of the hill.

CORBY: In reverse?

BARHOOTER: Yes. And the baby is very backward.

CORBY: It seems to me there is something wrong with all your sister's children. Look at Julia!

(BARHOOTER *and* LAFFLER *look in all directions, as if trying to locate Julia*)

BARHOOTER: (*To* CORBY) Can you imitate birds?

CORBY: No. Why?

BARHOOTER: I'm always afraid I'll be near somebody that can imitate birds.

CORBY: (*To* BARHOOTER) That reminds me, Louis—Do you shave yourself?

BARHOOTER: Who would I shave?

CORBY: Well, when you shave, what do you do with your old whiskers?

BARHOOTER: I don't do anything with them.

CORBY: Will you save them for me?

BARHOOTER: What do you do with them?

CORBY: I play with them.

BARHOOTER: (*With no apparent interest*) You're a scream, Corby.

LAFFLER: (*To* BARHOOTER) Is your first wife still living?

BARHOOTER: I'm not sure. I haven't been home for a long while. But I heard she was dead.

LAFFLER: What did she die of?

BARHOOTER: I think she got her throat caught between my fingers.

LAFFLER: Mr. Corby—

CORBY: Well?

LAFFLER: I often wonder how you spell your name.

CORBY: A great many people have asked me that. The answer is, I don't even try. I just let it go.

LAFFLER: I think that's kind of risky.

CORBY: I'm getting hungry. I wish we could catch some fish.

BARHOOTER: I'm hungry, too, but not for fish.

LAFFLER: I can't eat fish either. I've got no teeth. (*Opens his mouth and shows his teeth*) About all I can eat is broth.

BARHOOTER: Well, let's go to a brothel.

BLACK OUT

The Bull Pen

CAST OF CHARACTERS *

Bill Carney, *a pitcher* ....AL OCHS
Cy Walters, *a pitcher* ....WILL ROGERS
Joe Webb, *a Busher* ....ANDY TOOMBES

SCENE—*"Bull Pen" at the Polo Grounds during a game between the Yankees and Cleveland. Bill and Cy are seated on empty boxes.*

JOE: What innings is it?

CY: Third.

JOE: What's the score?

CY: One and one. And in case you don't know who's playing, it's us and Cleveland. And you're in the American League.

JOE: I know what league I'm in and I know what league I wisht I was in. I wisht I was back in the Central League.

CY: Looks to me like you was going to get your wish.

JOE: They'll keep me longer than they will you.

CY: Well, I've got a good start on you. You only been here part of one season and I was here all last year besides.

JOE: Yes, but how many games did you pitch?

CY: Well, I pitched 154 games last year and about fifty so far this year. And I pitched 'em all right here where we're standing. Some guys gets all swelled up over pitching one no-hit game. Well, the Yankees has played over 200 games since I been with them and nobody's got a hit off me yet.

JOE: I wisht I was where they paid some attention to a man.

CY: That's what I wished the first part of last season. But the last part of the season, I wished they'd ignore me entirely. I used to make ugly faces at Huggins in hopes he'd get mad and quit speaking to me. But just before every game he'd say, "Go down to the Bull Pen and warm up." *WARM UP!* Say, there may be better pitchers than me in this league, but there ain't none that's hotter.

* As played in the Ziegfeld Follies of 1922.

BILL (*commenting on game*): Bob was lucky to get by that inning! Did you see that one Scotty grabbed off Speaker?

JOE: Them guys don't know how to pitch to Speaker.

CY (*gives him a look*): No? How would *you* pitch to him?

JOE: First I'd give him my fast one——

CY: Hold on! Now you're pitching to the next batter. Speaker's on third base.

JOE: How would he get to third base?

CY: He'd slide.

JOE: You ain't seen my fast one when I'm right. It goes zooy! (*Makes motion with hands.*)

CY: Yes, and after it bounced off Speaker's bat, it'd go zeet! (*Makes similar motion.*) Especially this ball they're using these days with a raisin in it.

BILL: The Babe's up. (*Without raising his voice*) Come on, Babe! Bust one!

JOE: He wouldn't bust one if I was pitching!

CY: How would you pitch to *him*?

JOE: High and on the outside.

CY: And that's just where it'd go.

BILL: No, he popped up.

JOE: Just the same, I bet Ruth's glad I ain't with some other club.

CY: He don't know you ain't.

JOE: I bet he don't break no home run record this year.

CY: Look how long he was out!

JOE: Well, it was his own fault. I bet if *I'd* went barnstorming, Landis wouldn't of dast suspend *me* that long!

CY: He wouldn't of suspended you at all. He wouldn't of never heard about it.

BILL: Coveleskie must *have* something in there. He made Baker pop up!

JOE: I wisht I could go in there to the bench.

CY: What for?

JOE (*with a self-conscious smile*): Well, do you remember before the game, when I was up there throwing to Schang? Well, they was a swell dame come in and set down right behind our bench. She looked like a Follies dame. And she give me *some* smile!

CY: She done well to keep from laughing outright.

JOE: She was trying to make me.

CY: She was trying to make you out.

JOE: I bet if Huggins had of left me stay on the bench, I'd be all set by now.

CY: Yes, and that's why Huggins don't let you stay on the bench. He told me the other day, he says, "Cy, old pal, I hope it won't bother you to have this gargoyle down there warming up with you all the time. But it's against the rules to have gals on the bench, and if he was there I simply couldn't keep them off." He says, "I've got a hard enough bunch to manage without adding Peggy Hopkins."

JOE: How do *you* know that's her name?

CY: Oh, I seen her looking at you and I asked one of the ushers.

JOE: Peggy Hopkins! Do you know if she's married?

CY: I can't keep track.

JOE: Do you s'pose her name's in the book?

CY: Well, seems like I've seen it in print *somewheres*.

JOE (*as if to memorize it*): Peggy Hopkins.

BILL: Bob's wild. It's three and nothing on Sewell.

CY (*to* JOE): You better cut loose a little, kid. This may be our day.

JOE: Not both of us.

CY: Sure, providing he picks you first. (*Slight pause.*) But, listen, kid, if I was you I'd leave the dames alone. Wait till you've made good.

JOE: I ain't after no dames. But I can't help the looks they give me.

CY: No more than you can help the looks *God* give you. And he certainly didn't spread himself.

BILL: He's walked Sewell.

JOE: The *gals* seem to think I look O.K.

CY: How do you know?

JOE: The way they act. Do you remember that poor little kid in New Orleans?

CY: What kid?

JOE: The telephone gal in the hotel. She was down to the depot when we went away. But I ducked her. And that dame in Philadelphia.

CY: What do you owe *her?*

JOE: I don't owe you nothin', but she was out to the game every day, tryin' to flirt.

CY: Oh, *that* woman!

JOE: What woman?

CY: That's the woman that goes to the games in Philadelphia. You know those Philadelphia fans? Well, she's their sister.

JOE: I don't know who she is, but she certainly made eyes at me.

CY: She don't mean to make eyes. That's a nervous disease. She's been looking at the Athletics for six years. But you want to quit thinking about the dames and pay attention to your work.

JOE: *I* pay attention to my work!

CY: Well, at that, I can see you've made quite a study of the batters. You know how to pitch to Speaker and Ruth.

JOE: Yes, and some of them other high monkey monks.

CY: Well, how would you go to work on George Sisler?

JOE: Say, that guy won't never get a hit off me.

CY: I guess you're right. He told me one day that when he was through in the big league, he was through.

BILL: There goes Gardner. Another base on balls.

JOE: But there's one guy I *could* fool, is Sisler!

CY: Oh, anybody could *fool* him.

JOE: Well, how would *you* fool him?

CY: I'd say, "Hit this one, George." And then I'd throw him an orange. Then there's another way I bet I could fool him. I could say, "George, come out to the house to dinner to-night. My wife's a great cook. We live at 450 Riverside Drive." When he got there, he'd find out I don't live at that address, and besides, I ain't married.

JOE: Well, I'd like to get a chance at him. And another guy I'd like to pitch against is Cobb.

CY: Irvin?

JOE: That ain't his name is it?

CY: You mean the man that writes the outfield for Detroit. That's Irvin.

JOE: That's right, Irvin.

BILL: He hit O'Neill in the arm. The bases is choked, boys.

CY (*to* JOE): Put something on her, kid! If he can just get Coveleskie! (*Warming up at top speed*) Listen, kid, if you get in, don't be scared to cut loose! You got nothing to lose.

JOE: Do you think it'll be me?

CY: Well, it's one of us.

BILL (*with feeling*): Damn! Damn! And he had a double play right in front of him. Cy! He's waving to you!

CY (*jumps up and tears off his sweater*): Get out of the way, boy!

He wants me in there! (JOE, *dazed, gets out of his way and mournfully goes to the bench and sits down.* CY *throws one ball.*)

CY: I'm ready. (*He picks up his sweater and goes offstage, carrying it on his arm.*)

JOE: A fine manager we're workin' for!

(*Curtain*)

Quadroon

A Play in Four Pelts
Which May All Be Attended in One Day
or Missed in a Group

*Quadroon is a parody on O'Neill's lengthy "Mourning Becomes Electra,"
where the audience went out for dinner at intermission. Mr. Lardner
has concentrated largely on the dinner.*

(Author's Note: The characters were all born synonymously; that
is, in the "S'uth," they are known as half-castes. The only time the
play, or series of plays, was performed with a whole cast, it was
stopped by a swarm of little black flies, which don't bite, but are
annoying. One time, in Charlotte, Utah, I forget what did happen.

At this point, a word or two concerning the actors may not
embarrass you. Thomas Chalmers and Alice Brady are one and the
same person. I owned some Alice-Chalmers before the crush in the
market and had to give Kimbley & Co. twelve dollars hush money. I
asked Mr. Nymeyer one of the partners to get me out of Wall Street
and he said he had already moved me as far as Nassau. That is the
kind of a friend to have in the stock market. He says one of the men
in the firm paid $195,000 for a seat. Imagine, when you can get one
for $22.00 to a Ziegfeld opening if you know Goldie or Alice. I can
generally most always get one for nothing if he invites me to Boston
or Pittsburgh to look at one of his shows and see whether I can improve it. Those kind, as Percy Hammond would say, are usually so
good that they can't be improved and after I have heard the second
comic's first wow, I wish I had stayed in the hospital, where men are
orderlies.

Speaking of hospitals, I turned the last one I visited into a pretty good roadhouse. Harland Dixon came up and tap-danced, Vince Youmans and Paul Lanin dropped in twice and played, and Vic Arden made the piano speak a language with which it was entirely unfamiliar. Phil Ohman would have been there, too, if the doctor had given me a little more nerve tonic and Mrs. Bechlinger, the housekeeper, had had two pianos. Our gracious hostess told me, *con expressione*, that she had never heard of Messrs. Youmans, Lanin, Arden, and Dixon, but had read my stuff ever since she arrived in this country, ten years ago. This gave me a superiority complexion over all musicians and tap-dancers until, at parting, she called me Mr. Gardner. And dropping the subject of roadhouses entirely for the moment, Miss Claudette Colbert came up to call one day and almost instantly, piling in like interferers for Marchmont Schwartz, appeared fifteen internes, to take my temperature. Previously they had treated my room as vacant.

This play, as hinted in the subtitle, is actually four separate plays with four separate titles: "Hic," "Haec," "Hoc," and "Hujus." It can be seen that the original author was a born H lover. He was the first Manny O'Neill and a great friend to William A. Brady. He promised the latter, "If you ever have a daughter, I will provide her with a vehicle." Well, Bill had a daughter, but Manny passed on without leaving her even a roller-coaster. However, he had a great grandson, Eugene (("Greasy")) O'Neill, who acquired a fine sense of after-dinner speaking by playing the outfield for Cincinnati and coaching football at W. and J. He took up the work where the old man had left off, at the top of a blank sheet of fools cap paper, and I kind of monkeyed with it until now it begins at ten in the morning and lasts until Walter Winchell goes to bed.

Remarks have been brandied back and forth concerning the difference in the number of lines given the male and female characters in the piece. The women have a great deal many more lines to speak than the men. There is, of course, a two-fold purpose in this arrangement. The first fold is that it pleases the women. The second fold is that it promotes harmony in the cast. During the intermissions, the ladies, God use his own judgment, have said so much that they are out of lewd words. End of notatum.)

HIC

Part One of "Quadroon"

CAST
(In Order to Confuse)

Christine, *his sister, played by Alla Nazimova*
Lavinia, *her daughter, played by Alice Brady*
Casey Jones, *a midwife, played by William A. Brady*

SCENE: *A Park Avenue Push-Wagon, Armistice Day, 1860.*

Luncheon Intermission of Half an Hour

The Roth Lunch
127 West Fifty-second Street

November 22, 1931

Special Luncheon, 65 Cents.

Chopped Tenderloin Steak
or Calves' Liver and Bacon.
Carrots Shoestring Potatoes String Beans
Choice of Desserts
Rice Pudding   Strawberry Tart
Tea, Coffee or Milk.

HAEC

Part Two of "Quadroon"

CAST

Christine, *his sister, played by Alice Brady*
Lavinia, *her daughter, played by Alla Nazimova*
Frankie and Johnnie, *played by A. H. Woods*

SCENE: *Department of Plant and Structures. An evening in 1850.*

(CHRISTINE *and* LAVINIA *meet off-stage, dancing.*)

LAVINIA: Did you-all evah see me-all in "Hedda Gabler"?

CHRISTINE: Does yo'all mean "Hedda Gabler" by William Anthony McGuire?

LAVINIA: Yo'all done said zac'ly wot Ah'm drivin' at. How did yo'all lak me?

CHRISTINE: Well, Ah seen Mrs. Fiske.

FRANKIE AND JOHNNIE: Let's you and I run up to Elizabeth Arden's and free ourselves from fatigue with an Ardena Bath.

Dinner Intermission of One Hour and a Half *

Typical Dinner, $1.50

———

Médaillon of lobster au caviar
Grapefruit
Suprême of fresh fruit, Maraschino
Blue Point oyster cocktail
Fresh shrimp cocktail
or
Cream of lettuce, Parmentier
Clear green turtle, Amontillado
(*Choice*)

Filet of sole, Farci Isabella
Broiled Boston scrod, Maître d'Hôtel
Tartelette of Fresh mushrooms,
Lucullus
Country sausages, apple sauce
Breaded spring lamb chop
with Bacon, tomato sauce
Chicken hash au Gratin
Roast sugar cured ham, cider sauce
Omelette Glacé aux Confitures
Cold—Fresh calf's tongue
with chow chow

———

Stewed celery or fresh string beans
Mashed or French fried potatoes

* It will doubtless promote good fellowship and good service if, when entering the hotel's dining-room, you say to the man in charge: "Hello, Maître d'Hôtel."

(*Choice*)

Pudding Creole   Coffee éclair
Assorted cakes
Vanilla, raspberry or chocolate
ice cream and cake

———

Delicious apple   Apple pie
French pastry   Coffee, Tea or Milk

Make the Plaza Central
your New York Home During the
Entire Performance. Ask Arnold.

HOC

Part Three of "Quadroon"

CAST

Lynn Fontanne, *a Mrs. Lunt, played by Grace George*
Casey Jones, *a midwife, played by Bert Lahr*
Frank Case, *proprietor of the Algonquin, played by Alice Brady*

SCENE: *Jimmy Walker's Wardrobe Trunk.*

(*The* MAYOR *and the* PRINCE OF WALES *meet outside the stage door, dancing.*)

THE MAYOR: New York is the richest market in the world.

THE PRINCE: Not only that, but the New York Theatre Market is an unrivalled concentration of spending power.

THE MAYOR: The New York Magazine Program reaches that market exclusively.

FRANK CASE: Pardon me, Officer, but can either of you boys play a cellophane?

Passengers will Please not Linger in Washrooms until
Other Passengers Have Completed Their Toilets.

HUJUS

Part Four of "Quadroon"

CAST

Christine, *her sister, played by Alla Nazimova*
Lavinia, *their little one, played by Alice Brady*
Fred Astaire, *a hoofer, played by Morris Gest*

SCENE: *An ambuscade in the Astor lobby.*

(FRED *and* LAVINIA *dance.*)

LAVINIA: The minute you try Pebeco Tooth Paste you know by its "bitey" tang that here is a tooth paste that really "gets somewheres."

FRED: Will you love me always?

LAVINIA: As long as you keep kissable.

(*She kills him with an oyster fork.*)

[*Leave your ticket check with an usher and your car will come right to your seat.*]

Dinner Bridge

Dinner Bridge was written for a Dutch Treat Show in 1927 (Edmund Wilson published it that year in The New Republic), with a rather unusual cast, some of its members being Robert Benchley, George S. Kaufman, Percy Hammond and Robert Sherwood.

CHARACTERS

Crowley, *the foreman*
Amorosi, *an Italian laborer*
Taylor, *a Negro laborer*
Chamales, *a Greek laborer*
Hansen, *a Scandinavian laborer*
Llanuza, *a Mexican laborer*
The Inquisitive Waiter
The Dumb Waiter

PROGRAM NOTE

This playlet is an adaptation from the Wallachian of Willie Stevens. For a great many years, Long Islanders and Manhattanites have been wondering why the Fifty-ninth Street Bridge was always torn up at one or more points. Mr. Stevens heard the following legend: that Alexander Woollcott, chief engineer in charge of the construction of the bridge, was something of a practical joker; that on the day preceding the completion of the bridge, he was invited to dinner by his wife's brother; that he bought a loaded cigar to give his brother-in-law after the meal, and that the cigar dropped out of his pocket and rolled under the unfinished surface planking. Ever since, gangs of men have been ripping up the surface of the bridge in search of the cigar, but an article the shape of a cigar is apt to roll in any and all directions. This is what has made it so difficult to find the lost article, and the (so far) vain search is the theme of Mr. Stevens' playlet.—*Adapter.*

SCENE: An area under repair on the Fifth-ninth Street Bridge. Part of the surface has been torn up, and, at the curtain's rise, three of the men are tearing up the rest of it with picks. Shovels, axes and other tools are scattered around the scene. Two men are fussing with a concrete mixer. Crowley is bossing the job. Crowley and the laborers are dressed in dirty working clothes. In the foreground is a flat-topped truck or wagon. The two waiters, dressed in waiters' jackets, dickies, etc., enter the scene, one of them carrying a tray with cocktails and the other a tray with caviar, etc. The laborers cease their work and consume these appetizers. The noon whistle blows. The waiters bring in a white table cloth and spread it over the truck or wagon. They also distribute six place cards and six chairs, or camp stools, around the truck, but the "table" is left bare of eating implements.

FIRST WAITER, *to* CROWLEY: Dinner is served.
(CROWLEY *and the laborers move toward the table.*)
TAYLOR, *to* AMOROSI: I believe I am to take you in.
(AMOROSI *gives* TAYLOR *his arm and* TAYLOR *escorts him to the table. The laborers all pick up the place cards to find out where they are to sit.*)
CROWLEY, *to* AMOROSI: Here is your place, Mr. Amorosi. And Taylor is right beside you.
(*Note to producer: Inasmuch as* TAYLOR *and* AMOROSI *do most of the talking, they ought to face the audience. In spite of their nationalities, the laborers are to talk in correct Crowninshield dinner English, except that occasionally, say every fourth or fifth speech, whoever is talking suddenly bursts into dialect, either his own or Jewish or Chinese or what you will.*
All find their places and sit down. The two waiters now reënter, each carrying one dinner pail. One serves CROWLEY *and the other serves* AMOROSI. *The serving is done by the waiters' removing the cover of the pail and holding it in front of the diner. The latter looks into the pail and takes out some viand with his fingers. First he takes out, say, a sandwich. The waiter then replaces the cover on the pail and exits with it. All the laborers are served in this manner,*

two at a time, from their own dinner pails. As soon as one of them has completed the sandwich course, the waiter brings him the pail again and he helps himself to a piece of pie or an apple or orange. But the contents of all the pails should be different, according to the diner's taste. The serving goes on all through the scene, toward the end of which everyone is served with coffee from the cups on top of the pails.)

CROWLEY, *to* AMOROSI: Well, Mr. Amorosi, welcome to the Fifty-ninth Street Bridge.

AMOROSI: Thank you, I really feel as if this was where I belonged.

HANSEN, *politely*: How is that?

AMOROSI: On account of my father. He was among the pioneer Fifty-ninth Street Bridge destroyers. He had the sobriquet of Giacomo "Rip-Up-the-Bridge" Amorosi.

TAYLOR, *sotto voce, aside to* HANSEN: This fellow seems to be quite a card!

LLANUZA: I wonder if you could tell me the approximate date when your father worked here.

AMOROSI: Why, yes. The bridge was completed on the fifth day of August, 1909. So that would make it the sixth day of August, 1909, when father started ripping it up.

TAYLOR, *aside to* HANSEN, *in marked Negro dialect:* I repeats my assertation that this baby is quite a card!

AMOROSI, *in Jewish dialect*: But I guess it must be a lot more fun nowadays, with so much motor traffic to pester.

TAYLOR: And all the funerals. I sure does have fun with the funerals.

CROWLEY, *in Irish brogue:* Taylor has a great time with the funerals.

HANSEN, CHAMALES *and* LLANUZA, *in unison:* Taylor has a great time with the funerals.

AMOROSI, *to* TAYLOR: How do you do it?

TAYLOR, *in dialect:* Well, you see, I'm flagman for this outfit. When I get out and wave my flag, whatever is coming, it's got to stop. When I see a funeral coming, I let the hearse go by and stop the rest of the parade. Then when I see another funeral coming, I stop their hearse and let the rest of *their* procession go on. I keep doing this all morning to different funerals and by the time they get to Forest Hills, the wrong set of mourners is following the wrong hearse. It generally always winds up with the friends and relatives of the late Mr. Cohen attending the final obsequies of Mrs. Levinsky.

CROWLEY, HANSEN, CHAMALES *and* LLANUZA, *in unison:* Taylor has a great time with the funerals.

AMOROSI: I'm a *trumpet* medium myself.

TAYLOR, *aside to* HANSEN: This boy will turn out to be quite a card!

LLANUZA: Why do you always have to keep repairing it?

CROWLEY: What do you mean, what's the matter?

LLANUZA: Why do they always have to keep repairing it?

AMOROSI: Perhaps Mr. Crowley has the repairian rights.

TAYLOR, *guffawing and slapping* HANSEN *or* CHAMALES *on the back:* What did I tell you?

LLANUZA, *in dialect:* But down in Mexico, where I come from, they don't keep repairing the same bridge.

AMOROSI, *to* LLANUZA: If you'll pardon a newcomer, Mr. ——, I don't believe I got your name.

LLANUZA: Llanuza.

AMOROSI: If you'll pardon a newcomer, Mr. Keeler, I want to say that if the United States isn't good enough for you, I'd be glad to start a subscription to send you back to where you came from.

LLANUZA: I was beginning to like you, Mr. Amorosi.

AMOROSI: You get that right out of your mind, Mr. Barrows. I'm married; been married twice. My first wife died.

HANSEN: How long were you married to her?

AMOROSI: Right up to the time she died.

CHAMALES, *interrupting:* Mr. Amorosi, you said you had been married twice.

AMOROSI: Yes, sir. My second wife is a Swiss girl.

HANSEN: Is she here with you?

AMOROSI: No, she's in Switzerland, in jail. She turned out to be a murderer.

CROWLEY: When it's a woman, you call her a murderess.

TAYLOR: And when it's a Swiss woman, you call her a Swiss-ess.

(*One of the waiters is now engaged in serving* AMOROSI *with his dinner pail.*)

WAITER, *to* AMOROSI: Whom did she murder?

(WAITER *exits hurriedly without seeming to care to hear the answer.*)

AMOROSI, *after looking wonderingly at the disappearing waiter:* What's the matter with *him*?

TAYLOR: He's been that way for years—a born questioner but he hates answers.

CROWLEY: Just the same, the rest of us would like to know whom your wife murdered.

TAYLOR, HANSEN, CHAMALES and LLANUZA, *to* CROWLEY: Speak for yourself. We don't want to know.

CROWLEY: Remember, boys, I'm foreman of this outfit. (*Aside to* AMOROSI): Who was it?

AMOROSI: (*Whispers name in his ear.*)

CROWLEY: I don't believe I knew him.

AMOROSI: Neither did my wife.

CROWLEY: Why did she kill him?

AMOROSI: Well, you see, over in Italy and Switzerland, it's different from, say, Chicago. When they find a man murdered over in those places, they generally try to learn who it is and put his name in the papers. So my wife was curious about this fellow's identity and she figured that the easiest way to get the information was to pop him.

TAYLOR: I'm a *trumpet* medium myself.

(WAITER *enters and serves one of the laborers from his dinner pail.*)

WAITER: How long is she in for?

(WAITER *exits hurriedly without waiting for the answer.* AMOROSI *again looks after him wonderingly.*)

HANSEN, *to* AMOROSI: Did you quarrel much?

AMOROSI: Only when we were together.

TAYLOR: I was a newspaper man once myself.

LLANUZA, *skeptically*: You! What paper did you work on?

TAYLOR: It was a tabloid—The Porno-graphic.

(WAITER *enters to serve somebody.*)

WAITER, *to* TAYLOR: Newspaper men must have lots of interesting experiences. (*Exits without waiting for a response.*)

AMOROSI: I suppose you've all heard this story——

THE OTHER LABORERS, *in unison*: Is it a golf story?

AMOROSI: No.

THE OTHERS, *resignedly*: Tell it.

AMOROSI, *in dialect*: It seems there was a woman went into a photographer's and asked the photographer if he took pictures of children.

(WAITER *enters to serve somebody*.)

WAITER: How does it end? (WAITER *exits hurriedly*.)

AMOROSI: She asked the photographer if he took pictures of children. "Why, yes, madam," replied the photographer——

TAYLOR: He called her "madam."

AMOROSI: The photographer told her yes, that he did take pictures of children. "And how much do you charge?" inquired the madam, and the photographer replied, "Three dollars a dozen." "Well," said the woman, "I guess I'll have to come back later. I've only got eleven."

(*The other laborers act just as if no story had been told*.)

LLANUZA: Down in Mexico, where I come from, they don't keep repairing the same bridge.

TAYLOR, *to* HANSEN: Can you imitate birds?

HANSEN: No.

TAYLOR, *to* CHAMALES: Can you imitate birds?

CHAMALES: No.

TAYLOR: Can anybody here imitate birds?

THE OTHER LABORERS, *in unison*: No.

TAYLOR: *I* can do it. Long before I got a job on this bridge, while I was helping tear up the crosstown streets, I used to entertain the boys all day, imitating birds.

AMOROSI: What kind of birds can you imitate?

TAYLOR: All kinds.

AMOROSI: Well, what do you say we play some other game?

CROWLEY, *rising*: Gentlemen, we are drawing near to the end of this dinner and I feel we should not leave the table until some one has spoken a few words of welcome to our newcomer, Mr. Amorosi. Myself, I am not much of a talker. (*Pauses for a denial*.)

TAYLOR: You said a full quart.

CROWLEY: Therefore, I will call on the man who is second to me in length of service on the Fifty-ninth Street Bridge, Mr. Harvey Taylor. (*Sits down*.)

TAYLOR, *rising amid a dead silence*: Mr. Foreman, Mr. Amorosi and gentlemen: Welcoming Mr. Amorosi to our little group recalls vividly to my mind an experience of my own on the levee at New

Orleans before Prohibition. (*He bursts suddenly into Negro dialect, mingled with Jewish.*) In those days my job was to load and unload those great big bales of cotton and my old mammy used to always be there at the dock to take me in her lap and croon me to sleep. (WAITER *enters, serves somebody with coffee.*)

WAITER: What was the experience you was going to tell? (*Exits hurriedly.*)

TAYLOR: It was in those days that I studied bird life and learned to imitate the different bird calls. (*Before they can stop him, he gives a bird call.*) The finch. (*The others pay no attention. He gives another call.*) A Dowager. (TAYLOR *is pushed forcibly into his seat.*)

AMOROSI, *rising to respond*: Mr. Foreman and gentlemen: I judge from Mr. Taylor's performance that the practice of imitating birds is quite popular in America. Over where I come from, we often engage in the pastime of mimicking public buildings. For example (*he gives a cry.*) The American Express Company's office at Rome. (*He gives another cry.*) The Vatican. (*He gives another cry.*) Hotel McAlpin. (*A whistle blows, denoting that the dinner hour is over.*)

CROWLEY, *rising*: Shall we join the ladies?

(*All rise and resume the work of tearing up the bridge. The waiters enter to remove the table cloth and chairs.*)

WAITER (*the more talkative one*): How many Mack trucks would you guess had crossed this bridge in the last half hour? (*He exits without waiting for a reply.*)

(CURTAIN)

Cora or Fun at a Spa

An Expressionist Drama
of Love and Death and Sex—
in Three Acts

CHARACTERS

(In the order in which I admire them)

A Friend of the President.
Plague Bennett, *an Embryo Steeplejack.*
Elsa, *their Ward.*
Manager of the Pump Room.
A Man Who Looks A Good Deal Like Heywood Broun.
Mrs. Tyler.*
Cora.
Poultry, Game in Season, Etc.

ACT I

A Pharmacy at a Spa. The Proprietor is at present out of the city and MRS. TYLER *is taking his place. She is a woman who seems to have been obliged to leave school while in the eighth grade.* PLAGUE BENNETT *enters. His mother named him* PLAGUE *as tribute to her husband, who died of it. As* PLAGUE *enters,* MRS. TYLER *is seen replacing a small vial in a case behind the counter.*

PLAGUE: Well, Mrs. T.

MRS. TYLER: "Mrs. T." indeed! I see you're still the same old Plague!

PLAGUE: What are you doing?

MRS. TYLER: What do I look like I was doing, spearing eels? I'm

---

* Mrs. Tyler appears only when one of the other characters is out of the city.

just putting this bottle of germs back in its place. The little fellows were trying to escape. They said they didn't like it here. I said, "Don't bacilli!"

(*A* FRIEND OF THE PRESIDENT *enters.*)

PLAGUE: Hello, Doctor.

(*He calls him Doctor.*)

FRIEND OF THE PRESIDENT: (*As if to himself*) That old devil sea!

PLAGUE: Well, Doctor, I'm going to Washington tomorrow.

(*He repeatedly calls him Doctor.*)

FRIEND OF THE PRESIDENT: What of it?

PLAGUE: Well, they tell me you and the President are pretty close.

FRIEND OF THE PRESIDENT: *He* is.

(END OF FIRST ACT)

ACT II

A poultry yard at a Spa. The chairs and tables are in disarray as if a blotter salesman had been making his rounds. The MANAGER OF THE PUMP ROOM *is out of the city and the poultry are being fed by* MRS. TYLER. *A Dead Ringer for David Belasco enters, crosses stage.*

MRS. TYLER: You old master you! (*Aside*) I can never tell whether he's in first speed or reverse.

(*Dead Ringer for David Belasco exits.* MANAGER OF THE PUMP ROOM *returns to the city unexpectedly and* MRS. TYLER *goes into pictures.* MANAGER OF THE PUMP ROOM *stands in center stage as if he had been everywhere.*)

MANAGER OF THE PUMP ROOM: (*Aside*) I wonder what is keeping Elsa. (*Looks right*) Ah! There she comes now, dancing as usual!

(ELSA *enters left, fooling him completely. She is not even dancing. She looks as if she had taken a bath.*)

ELSA: Well——

MANAGER OF THE PUMP ROOM: (*Turns and sees her*) Elsa! I was just thinking about you. I was wondering what was keeping you.

ELSA: I presume you mean who.

(*The curtain is lowered and raised to see if it will work.*)

MANAGER OF THE PUMP ROOM: What's the difference between that curtain and Ziegfeld?

ELSA: It works. And that reminds me that I just met a man who looks something like Heywood Broun. Here he comes now, dancing as usual.

(*A* MAN WHO LOOKS A GOOD DEAL LIKE HEYWOOD BROUN *enters.*)

MANAGER OF THE PUMP ROOM: (*Aside*) I'll say so!

MAN WHO LOOKS A GOOD DEAL LIKE HEYWOOD BROUN: What's that?

MANAGER OF THE PUMP ROOM: Why, this young lady was just saying she thought you looked something like Heywood Broun.

MAN WHO ETC.: (*Throwing confetti in all directions*) She's conservative.

(END OF SECOND ACT)

ACT III

A Mixed Grill at a Spa. Two Milch Cows sit at a table in one corner, playing draughts. In another corner is seated a gigantic zebu.

FIRST MILCH COW: Don't you feel a draught?

SECOND MILCH COW: No. But we'd better be going. That gigantic zebu is trying to make us.

FIRST MILCH COW: He thinks he is a cow catcher.

SECOND MILCH COW: (*As they rise*) They say there are still a great many buffaloes in Yellowstone Park.

FIRST MILCH COW: So I herd.

(*The Milch Cows go out, followed at a distance by the Zebu.* CORA *enters. She is dressed in the cat's pajamas. She looks as if she had once gone on an excursion to the Delaware Water Gap.*)

CORA: (*Aside*) I wonder if it could be!

(PLAGUE BENNETT *and A* FRIEND OF THE PRESIDENT *enter in time to overhear her remark.*)

PLAGUE: (*To* FRIEND OF THE PRESIDENT) Go on without me, Doctor. (*He still calls him Doctor.* FRIEND OF THE PRESIDENT *exits and* PLAGUE *turns to* CORA.) You wonder if it could be who?

CORA: Why, I just met a man who looks a little like Heywood Broun. Here he comes now, dancing as usual.

(*A* MAN WHO LOOKS A GOOD DEAL LIKE HEYWOOD BROUN *enters.*)

PLAGUE: (*Aside*) He does, at that!

MAN WHO ETC.: At what?

PLAGUE: This little lady was just saying she thought you looked a little like Heywood Broun.

MAN WHO ETC.: A little! She's putting it mildly!

(Finds he is out of confetti and exits. A poisoned rat dashes into the open air, seeking water.)

PLAGUE: That rat acts like he was poisoned.

CORA: God! You ought to saw me last night!

(END OF THIRD ACT)

Abend di ᴄAnni Nouveau
A Play in Five Acts

CHARACTERS

St. John Ervine, *an immigrant.*
Walter Winchell, *a nun.*
Heywood Broun, *an usher at Roxy's.*
Dorothy Thompson, *a tackle.*
Theodore Dreiser, *a former Follies girl.*
H. L. Mencken, *a kleagle in the Moose.*
Mabel Willebrandt, *secretary of the League of American Wheelmen.*
Ben Hecht, *a taxi starter.*
John Roach Straton, *a tap dancer.*
Carl Laemmle, *toys and games, sporting goods, outing flannels.*
Anne Nichols, *a six-day bicyclist.*

ACT 1

*(A hired hall. It is twenty-five minutes of nine on New Year's Eve.
A party, to which all the members of the cast were invited, is supposed to have begun at thirty-four minutes after eight. A waiter
enters on a horse and finds all the guests dead, their bodies riddled
with bullets and frightfully garbled. He goes to the telephone.)*

WAITER: *(telephoning)* I want a policeman. I want to report a fire.
I want an ambulance.
*(He tethers his mount and lies down on the hors d'oeuvres. The cur-
tain is lowered and partially destroyed to denote the passage of four
days. Two policemen enter, neither having had any idea that the
other would come. They find the waiter asleep and shake him. He
wakes and smilingly points at the havoc.)*
WAITER: Look at the havoc.

FIRST POLICEMAN: This is the first time I ever seen a havoc.
SECOND POLICEMAN: It's an inside job, I think.
FIRST POLICEMAN: You WHAT?
WAITER: The trouble now is that we'll have to recast the entire play. Every member of the cast is dead.
FIRST POLICEMAN: Is that unusual?
SECOND POLICEMAN: When did it happen?
WAITER: When did what happen?
SECOND POLICEMAN: I've forgotten.

(END OF ACT 1)

ACT 2

(*The interior of an ambulance. Three men named* LOUIE BREESE *are playing bridge with an interne. The interne is* LOUIE BREESE'S *partner.* LOUIE *leads a club. The interne trumps it.*)

BREESE: Kindly play interne.
INTERNE: I get you men confused.
BREESE: I'm not confused.
THE OTHER TWO BREESES: Neither of us is confused.
(*They throw the interne onto Seventh Avenue. An East Side gangster, who was being used as a card table, gets up and stretches.*)
GANGSTER: Where are we at?
BREESE: Was you the stretcher we was playing on?
GANGSTER: Yes.
BREESE: There's only three of us now. Will you make a fourt'?
GANGSTER: There's no snow.

(END OF ACT 2)

ACTS 3, 4 AND 5

(*A one-way street in Jeopardy. Two snail-gunders enter from the right, riding a tricycle. They shout their wares.*)

FIRST SNAIL-GUNDER: Wares! Wares!
A NEWSBOY: Wares who?

FIRST SNAIL-GUNDER: Anybody. That is, anybody who wants their snails gunded.

(*Three men suddenly begin to giggle. It is a secret, but they give the impression that one of them's mother runs a waffle parlor. They go off the stage still giggling. Two Broadway theatrical producers, riding pelicans, enter almost nude.*)

FIRST PRODUCER: Have you got a dime?

SECOND PRODUCER: What do you think I am, a stage hand?

FIRST PRODUCER: Have you seen my new farce?

SECOND PRODUCER: No. I was out of town that night.

(END OF ACTS 3, 4 AND 5)

Clemo Uti—"The Water Lilies"

CHARACTERS

Padre, *a Priest.*
Sethso ⎫
Gethso ⎭ *Both Twins.*
Wayshatten, *a Shepherd's Boy.*
Two Capitalists.*
Wama Tammisch, *her daughter.*
Klema, *a Janitor's third daughter.*
Kevela, *their mother, afterwards their aunt.*

[TRANSLATOR'S NOTE: *This show was written as if people were there to see it.*]

ACT I

(The Outskirts of a Parchesi Board. People are wondering what has become of the discs. They quit wondering and sit up and sing the following song.)

CHORUS
What has become of the discs?
What has become of the discs?
We took them at our own risks,
But what has become of the discs?

(WAMA enters from an exclusive waffle parlor. She exits as if she had had waffles.)

ACTS II & III

(These two acts were thrown out because nothing seemed to happen.)

* NOTE: *The two Capitalists don't appear in this show.*

157

ACT IV

(A silo. Two rats have got in there by mistake. One of them seems diseased. The other looks at him. They go out. Both rats come in again and wait for a laugh. They don't get it, and go out. WAMA *enters from an off-stage barn. She is made up to represent the Homecoming of Casanova. She has a fainting spell. She goes out.)*

KEVELA: Where was you born?

PADRE: In Adrian, Michigan.

KEVELA: Yes, but I thought I was confessing to you.

(The PADRE *goes out on an old-fashioned high-wheel bicycle. He acts as if he had never ridden many of them. He falls off and is brought back. He is in pretty bad shape.)*

ACT V

(A Couple of Salesmen enter. They are trying to sell Portable Houses. The rest of the cast don't want Portable Houses.)

REST OF THE CAST: We don't want Portable Houses.

(The Salesmen become hysterical and walk off-stage left.)

KEVELA: What a man!

WAYSHATTEN *(the Shepherd's Boy)*: Why wasn't you out there this morning to help me look after my sheep?

CHORUS OF ASSISTANT SHEPHERDS
Why did you lay there asleep
When you should of looked after his sheep?
Why did you send telegrams
When you should of looked after his lambs?
Why did you sleep there, so old,
When you should of looked after his fold?

SETHSO: Who is our father?

GETHSO: What of it? We're twins, ain't we?

WAMA: Hush, clemo uti *(the Water Lilies)*.

(Two queels enter, overcome with water lilies. They both make fools of themselves. They don't seem to have any self-control. They quiver. They want to play the show over again, but it looks useless.)

SHADES

I Gaspiri (The Upholsterers)

A Drama in Three Acts
Adapted from the Bukovinan
of Casper Redmonda

CHARACTERS

Ian Obri, *a Blotter Salesman.*
Johan Wasper, *his wife.*
Greta, *their daughter.*
Herbert Swope, *a nonentity.*
Ffena, *their daughter, later their wife.*
Egso, *a Pencil Guster.*
Tono, *a Typical Wastebasket.*

ACT I

(A public street in a bathroom. A man named Tupper has evidently just taken a bath. A man named Brindle is now taking a bath. A man named Newburn comes out of the faucet which has been left running. He exits through the exhaust. Two strangers to each other meet on the bath mat.)

First Stranger: Where was you born?
Second Stranger: Out of wedlock.
First Stranger: That's a mighty pretty country around there.
Second Stranger: Are you married?
First Stranger: I don't know. There's a woman living with me, but I can't place her.
(Three outsiders named Klein go across the stage three times. They think they are in a public library. A woman's cough is heard offstage left.)

161

A New Character: Who is that cough?

Two Moors: That is my cousin. She died a little while ago in a haphazard way.

A Greek: And what a woman she was!

(*The curtain is lowered for seven days to denote the lapse of a week.*)

ACT III

(*The Lincoln Highway. Two bearded glue lifters are seated at one side of the road.*)

[Translator's Note: *The principal industry in Phlace is hoarding hay. Peasants sit alongside of a road on which hay wagons are likely to pass. When a hay wagon does pass, the hay hoarders leap from their points of vantage and help themselves to a wisp of hay. On an average a hay hoarder accumulates a ton of hay every four years. This is called Mah Jong.*]

First Glue Lifter: Well, my man, how goes it?

Second Glue Lifter: (*Sings "My Man," to show how it goes.*)

(*Eight realtors cross the stage in a friendly way. They are out of place.*)

CURTAIN

Taxidea *Americana*

A Play in Six Acts
Translated from the Mastoid

CHARACTERS

Fred Rullman, *an acorn huckster.*
Old Chloe, *their colored mammy.*
Thomas Gregory, *a poltroon.*
Mrs. Gregory, *his mother, afterward his wife.*
Phoebe, *engaged to* Chloe.
Prof. Schwartz, *instructor in Swiss at Wisconsin.*
Buddy, *their daughter.*
Students, *policemen, members of the faculty, sailors, etc.*
Time—*The present.*
Place—*Madison, Wisconsin.*

ACT 1.

(In front of the library. Two students in the agricultural college creep across the stage with a seed in their hands. They are silent, as they cannot place one another. DURAND *and* VON TILZER *come down the library steps and stand with their backs to the audience as if in a quandary.)*

DURAND: Any news from home?
(They go off stage left. Senator LaFollette enters from right and practises sliding to base for a few moments. RUBY BARRON *comes down the library steps.)*

RUBY: Hello, Senator. What are you practising, sliding to base?
(The Senator goes out left. RUBY *does some tricks with cards and re-enters the library completely baffled. Two students in the phar-*

163

macy college, PAT *and* MIKE, *crawl on stage from left and fill more than one prescription. On the second refrain* PAT *takes the obbligato.*)

PAT: I certainly feel sorry for people on the ocean to-night.

MIKE: What makes you think so?

PAT: You can call me whatever you like as long as you don't call me down.

(*They laugh.*)

CURTAIN

(*Note: Acts 2, 3, and 4 are left out through an oversight.*)

ACT 5.

(*Camp Randall. It is just before the annual game between Wisconsin and the Wilmerding School for the Blind. The Wisconsin band has come on the field and the cheer leaders are leading the Wisconsin battle hymn.*)

CHORUS

Far above Cayuga's waters with its waves of blue,
On Wisconsin, Minnesota and Bully for old Purdue.
Notre Dame, we yield to thee! Ohio State, hurrah!
We'll drink a cup o' kindness yet in praise of auld Nassau!
(*The Wilmerding rooters applaud and then sing their own song.*)

CHORUS

We are always there on time!
We are the Wilmerding School for the Blind!
Better backfield, better line!
We are the Wilmerding School for the Blind!
Yea!

(*Coach Ryan of Wisconsin appears on the field fully dressed and announces that the game is postponed to permit Referee Birch to take his turn in the barber's chair. The crowd remains seated till the following Tuesday, when there is a general tendency to go home.*)

CURTAIN

ACT 3.

*(Note: The coaches suddenly decide to send in Act 3 in place of
Act 6. A livery barn in Stoughton. Slam Anderson, a former Wisconsin end, is making faces at the horses and they are laughing
themselves sick. Slam goes home. Enter* DR. BONIFACE, *the landlord
of a switch engine on the Soo lines. From the other direction,*
FARMER HOOKLE *enters on a pogo stick.)*

DR. BONIFACE: Hello, there, Hookle! I hear you are specializing
in hogs.

HOOKLE: I don't know where you heard it, but it's the absolute
truth.

DR. BONIFACE: Well, do you have much luck with your hogs?

HOOKLE: Oh, we never play for money.

CURTAIN

June Moon

"*June Moon*," by *Ring Lardner and George S. Kaufman, was produced by Sam H. Harris. It opened October 9, 1929, twenty days before the première of the stock market crash. In spite of this, the production ran for two hundred and seventy-three performances and did well on the road.*

Lardner began work on "June Moon" early in 1929. He would submit a first draft and Kaufman would suggest changes. Lardner patiently accepted them, scrapped what had gone before and started all over again. The try-out was held in Atlantic City that summer, where it was discovered that Acts 2 and 3 were no good. Only the first act stood up. A friend of Lardner's met him on the boardwalk and asked him what he was doing in Atlantic City.

"I'm down here with an act," said Ring.

The play, with the newly revised second and third acts, was based on the Lardner short story "Some Like Them Cold," which ends with the brash young song writer notifying Edna, the ingénue, of his engagement to a city girl; he warns Edna not to go around picking up strange young men in railroad stations any more, as she might be misunderstood another time. (Edna is something less than a genius. In Act 2 of "June Moon," she reveals that she has been fired from her job in a doctor's office: "I made a mistake. I gave Mr. Mowrey's appointment to Mr. Treadwell, and Doctor scraped Mr. Treadwell's bones instead of Mr. Mowrey's.") In the play, the two innocents are brought together at the end, but no audience could doubt that before the morning papers were out the two would have bored each other into coma.

Here is the Prologue and Act One of "June Moon."

PROLOGUE

The scene is a section of a parlor car speeding toward New York, and not so very far from it when the curtain rises. We see only two chairs clearly; the ends of the car dissolve in shadows. On these less visible chairs are tossed vague overcoats and magazines; the racks

*above them are filled with baggage. There is a bag or two overhead;
on the floor are quantities of Sunday newspapers, along with plenty
of rotogravure sections, curling carelessly against the bottoms of the
chairs. It is night, and the shades are down.*

*In the two vital chairs sit a boy and a girl. The name of the boy,
as we presently find out is,* FRED STEVENS. *The girl is* EDNA BAKER.
*She sits with her back to him, and is absorbed in a magazine when
the curtain goes up. The boy, who is not exactly a literary type, is
a bit restless. He wriggles in his seat, sighs, peers discreetly at the
girl, who pays no attention. With a bit too much of a flourish, as
though he thus hoped to attract her attention, he whips out a time
table and studies it. Consults his watch; swings and peers out of the
window, hand cupped over eyes to exclude the light. Then he swings
back, relaxes—and looks toward the girl again. She swings her chair
around for a second; peers down the aisle, but swings back without
having permitted the boy to catch her eye. He rattles his newspaper
a trifle obviously; indulges in a bit of bad whistling; hums a little.
She swings around again; another look down the aisle.* FRED *girds
up his courage to break the ice. The girl, who has the situation well
in hand, gives sudden and demure attention to an imaginary spot
on her dress. She chips at it with a fingernail.*

FRED: (*diffidently extending his newspaper*) Would you—care to
look at the paper?

EDNA: (*ever so properly, in the manner of a young woman who
never has been spoken to on a train before*) Oh, thank you very
much. I don't think so, thank you. (*By turning away from him
again she indicates that she is not encouraging a continuation of
the interview.*)

FRED: I thought maybe you might want to read.

EDNA: No, thank you. (*She gives him a small smile.*)

FRED: (*trying desperately to keep things going*) We're due in New
York at ten-three.

EDNA: Yes, I know.

FRED: You got on at Hudson, didn't you?

EDNA: Yes.

FRED: I seen you. (*A pause after this momentous remark.*) I been
on ever since Schenectady.

EDNA: Really?

FRED: That's where I work. I mean, where I did work. At the G. E.

EDNA: G. E.?

FRED: General Electric. They call it the G. E. That's where their plant is, Schenectady.

EDNA: (*feeling that it's all right to help along*) I've got a girl friend from Schenectady.

FRED: Is that so?

EDNA: She's in New York now, or at least she was the last time I heard of her. Working at Saks'. Grace Crowell.

FRED: I used to know a Mildred Crowell, but her name wasn't Grace.

EDNA: (*refusing to give in*) This was Grace. I haven't seen her for years, and I never did know her very well.

FRED: Mildred Crowell's brother was quite a billiard player. Three cushions. Eddie, his name was.

EDNA: That's my name, too. (*Laughs.*) Of course it isn't my real name. It's just my nickname. My real name's Edna.

FRED: Oh! (*He comes back to vital matters.*) Eddie Crowell used to pretty near live on the billiard table. Then finally his health broke down and he went out West somewheres. I couldn't tell you now if he's dead or alive.

EDNA: It's funny how we lose track of people. Some of the girls I used to go with, they still live there yet, but I never look any of them up, except Gertie Hutton. I guess it's terrible of me not to, because if a person's got good friends, they ought to keep them.

FRED: I certainly got good ones. They showed that last night, at the banquet. (*He has finally managed to bring that up.*)

EDNA: Where you at a banquet?

FRED: I had to be. It was me they give it for. I mean, I was the guest of honor.

EDNA: How exciting!

FRED: It was a farewell testimonial on account of me going to New York. And then this afternoon ten or eleven of them come down to the station, and Ernie Butler had a hangover and bought me this seat in the parlor car; he said it would be a disgrace for me to ride in the day coach with this new bag. (*He indicates a shining yellow suitcase at his side.*)

EDNA: It's a beautiful bag!

FRED: They give it to me at the banquet. It's got my initials. See? F. M. S. Frederick M. Stevens.

EDNA: What's the M for?

FRED: Martin.

EDNA: I like a man to have a middle name. Girls don't usually have them. I'm just plain Edna.

FRED: (*pretty daring, for him*) I wouldn't say "plain."

EDNA: You know how to make pretty speeches.

FRED: I bet you're used to them.

EDNA: There's another one. I'm not so used to them that I don't like to hear them, especially from people whom I think they're sincere.

FRED: I don't say things unless I mean them.

EDNA: I'm glad of that.

FRED: Talking about speeches, you ought to heard the speech Carl Williams made when he give me this bag. At the banquet, I mean. I guess I blushed, the things he said about me. A lot more than I deserve.

EDNA: I bet they were sorry to see you go. You look like the kind of a man men would like. And girls, too.

FRED: I don't go around much with girls.

EDNA: I don't go much with men, either.

FRED: Neither do I. (*A pause; that* subject's cleaned up.) It's comfortable in here, ain't it? Like being home. I never been in a parlor car before.

EDNA: My brother always insists on me riding in it. He says the day coach is generally dirty, for one thing—and another thing, the men that ride in the day coach are the kind that try and make up to pretty girls. That sounds like I was throwing a bouquet at myself, but I'm just repeating what Dick said. That's my brother's name, Dick. I guess a brother always thinks their sister is good-looking.

FRED: I believe in a man sticking up for their sister, or any woman. I got no use for a man that don't respect woman's hood. Where would a man be if it wasn't for their mothers and sisters and wives?

EDNA: Some men haven't got wives.

FRED: I haven't got one myself—yet. I ain't been lucky enough to meet a woman who would be a good pal as well as a sweetheart. I want my wife to be like mother used to be.

EDNA: I love to have a man love their mother.

FRED: I wished mine was still here. Like Carl Williams said in his speech last night—if she was still here, maybe she would be a little proud of me.

EDNA: I'll bet she would.

FRED: He made quite a speech, all right. He said the boys expected me to make Irving Berlin jealous. I said I didn't want to make nobody jealous, but I wanted to make my friends proud. I said my only regret in going to New York was on account of leaving so many good friends behind, and as soon as my songs begun to sell up in the hundred thousands, and my dreams came true, I would invite them all down to visit me on Broadway and show them the sights.

EDNA: (*a bit too eagerly*) Is that what you are? A song-writer?

FRED: (*nods*) Not the music part; just the words. Lyrics, they're called.

EDNA: It must be wonderful to have a gift like that.

FRED: That's what Benny Davis called it—a gift. I guess you've heard of him—he's turned out a hundred smash hits.

EDNA: I guess I must have.

FRED: He wrote, "Oh, How I Miss You To-night!" It was a song about how he missed his mother—he called her his "Old Pal."

EDNA: That's sweet!

FRED: Well, he happened to be playing in Schenectady in vaudeville, and I happened to meet him and I happened to show him some of my lyrics. And he said a man like I with the song-writing gift was a sucker not to go to New York, because that's where they have the Mecca for a man if you got the song-writing gift. So he give me a letter to the Friars' Club, asking them to give me a two weeks' card, they call it. The Friars' Club is where they have the Mecca for song-writers. And he give me a letter of introduction to Paul Sears, the composer. He wrote "Paprika." You remember "Paprika"? (*He sings a strain of it.*) "Paprika, Paprika, the spice of my life——"

EDNA: (*with quick concurrence*) I think so.

FRED: When you write a song like "Paprika" you don't ever have to worry again. He's one of the most successful composers there is, Paul Sears. I bet you I and he will turn out some hits together.

EDNA: Are you going to be partners with him?

FRED: If he wants me to, and I guess he will when I show him

Benny Davis's letter. That's the hard part, getting acquainted. I'd have broke away a long while ago only for my sister. I couldn't leave her alone.

EDNA: Is she in Schenectady?

FRED: (*nods*) She got married a week ago Saturday. A fella I been working with in the shipping department—Bob Gifford.

EDNA: She'll miss you just the same. I know how sisters feel, especially when their brother is like you or Dick.

FRED: Well, anyway, she got married, and I give them a pair of book-ends.

EDNA: She'll love them!

FRED: She always done everything for me—I mean, cooked my meals and sewed things for me. Look! (*Dives for his bag and starts opening it.*) She made me a half a dozen shirts before I left. Different colors. Here's one of the blue ones. I bet if you was to buy a shirt like that, you couldn't buy a shirt like that under a dollar seventy-five.

EDNA: I'll bet it would cost more than that.

FRED: Marion can sew, all right. My mother used to say she was a born seamstress.

EDNA: I love to sew. (*Looks at the shirt.*) Has it got your monogram, your initials?

FRED: No. She was going to put a "F" on the sleeve, but she was too busy.

EDNA: It's too bad you're not my brother and I'd embroider your whole initials.

FRED: You don't have to be a man's sister to embroider their shirt.

EDNA: I don't want you to misjudge me, Mr. Stevens. I'm not the kind of a girl that talks to strangers. My friends would die if they knew I was talking to a man whom I had not been properly introduced.

FRED: You don't have to be scared of me, girlie. I treat all women like they was my sister. Till I find out different.

EDNA: A girl alone in New York can't be too careful, especially a girl in my position. You take at Dr. Quinn's, where I work—he's one of the best dentists there is, and he has lots of men patients that would be only too glad to start a little flirtation. Why even Doctor himself was fresh, the first day I met him. It turned out he wasn't really, but it seemed that way. He put his arm around my shoulders and I jumped away from him like he was a leopard or something, and I told him, I said, "Doctor, I guess I don't care to work here after all." Then he laughed and said forget it, that he was just testing me. He said he didn't want an assistant who was inclined to flirt. And from that day he's never made any advances, except once or twice.

FRED: He'd keep his distance if I was around.

EDNA: I wish you could be.

FRED: I got plenty of excuses for being there. I got a cavity as big as the Grand Canyon.

EDNA: (*laughing a little harder than is necessary*) You must forgive me laughing. Caroline used to tell me I had the keenest sense of humor of any person she ever met.

FRED: First thing you know I'll be in to see Dr. What's-His-Name myself.

EDNA: He'll fix it for you. He's a wonderful dentist.

FRED: If I come, it'll probably be when he's out to lunch.

EDNA: Then what would you come for?

FRED: I'll let you guess.

EDNA: I'd rather you told me. I'm a bad guesser.

FRED: I might come to see you. Would you let me?

EDNA: I'd love it, if you wanted to.

FRED: I wouldn't say so if I didn't.

EDNA: You'll forget all about it.

FRED: No, I won't. Your smile will always haunt me.

EDNA: I'll bet you're a wonderful song-writer. No wonder your friends gave you that big dinner.

FRED: It certainly was quite a banquet. I bet some of my pals got a headache to-day, all right.

EDNA: I hope you haven't got one.

FRED: No. Liquor don't afflict me like most people.

EDNA: I hardly ever touch it myself, only once in a great while, at a party.

FRED: Girls ought to lay off it entirely.

EDNA: (*quickly covering her slip*) I never touch it.

FRED: Take some of those women in Schenectady and they want to go out somewhere every night and guzzle. Married women, too.

EDNA: I don't see how they can, with a home to take care of.

FRED: Either they get all dressed up and drag their husband to a dance or a card party every night, or either they lay around the house in a wrapper.

EDNA: When I marry I'll be just as careful of my appearance as I am now. I believe a husband appreciates a wife dressing up for him.

FRED: (ever the practical soul) If it ain't too expensive.

EDNA: The man I marry won't have any complaints. I make practically all my own clothes. Caroline—she's the girl I used to live with—she used to say I always looked like I had just stepped out of a bandbox, even if we were only sitting in our room. We hardly ever went out evenings; personally I prefer to stay home and read, or else just sit and dream. But still I always bathe and change my clothes even when I'm only going to cook dinner.

FRED: I think I'll take a room with a bathroom when I get to the hotel.

EDNA: Where are you going to stay?

FRED: The Hotel Somerset. They got rooms with a bathroom right in the room, so you don't have to go out of the room. And it's close to the music publishing houses and the Friars' Club—any place I want to go, I can walk. Except to Paul Sears' place. He probably lives in some swell apartment, or maybe a country place in Great Neck or Jamaica.

EDNA: A successful man like he wouldn't live in Jamaica.

FRED: Well, some place. I don't know much about New York; I only been there once before, with Carl Williams. He's the fella that made the speech last night. It was the first time he's been away from home in the evening since he was married. He's got a wife and baby now.

EDNA: (so impulsively) Oh, I'm dying to have a baby! (She catches herself.) Heavens! I didn't mean to say that. I love them so.

FRED: It's nothing against a woman to like babies. Carl's wife certainly likes hers. She's made him a nice home, too. He didn't have to buy hardly anything in the way of furniture; her grandmother gave her a bedroom suit and she bought some herself with money she saved while she was working at Berger's.

EDNA: She must be a good deal like myself. I could almost start housekeeping with the things I've got. I suppose I'm silly and old-fashioned, but I always thought a girl should bring her husband something besides herself. I even wouldn't mind going on working after I was married, till my husband established himself.

FRED: The girl I marry won't never have to work. I don't believe God ever meant for a woman to endure a life of druggery.

EDNA: Oh, Mr. Stevens, if only all men felt the same way!

FRED: (*a look at his watch*) My, it's nine twenty-six already.

EDNA: It's been a shorter trip than usual, for some reason.

FRED: (*trying to peer out the window*) I wonder where we're at now?

EDNA: (*also peering*) Pretty near Yonkers, I guess.

FRED: If we was on the other side we could see the Hudson River.

EDNA: My, but it's dark!

FRED: There's a moon out.

EDNA: Yes, I love it.

FRED: June—moon.

EDNA: What?

FRED: I just said June moon.

EDNA: It isn't June. It's October.

FRED: I know, but June and moon go together. They rhyme. I'm always thinking of words that rhyme, even when I ain't working.

EDNA: That'd be a catchy name, June Moon. For a song, I mean.

FRED: Yes, you could get other words to go with it. Spoon, and croon, and soon. Marry soon, or something.

EDNA: And macaroon.

FRED: Yeah. I wish I had some. I'm hungry.

EDNA: I am, too, kind of. (*After a pause.*) Some day when that song is published and people are singing it everywhere, I'll say to my friends, "I knew the man that wrote that. We were riding on a train and he looked out and saw the moon, and he thought of this song, and then the train got to New York and he never saw poor little me again."

FRED: You won't be telling the truth, because I'm going to see you again.

EDNA: You say that now. But you'll forget all about me.

FRED: No, I won't. Are you going right home when we get in?

EDNA: Why—I intended to. (*She sits up, expectantly.*)

FRED: I thought I'd go and get something to eat some place, only I wouldn't know where to go if I didn't have somebody with me that knowed where to go.

EDNA: I can tell you a place where I go once in a while, the Little Venice. Though most of the time I stay home and cook my own dinner, just because I love to cook.

FRED: It'll be a little late to cook to-night. I was wondering if you wouldn't go along to this place, and maybe we could eat together.

EDNA: I'd love to.

FRED: It ain't a very expensive place, is it?

EDNA: Oh, no. The last time I went, there was two of us and we had hot roast beef sandwiches, and peas, and coffee, and it only came to a dollar-twenty.

FRED: (*with vast relief*) All right. I guess we can each afford sixty cents.

(THAT WINDS UP THE PROLOGUE)

ACT I

The scene is one of those Riverside Drive apartments, in a place called New York City. It is up in the neighborhood of One Hundred and Sixteenth Street, and once it was pretty good. It's a bit run down now, and since people began moving to the East Side the neighborhood has become somewhat declassée—not more so, however, than PAUL SEARS, *the tenant of this particular apartment.*

We see the living-room, if you can call it living. There is a piano, because PAUL SEARS *is a composer. The rest of the furniture is what you might imagine, or worse.*

PAUL, *a commonplace-looking man in his middle thirties, is at the piano when the curtain rises. He is in his shirt sleeves and is alternately hitting a few discouraged keys and making probably meaningless notations on the music sheet in front of him. He lacks one finger of being a two-fingered piano player. He is laboriously going over the same phrase again and again. And if you had never even heard it once, it would be too often.*

LUCILLE, *his wife, comes on from the rear rooms of the apartment. A spare but still attractive woman, on whom three years of marriage with* PAUL SEARS *have left their mark. She looks around for something. Finds it. It turns out to be a copy of the "Graphic." She drops listlessly into a chair and starts to read.* PAUL *continues torturing the piano.*

LUCILLE: (*addressing herself more than* PAUL, *as she scans her paper*) What do you know about that! Myra Vale's engaged!

PAUL: I read it. Automobile man. Probably drives a truck.

LUCILLE: If he does, at least she'll have something to go places in.

PAUL: I got Myra her first job; I introduced her to Dillingham.

LUCILLE: Yes, you did! She was in "Nanette" with Eileen and me before you ever saw her.

PAUL: (*belligerently*) Who says so?

LUCILLE: Ask the doorman down at the Globe. He used to have to carry her in.

PAUL: She never took a drink when I knew her.

LUCILLE: I can vouch for that.

PAUL: (*jumping up from the piano*) This is the last time I'll work with Fagan! I rewrite two whole bars of the melody for him, and when I ask him to change one word of his lyric, he squawks. He's got it "as a rose in June," and I want him to make it "as roses in June." Listen—here's his way (*he plays and sings*): "As a rose in June." And here's the way I want it: "As roses in June." All the difference in the world.

LUCILLE: (*wearily*) It sounds just the same to me.

PAUL: My way gives me a triplet and makes it twice as effective! Listen! (*Starts hitting the same old notes.*)

LUCILLE: Oh, isn't that enough? (PAUL *stops.*) Must I sit around all night listening to that?

PAUL: Why don't you go out? You could go out if you want to.

LUCILLE: Who with?

PAUL: You could go out with Eileen. You and *her* could go somewhere.

LUCILLE: You know she's got a date with Hart. I suppose you want me trailing along.

PAUL: Well, I explained to you *I* can't go no place, with this fella coming up. I told you a dozen times.

LUCILLE: I don't expect you to take me anywhere, except maybe for a walk around the block. That's free.

PAUL: I don't enjoy laying around here no more than you do. I'm not a nun.

LUCILLE: That's the first I've heard about it.

PAUL: You wait till this number gets over. We'll go everywhere then.

LUCILLE: (*tiredly*) Oh, sure!

PAUL: You haven't heard it played yet. It'll be another "Paprika."
Did I tell you what Dave Stamper said about it?

LUCILLE: (*quickly*) Yes!

PAUL: (*just as though she'd said "No"*) He said it was another
"Paprika." You wait till you hear it played. Dave Stamper says it's
sure fire. (*Back to his "playing" again.*)

LUCILLE: The silliest thing in the world to me is a man trying to
be a composer when he can't even play "Chopsticks."

PAUL: I can play as good as I need to. I can play as good as Berlin, and he's turned out twice as many hits as anybody.

LUCILLE: He knows what people want. He appeals to the women.

PAUL: It ruins a composer to play the piano too good. They depend on fancy harmony and tempo, instead of pretty melodies.

LUCILLE: (*giving up*) All right.

PAUL: (*his eye drawn to the newspaper*) Did you read that thing
from that Boston paper about "Pretty Polly"? They say Gershwin
hasn't given them one tune. (*He's pretty pleased about it, too.*) Ten
years from now, nobody'll know there *was* a Gershwin. He won't
live.

LUCILLE: At least he won't starve to death.

PAUL: It was me that was responsible for Gershwin getting his
start. I brought him and Georgie White together.

LUCILLE: (*simply not listening*) Why can't you see this man in the
daytime instead of asking him up here?

PAUL: Because I don't want him to come in the office yet, that's
why. I'm keeping him under cover till I get rid of Fagan.

LUCILLE: If there's one thing that'll round out my day, it's entertaining a lyric-writer.

PAUL: This fella ain't like the rest of them. He's got a fresh slant.
Take fellas like Fagan, that's been around Broadway all their life,
and all their lyrics sound just alike. If Fagan gave me a new idea,
I'd drop dead. But this fella's got a fresh slant.

LUCILLE: Fagan would drop even deader if you gave him a new
tune.

PAUL: I gave him "Paprika," didn't I?

LUCILLE: That's so long ago I don't see how you remember it.

PAUL: Old man Goebel remembers it, and so does Hart. They
made enough money out of it.

LUCILLE: (*the eternal wife*) Everybody makes money but you.

PAUL: Yes, they do! There's plenty fellas around the club that's just as flat as I am.

LUCILLE: (*ever so brightly*) That makes everything all right.

PAUL: I'll tell you who's got money, if you want to know, and that's Stevens.

LUCILLE: Who?

PAUL: This lyric-writer, Stevens. He's got money.

LUCILLE: A lot of good that'll do me.

PAUL: He's a nice kid, too. (*His eye falls on his watch.*) If Eileen's got a date with Hart, why don't she keep it? It's half past eight.

LUCILLE: Don't you worry about that.

PAUL: What about him and her, anyway? If she's engaged to him, aren't they ever going to get married?

LUCILLE: You'll know as soon as there's anything to know.

PAUL: He'll wriggle off the hook some way. If you ask me he's getting tired of her already.

LUCILLE: (*with sudden interest*) What makes you think so?

PAUL: Just the luck I'm running in. If I ever marry again, it'll be a woman without a sister.

LUCILLE: She don't cost you much, and she's company for me.

PAUL: What's the matter with her getting a job somewheres? (*The telephone rings.*)

LUCILLE: Yeah. You ought to be able to place her, with your influence.

PAUL: (*at the telephone*) Hello. . . . Oh, hello, Maxie! (*There enters, from the rear rooms,* EILEEN. *She has been drawn by the ring of the telephone, and comes on eagerly, expectantly. She is a young woman in her late twenties, and has plenty of good old fashioned sex appeal. But with it she is a bit hard, a trifle worldly. She wears a good-looking and rather revealing negligée, and is carrying what seems to be an evening dress, on which she has been sewing, or trying to sew. She stops short as she senses that the phone call is not for her; relaxes. From her mouth comes a cloud of cigarette smoke.* PAUL, *of course, has kept right on with his phone conversation.*) Sure—going to be here all evening. . . . All right. . . . Fine! (*He hangs up; turns to* LUCILLE.) Maxie's coming over. Wait till you hear him play it—(*a gesture toward his music*)—then you'll see!

EILEEN: (*drifting over to* LUCILLE) What time is it?

PAUL: (*going right on*) It's going to be another "Paprika."

LUCILLE: (*reaching for the dress that* EILEEN *has brought along*) Want me to do that?

EILEEN: I'll go crazy, waiting around here!

PAUL: (*you can't stop him.*) If I team up with this new fella you'll hear some hits.

LUCILLE: (*handing over the paper to* EILEEN) Did you see this? Myra Vale's announced her engagement.

EILEEN: Who to, for God's sake?

LUCILLE: Nobody we know.

EILEEN: (*reading*) No. And nobody that knows her, you can bet on that.

LUCILLE: Paul was trying to tell me he got her her first job; introduced her to Dillingham.

EILEEN: Oh, sure. He introduced Rogers to Peet, didn't he?

LUCILLE: (*indicating the dress*) This isn't going to last much longer.

EILEEN: I know it.

LUCILLE: Why don't you look around Monday? See what you can find.

EILEEN: Maybe I will. I've just been putting it off. I'm lazy, I guess.

LUCILLE: I'd never be too lazy to shop, if I had anything to shop with.

PAUL: You wait till this number gets over.

LUCILLE: (*quite pleasantly*) By that time I'll only want a shawl.

PAUL: (*finally flaring up*) There's nothing helps a man like being married to a woman that always encourages you and looks on the bright side. I'm going to write an article for the *American Magazine,* saying I attribute my success to my wife.

EILEEN: Why don't you try writing articles? They might be pretty near as good as your tunes.

PAUL: You don't have to worry about my tunes. Anyhow, I was talking to Lucille.

EILEEN: It's time you did something more for Lucille besides talk to her!

PAUL: If I was in your place, I'd keep pretty still in this house. That is, unless I was paying board.

EILEEN: (*it's a good battle, by this time.*) Don't you dare say I'm dependent on you, because I'm not!

PAUL: Only for your meals and a place to sleep!

EILEEN: You wouldn't even have a job if it wasn't for me! Do you think Hart is keeping you on the staff because you wrote a hit three years ago?

LUCILLE: Now!

EILEEN: Well, make him lay off me, if he knows what's good for him. If he keeps riding me, he'll be looking for a new job!

PAUL: Swell chance of them letting me out when I've got a number like "Montana." I'd run right to Harms with it.

EILEEN: Harms wouldn't let you in their elevator!

PAUL: (*as he goes proudly into the next room*) I was in it this afternoon!

EILEEN: (*a long, long sigh*) Is Hart going to phone or isn't he? It gets me crazy, this waiting.

LUCILLE: I wouldn't mind waiting if there was something to wait for. I nearly go out of my mind, just sitting. You hear women brag about the nice, cozy evenings they spend at home with their husband. They're not married to a piano tuner with ten thumbs.

EILEEN: (*hoping against hope*) Maybe he didn't get back from Philadelphia. He might still be over there.

LUCILLE: What time was he going to call up?

EILEEN: Six o'clock. He said he'd call me the minute he got in. Maybe the train was late.

LUCILLE: They aren't late very often, from Philadelphia.

EILEEN: It's the only evening we'll *have* for three weeks, with him going away again to-morrow. (*Restlessly pacing*) If he was going to be late you'd think he'd try to reach me.

LUCILLE: Of course, you know him better than I do, but when a man's really crazy about a girl, he calls her up, I don't care what he's doing. It's only when he begins cooling off that he finds excuses, like being in Philadelphia.

EILEEN: But he was in Philadelphia.

LUCILLE: I know, but they've got phones there now, too.

EILEEN: If you think he's cooling off you're crazy! He's insanely jealous. When I told him I was thinking of going out with Bert Livingston he was sore as hell. He said, "All right, go ahead and go out with him." I asked him if he meant it, and he said, "Sure! Go out with the whole Lambs Club!" He's insanely jealous and tries to hide it.

LUCILLE: I'd go out with the janitor if he asked me. God, I'm sick of this place!

EILEEN: Why don't you go to a picture?

LUCILLE: They charge admission. (*A little sardonic laugh*) Remember the way I used to figure when Paul first came along? I thought marrying a song-writer meant going to all the first nights, meeting everybody that was worthwhile, going down to Palm Beach——

EILEEN: You would, too, if Paul was any good.

LUCILLE: I wonder what it'd be like if we'd stayed in Stroudsburg. I'd probably be married to Will Broderick, and we'd have a car——

EILEEN: To drive over to Scranton in.

LUCILLE: (*a sigh*) I suppose I ought to get consolation out of one thing. I never expect a phone call or a mash note or an invitation or even a half pound box of candy. Whatever happens is velvet.

EILEEN: You're a fool if you keep it up. You ought to break away while there's still time.

LUCILLE: That's an easy thing to say. I haven't got any grounds, in the first place.

EILEEN: You wouldn't need grounds. Just get him up in court and let the judge look at him.

LUCILLE: And even if I did get free, where am I? I'm not young any more. No man under sixty would look at me.

EILEEN: Well, men over sixty are more liable to have money than boy scouts.

LUCILLE: I don't like old men.

EILEEN: Who does? Just the same, they've got their good points. They sleep eighteen hours a day. And they're like little kids—they believe everything you tell them.

LUCILLE: I never could fool anybody. That's why I've been afraid to try anything, with Paul. He knows when I'm lying to him, every time.

EILEEN: Him! He isn't even listening to you! You could have callers right in this room and he wouldn't hear them come in—not with all those God-given melodies ringing in his ears.

LUCILLE: What's the use of talking about it? There haven't been any volunteers. Women can't go wrong if they're not invited.

EILEEN: All I can say is, if you don't break away from him, you're crazy!

LUCILLE: And if I did, do you know what would happen? He'd write ten smash hits in a week. That's my luck. . . . God! It would be wonderful to have some clothes and hold up my head again!

EILEEN: I'm through arguing with you. You're hopeless.

LUCILLE: You'd better be thinking about Mr. Hart. You may be as bad off as I am.

EILEEN: Don't you worry about me! If he wasn't crazy about me, why would he be so insanely jealous? He's insanely jealous!

LUCILLE: Has he ever said anything half-way definite? About marrying, I mean?

EILEEN: Not in words, exactly.

LUCILLE: What did he say it in?

EILEEN: He must be thinking of it. He doesn't ever go out with anybody else.

LUCILLE: (*trying to recall what* EILEEN *had said*) How long's he going to be gone this time—three weeks?

EILEEN: Yeah—about. He's got to go to Chicago, and—a lot of places.

LUCILLE: What are you going to do with yourself all that time— just sit around?

EILEEN: Maybe he'll treat us to some shows—I'll ask him to-night. Maybe he'll get us seats for some shows.

LUCILLE: Do they still have seats at shows?

EILEEN: (*restless again*) Only I wish that thing would ring!

LUCILLE: Why *don't* you go out with Bert or somebody, while he's gone? It might be a good thing for him.

EILEEN: Do you want to get me murdered? I tell you he's insanely jealous. (*The door bell rings.*) Who's that?

LUCILLE: Maxie, I guess. (*Starting for the door.*) Or maybe that lyric-writer.

EILEEN: Who?

LUCILLE: (*disappearing into the hallway, talking as she goes*) You know, that's coming to see Paul. From Albany or some place.

EILEEN: Oh!

LUCILLE: Of course he couldn't meet him in the daytime. He has to bring him up here in the middle of the night— (*Having opened the outside door*) Oh, it's you!

MAXIE (*outside*) Hello, there!

(PAUL *comes back into the room.*)

PAUL: Who is it? Maxie?

MAXIE: Yah, Maxie. (*He is a man in his late forties, easy-going, kindly. Wears a dinner coat. He is an arranger for Goebel's, and he knows the popular song business backwards.*)

PAUL: Hello!

MAXIE: Well! All staying home on a Saturday night?

LUCILLE: All nights are alike up here.

EILEEN: You didn't come right up from the office, did you?

MAXIE: (*indicates his dinner coat*) Do I look it? I'm playing down at the Orchard this week. Pounding the piano for a lot of morons. I envy you people that can spend an evening at home.

LUCILLE: (*with emphasis*) Yes. It's a great treat.

PAUL: I want the girls to hear the "Montana" number, the way it sounds when it's really played.

(EILEEN *starts to go.*)

MAXIE: O. K.

PAUL: (*stopping* EILEEN) Hey! He's going to play the "Montana" number.

EILEEN: That's all right. I'll close the door. (*She leaves.*)

PAUL: Go ahead, Maxie. She don't know anything.

MAXIE: Think of me slaving down at the Orchard while you people enjoy all the comforts of home.

(*An impatient movement from* LUCILLE)

PAUL: Go ahead with "Montana."

MAXIE: It certainly was a tough day for me when Edison invented the piano. Fixing up other people's tunes—there's a life work for you.

PAUL: Go on.

MAXIE: (*his fingers rambling over the keys*) You know, I might have been a song-writer myself but I got stuck on my own stuff. I wrote tunes nobody ever heard before—they wouldn't stand for it.

PAUL: (*prompting with a gesture*) "Montana."

MAXIE: (*about to start, but resumes talking instead*) That was a great idea of Fagan's, writing a lyric about Montana. I've often wondered why lyric writers stayed out of the Northwest.

PAUL: Maybe Fagan was born there.

MAXIE: Naw! Shamokin, Pennsylvania. If song-writers always wrote about their home state, what a big Jewish population Tennessee must have. (*He starts playing a popular tune—the telephone rings.* PAUL *takes it up.*)

PAUL: Hello. . . . This is him. . . . Oh, hello! . . . Where are you at now? . . . Well, you better hop in a taxi—it's quite a ways yet. (EILEEN *makes another expectant appearance in the doorway—departs in disappointment as she learns that it still isn't her call.*) 448 Riverside Drive. Tell him just above 116th Street. . . . That's it. (*He hangs up; addresses* MAXIE, *who continues to drum.*) That's Stevens, the lyric writer I was telling you about. From Schenectady.

MAXIE: Thank God he can't get that in a lyric.

PAUL: He had the phone number, but he didn't know the address.

LUCILLE: How'd he get the phone number?

PAUL: Telephone book, I guess.

LUCILLE: And then he called up for the address? (*She shakes her head—it's too much for her.*) I want to meet him.

PAUL: (*to* MAXIE) You'll like this fella. He's young yet. He's got a fresh slant.

MAXIE: What does he do—write about counties instead of states?

PAUL: I've been thinking maybe he and I could do something together, if I can get rid of Fagan.

MAXIE: Fagan isn't so bad. Only he's using up his ideas too fast. "Montana Moon." He puts a state and a moon all in one song.

PAUL: Are you going to play it? (MAXIE *plunges into the preliminary chords;* PAUL *comes to life and sets himself to sing. Raises a warning finger in the direction of* LUCILLE.) Now listen!

> "Golden West that seems so far away,
>   Golden girl for whom I'm always pining,
>   Don't you know I love you night and day,
>   But chiefly when the full bright moon is shining!"

(*He takes new breath for the chorus.* LUCILLE, *meanwhile, is listening intently, but hardly enthusiastically. In fact, you might almost think she didn't like it so much.*)

> "Montana moonlight,
>   As bright as noon light,
>   Oh, may it soon light
>   My way to you!
>   I know you're lonely,

My one and only,
For I am lonely,
   Yes, lonely, too."

(*At this point* LUCILLE *simply goes back to her sewing.* PAUL'S *tone grows sharper as he sings, and she resigns herself to further listening.*)

"My heart is yearning
   For kisses burning,
   For lips as sweet as a rose in June.
   I'm always dreaming
   Of your eyes gleaming,
   Beneath the beaming
      Montana Moon!"

(MAXIE *plunges into a second chorus as* PAUL *presses* LUCILLE *for an opinion.*) Don't it sound great? The way Maxie plays it?

LUCILLE: (*delivering the verdict*) I don't think Berlin will kill himself.

PAUL: It's nothing like Berlin. Play it in two-four and it's a great dance tune. (MAXIE *is obliging.* PAUL *sings a strain of it and dances.*)

LUCILLE: You don't get Berlin's songs to dance to. You get them to cry to.

PAUL: All right. You can cry to this, too. "My heart is yearning for kisses burning." That's sad.

LUCILLE: Yes, but there's something behind his songs. (*Sighs*) They're sympathetic.

PAUL: Do you want to know why? Because he gets a little sympathy now and then! He's appreciated at home! He don't sit around here night after night with you yapping your head off at him, telling him he's all through!

MAXIE: Now, now! You're going to write plenty of hits.

PAUL: (*sits*) Well, it makes a fellow lose confidence in himself.

LUCILLE: I'm trying to help you, not hurt you.

PAUL: You go about it in a funny way.

(EILEEN *comes back; is lighting a cigarette.*)

MAXIE: She doesn't mean anything. Of course she wants to help you. But this number—I wouldn't count on it too much if I were you.

LUCILLE: What do you mean?

PAUL: Why not?

MAXIE: I just wouldn't—that's all. You can't tell which way they're going to jump these days.

PAUL: They'll snap this one up. Unless they're crazy.

LUCILLE: Keep still a minute. (*To* MAXIE) What's happened?

MAXIE: (*reluctant*) Nothing definite. Only they were talking about it—Hart and Goebel.

PAUL: When were they?

EILEEN: (*has heard just enough*) What did you say?

MAXIE: Huh? I said Hart and Goebel were talking about Paul's new number.

EILEEN: When?

PAUL: What did they say about it?

EILEEN: You mean they were talking about it to-day?

MAXIE: Sort of.

EILEEN: In the office, you mean?

MAXIE: Yah. Sure.

EILEEN: What time?

MAXIE: I don't know. Five o'clock.

EILEEN: Goebel and—Hart both?

MAXIE: Yah. Why? (EILEEN *takes a moment to digest this bit of information; her eyes meet* LUCILLE'S. *Then, with a sudden movement, she turns and leaves the room.* LUCILLE, *after a thoughtful second, follows her out.* MAXIE *looks after them, uncomprehending. Then he turns back to Paul.*) Did I say something dirty?

PAUL: That don't matter. What did they say about the song?

MAXIE: But I don't understand——

PAUL: Listen—what did they do? Turn it down?

MAXIE: (*he has to say it.*) Right now they don't want it.

PAUL: (*hotly*) When did they hear it? After I left?

MAXIE: They asked me, so there was nothing for me to do but give it to them. I had Nate sing it.

PAUL: It's the lyric kills it! The melody's sure fire! Even if it don't sell over the counter it'd get a good mechanical break.

MAXIE: (*brightly*) Maybe you could sell it outside.

PAUL: It makes a man look like a fool, working for one house and selling your stuff to another. (*He drops into a chair, discouraged.*)

MAXIE: You mustn't let it worry you. The next one'll be great, and you'll forget all about this.

PAUL: What else did they say—when they heard it? Anything about me?

MAXIE: What could they say about you?

PAUL: If I don't deliver pretty soon they'll let me out. I'll be like all those fellows that come around every day with another tune. (*The door bell sounds.*) I guess this is Stevens.

MAXIE: Who?

PAUL: Stevens—that lyric writer.

MAXIE: Maybe he's just what you need. Maybe he'll make all the difference in the world.

PAUL: His stuff's pretty good—what I've seen of it. (*Disappears into the vestibule.*)

MAXIE: (*cheerily*) There you are! Everything'll be fine! You see! (*He is playing the piano again.*)

PAUL: (*in the hallway*) Hello, Stevens! Glad to see you!

FRED: Hello, Mr. Sears!

PAUL: Put your hat and coat on the chair. Come right in! This is Maxie—Mr. Schwartz. Shake hands with Mr. Stevens.

FRED: Glad to meet you, Mr. Schwartz.

MAXIE: (*playing with one hand and shaking hands with the other*) Hello, Stevens.

(LUCILLE *strolls back, eyeing the new arrival.*)

PAUL: And this is my wife. Dear, this is Mr. Stevens.

LUCILLE: How are you?

FRED: (*right there with an answer*) I'm all right.

LUCILLE: Paul tells me you're a song-writer yourself.

FRED: (*modestly*) Just the words.

LUCILLE: Well, that's all Paul needs—that and the music.

FRED: I've always been one of Mr. Sears' greatest admirers. I've admired Mr. Sears ever since he wrote "Paprika."

LUCILLE: You've got a good memory.

PAUL: Maybe Stevens and I will turn out another "Paprika."

FRED: I'm anxious to get started, all right. Since I got to town, all I've done so far is spend money.

LUCILLE: (*expansively*) Well, you're quite a stranger!

PAUL: Sit down.

FRED: Thanks. I guess I'm a little late. I got off the wrong subway station and there was an old woman there selling papers, and I stopped and talked to her because I knew she must be somebody's mother.

MAXIE: (*who has never stopped playing*) A fresh slant.

FRED: I was right too, because she told me she has six sons. I feel sorry for old women that has to earn their living.

LUCILLE: What do the boys do—rent her the stand?

FRED: No, most of them are in a hospital and two of them had their foot cut off. She told me all about it and I give her a dollar.

PAUL: You want to be careful in a place like New York. There's all kinds of people waiting to take your money away from you.

FRED: It's a great city, all right. To-day I took the ferry-boat over to Staten's Island and back. (*He explains it to* LUCILLE.) It's an island and you have to take a ferry-boat. But I suppose you been there.

LUCILLE: I go there a lot—just for the trip.

FRED: I seen the Goddest of Liberty, too—I mean the statue. It cost a million dollars and weighs 225 ton.

MAXIE: (*gently*) She ought to cut out sweets. (*He indulges in a fancy run.*)

FRED: (*a gesture in the direction of* MAXIE) He can play the piano! . . . And I seen some of the big ocean liner steamboats. I seen the *President Harding* just coming in from London or Europe or somewheres, and the other day I seen the *Majestic* tied up to the dock. She's pretty near twicet as long as the *President Harding* and weighs 56,000 ton. The *President Harding* only weighs 14,000 ton.

LUCILLE: Imagine!

FRED: (*to* LUCILLE) Have you been through the Holland Tunnel?

LUCILLE: No, I haven't.

FRED: (*to* PAUL) Have you been through the Holland Tunnel?

PAUL: No.

FRED: (*not for a minute giving up*) Have you been through the Holland Tunnel, Mr. Schwartz?

MAXIE: I've been waiting for somebody to go with.

FRED: I'll go with you!

MAXIE: Fine!

FRED: I want to go every place so as to get ideas for songs. I was telling Mr. Sears about one idea—I haven't got it written yet—it's a song about the traffic lights. Green for "Come ahead!" and red for "Stop!" Maybe a comical song with a girl signaling her sweetheart with different colored lights in the window; a green light when it's all right for him to call——

LUCILLE: And a red one when her husband's home.

FRED: (*shocked*) No, I was thinking about her father. I wouldn't write about those kind of women—I got no sympathy for them.

LUCILLE: I guess you're right.

FRED: I was thinking of another idea on the way up here. Maybe a song about the melting pots—all the immigrants from overseas who've come to the Land of Liberty. Take the Jews—do you know there's nearly two million Jews in New York City alone?

MAXIE: What do you mean alone?

FRED: And then there's the Hall of Fame, up to Washington Heights. They got everybody up there. Washington, Lincoln, Longfellow. They got two dozen—what do you call 'em—busts?

LUCILLE: (*sweetly, to* PAUL) That's the place for you, dear.

FRED: No. A man's got to be dead for twenty-five years.

LUCILLE: Well, that fits in.

MAXIE: (*it's too much for him*) I've got to be going along.

PAUL: Wait! I want Stevens to show you one of his lyrics—have you got that one with you? About the game?

MAXIE: I've got to be downtown at ten.

PAUL: This won't take a minute. (*To* FRED.) Go ahead.

FRED: I'll have to explain first, so you'll understand. The idea came to me at a football game between Syracuse and Colgate. They beat them, and they felt pretty bad, so the idea come to me for this little song. I call it "Life Is a Game."

MAXIE: A novelty!

FRED: Here's the verse. Are you ready?

PAUL: Yeah.

FRED: "I don't know why some people cry
　　　　When things appear to go wrong;
　　　　I always say 'Laugh and be gay!'
　　　　Things cannot always go wrong!
　　　　No use to pine, no use to whine,
　　　　Things will come right if you just give them time."
That's the verse.

LUCILLE: Uh-huh!

FRED: Then here's the refrain:

> "Life is a game; we are but players——"

MAXIE: Hey, bring it here! Maybe we can put some music to it.

FRED: Just play some chords.

MAXIE: I'll see if I know any.

FRED: (*sings as well as he can to* MAXIE'S *improvisation*)

> "Life is a game; we are but players
> Playing the best we know how.
> If you are beat, don't let it wrangle;
> No one can win all the time.
> Sometimes the odds seem dead against you;
> What has to be, has to be,
> But smile just the same, for life is a game,
> And God is a fine referee."

(MAXIE *picks up the last line and sings it again, tacking on a rousing musical finale to fit. It is really the finish of "All Those Endearing Young Charms," but so far as* FRED *is concerned it has been composed especially for his lyric. He is beaming with pleasure.*) I haven't got the second verse yet.

MAXIE: You won't need one.

LUCILLE: I like a song with love interest.

FRED: Well, I got an idea and a title for another one—I mean, of course I got lots of ideas, but this one, I told it to a party and she— (*he catches himself, embarrassed.*)—I mean, this party seemed to think it was pretty good.

PAUL: Let's hear it.

FRED: It's just a title. You told me you'd rather have just a title and then write the tune first.

PAUL: What's the title?

FRED: "June Moon." That's the title—"June Moon."

MAXIE: A war song.

FRED: No, no. The verse will be about a fella that's met a girl in June, when there was a moon shining, and then something happened so that she went away, or maybe he went away, and then whenever he looks up at the moon after that, he thinks of her. In the second verse, she'll be doing the same thing for him.

LUCILLE: That's fair enough.

PAUL: I don't know—another moon song.

MAXIE: (*dashing to the piano*) "June Moon"—I've got it!

(*He ad-libs a melody; FRED chimes in with some extemporized words.*)

FRED: (*singing*) June Moon, how I wish you so-and-so, how I miss my so-and-so, spoon! (*He comes out strong on the "spoon."*—that's right, anyhow.)

(*Meanwhile the phone has rung again, and under cover of the music LUCILLE has answered it.*)

LUCILLE: Hello. . . . No, this is Lucille. Just a minute. (*She puts down the receiver.*) Eileen!

PAUL: (*who has managed, despite the confusion, to make mental note of MAXIE's melody*) Well, I might be able to dig up something for that.

FRED: (*plunging expansively into explanation*) I got the idea coming in on the train. I happened to look out of the window——

(*He stops abruptly as EILEEN comes back on. She has put on a dress, but, in view of the news that MAXIE had brought, not the evening dress. She looks smart, however, and FRED is impressed, to say the least. Paying no attention to any one, she heads straight for the telephone.*)

EILEEN: Hello! . . . Oh, no, not at all. (*To say that the lady is sarcastic is putting it mildly.*) What train? . . . You're sure of that, are you? . . . Nothing, only I thought you might be mistaken. Everybody makes mistakes, you know. (*It's a good chance for MAXIE to escape, and he leaps up. While EILEEN is still talking he manages to get out—*"Good-by, everybody! I'm due at the Orchard! Glad to have met you, Stevens," *etc.* PAUL *follows him out with:* "Now look! Don't say anything to Fagan, because I don't want him to know until—" *The voices die out.* FRED, *a bit embarrassed, is left alone with the two girls, while* EILEEN *continues her phone talk.*) Yes, I can imagine. It must have been terribly tiresome in Philadelphia all day. . . . What? . . . Oh, really? (*Her tone indicates that this is the body blow.*) I thought you were leaving to-morrow. . . . What time to-night? . . . My, it must be important! . . . Then—I won't have a chance to say good-by before you go. . . . Oh, no, don't trouble yourself—it's quite all right. . . . Yes, I'm sure you are. . . . No, I don't mind a bit. I'm just sorry you have to spend the night on a train, that's all. . . . Oh, perfectly! . . . Have a pleasant trip. (*But she doesn't mean "pleasant trip." She hangs up; a look flashes between her and* LUCILLE.)

LUCILLE: (*coming back to the present*) Mr. Stevens, this is my sister, Miss Fletcher. Eileen—Mr. Stevens. (*She gives a broad wave of the hand, as if to say, "And if you want him, he's yours."*)

EILEEN: (*her mind on the telephone*) Hello.

FRED: I'm glad to meet you, Miss Fletcher.

EILEEN: Thanks.

LUCILLE: Mr. Stevens is a lyric writer. He's from Schenectady.

EILEEN: Oh, yes. Have you been in New York long?

FRED: Just a couple of weeks. I'm from Schenectady.

EILEEN: (*a lot she cares*) Schenectady, eh?

LUCILLE: (*with the air of a person who is washing that up*) Schenectady.

FRED: I was with the General Electric Company, but I left them.

EILEEN: I suppose they've closed down?

FRED: (*who knows better than that*) No. I had a post-card to-day from a fella that works there.

LUCILLE: Mr. Stevens has been all over New York, getting ideas for songs.

EILEEN: Do you like it?

FRED: Yes, I like it fine, but it costs money to live here. For instance, I had breakfast in the hotel this morning and it was ninety cents for salt mackerel and mashed potatoes and a cup of Instant Postum.

LUCILLE: No wonder you think New York's expensive! A few more breakfasts like that and you won't have any money left.

FRED: I still got plenty.

LUCILLE: Really? (*She flashes a look to* EILEEN.) I'll bet you haven't been to any of the real places, have you? It takes a New Yorker to find those.

FRED: I seen the Goddess of Liberty.

LUCILLE: Oh, I mean the night places!

FRED: I seen it at night.

LUCILLE: Oh, no! Restaurants!

FRED: Huh?

LUCILLE: Mr. Stevens would love those. (*To* EILEEN.) Wouldn't he?

EILEEN: *(slowly coming to)* Yah.

LUCILLE: I'll tell you what! Why don't we make up a party—the four of us—and show Mr. Stevens the town!

FRED: You mean to-night?

LUCILLE: What do you say, Eileen? How about it?

EILEEN: *(thinking hard; her eyes go involuntarily to the telephone)* Why—sure! I don't know why not! Sure!

FRED: Well, wait! It'd be great to go, all right, only the trouble is I got another engagement!

LUCILLE: Oh, but you could put that off!

EILEEN: Of course you could!

LUCILLE: *(as PAUL re-enters)* Paul had another engagement, too. He broke it on your account, didn't you, dear?

PAUL: *(to whom this is news)* What?

LUCILLE: We thought it would be fun for the four of us to go out some place, but Mr. Stevens doesn't want to.

FRED: It ain't that I don't want to, but——

LUCILLE: You know, you really ought to. Paul was just saying that what you needed was to go places where they do the latest numbers and hear what kind of songs are getting over! That's true, isn't it, Paul?

PAUL: Ah, yes! Sure!

LUCILLE: Of course it is! Are we all set?

FRED: Well, I want to go all right. It's only I don't know on account of this other engagement.

EILEEN: But you could do something about that. You could if you really wanted to. *(So close to him that he is groggy.)* Don't you—want to?

FRED: *(hesitating)* Well, I ain't dressed to go out. I mean, to some swell place.

EILEEN: We'll go where we don't have to dress.

LUCILLE: How about the Orchard? Wouldn't Maxie be surprised to see the four of us stroll in?

EILEEN: Lucille and I'll go right in and get our things on. *(A movement)*

PAUL: Well, wait a minute! It's just that I didn't happen to bring much money with me——

LUCILLE: Oh, that's all right. Mr. Stevens can be the treasurer to-night and you can fix it up with him later!

EILEEN: As long as you're going to be partners!

LUCILLE: Come on! Let's hurry!

(*The* GIRLS *rush off.*)

PAUL: Is that all right with you?

FRED: (*looking after the pair*) Say, she's quite a girl, isn't she?

PAUL: Who? Eileen?

FRED: Does she live here with you all the time?

PAUL: Yah. She does.

FRED: She's a regular New York girlie.

PAUL: Maybe it wouldn't be a bad notion for you to knock around a few nights—I mean, before we start working. Might give you some ideas.

FRED: I'm willing.

PAUL: Great!

FRED: Say, can I use your phone a minute?

PAUL: Sure. Do you want the book?

FRED: No, I know the number. (*Takes receiver off*) Rhinelander 4160.

PAUL: I'd better clean up a bit.

FRED: Look! They was talking about this Orchard. That ain't one of them expensive places, is it?

PAUL: No. Just about average.

FRED: Hello. . . . I want to speak to Miss Edna Baker, please. . . . Yes. (*To* PAUL.) I mean, what do you think it would be likely to come to for the four of us? More than ten dollars?

PAUL: (*vaguely*) No—not unless we go on to some other place. You've got more with you, haven't you?

FRED: What other place?

PAUL: One of the other clubs.

FRED: But I don't—hello. . . . Hello. . . . Eddie? . . . I want to tell you something.

PAUL: I'll go and wash up. (*Departs*)

FRED: Well, I'm up there now, but that isn't— Sure. . . . Yeah, it looks all right. . . . No, I'm still here. There was a piano player here from Goebel's. He liked my stuff and made up a tune to some of it. . . . Yeah. . . . He said it was all right. But that isn't . . . what I called up to say was I can't get around there till late. . . . No, it'll be later than that. There's no telling what time it'll be. . . . We got to study some songs. . . . Paul Sears and his wife. . . .

No, no, don't think that. It's a business proposition. They're taking me to a place where we'll get some ideas. . . . Just the three of us. . . . But you know I'd rather be with you. (EILEEN *comes back, coat over arm.*) But I can't. . . . I can't. . . . *They're* taking *me.* I'll tell you all about it in the morning. . . . That's all I can say now. . . . I can't. . . . In the morning. . . . Good night. (*Hangs up.*)

EILEEN: You seem to be having your troubles.

FRED: No, that wasn't anything. Just a—friend of mine.

EILEEN: Is she nice?

FRED: It isn't anybody. Just a little girl I happened to meet.

EILEEN: I understand.

FRED: She's just a—a girl from a little town.

(LUCILLE *comes back, full of life. Pulling on gloves, etc.*)

LUCILLE: Listen—it's kind of early for the Orchard anyhow. So why don't we take in the second show at the Capitol?

(PAUL *is on again.*)

PAUL: Is everybody ready?

EILEEN: Oh, that's fine! And I know what you'd love! After the Orchard what do you say we go to the Cotton Club? (*She throws a quick explanation to* FRED.) That's Harlem!

LUCILLE: Great!

EILEEN: They've got a wonderful tap dancer up there! Better than Bill Robinson!

PAUL: But say, the Cotton Club don't get hot till three!

FRED: (*who has never heard of that hour*) What time?

EILEEN: Oh, that's all right! We can go to the Madrid or Richman's in between!

LUCILLE: Oh, great!

PAUL: But say, Richman's burned down the other night!

FRED: Let's not go there!

LUCILLE: I'll tell you where I haven't been for a long while! The St. Regis Roof!

EILEEN: Grand!

LUCILLE: They've a wonderful view!

FRED: Where?

LUCILLE: The St. Regis Roof.

FRED: I get dizzy if I climb a ladder!

(*The voices of the others pick up in a confused jumble as*

THE CURTAIN FALLS

By the beginning of Act 2, Fred has become adjusted to metropolitan life . . . he tells Maxie about a suit he is having made: "It's a blue search with a hair-bone strip. He took my measurements all over. Like I was a fighter. I'm thirty-eight inches around my chest, thirty-three around my stomach—and I forget my thigh. Anyway, he's got it all wrote down." Maxie answers, "I must get a copy."

Edna tries to warn Fred of the perils he faces: "You can't tell, Fred —the most terrible things can happen. There was a near friend of mine, a man, and he was acquainted with a count, an international count, and he came here to New York and one night they went on a wild party and he fell in love with a beautiful chorus girl from the Metropolitan Opera Company—I forget the name of the opera. And he bought her pearls and diamonds, and in less than a week's time he found out they was both married. That's just what could happen to you, dear." Fred says, "He must have been a fine count, not to know he was married," and goes right on seeing the wicked Eileen. Eileen has been having her troubles with Hart. From his latest trip he mailed her only picture post-cards, which causes Lucille to observe, "He certainly sent you a beauti-ful view of the Detroit Athletic Club. And that new waterworks in Cleveland. A man that didn't care about you would have sent a picture of the old waterworks."

But Eileen and Fred become engaged after Fred's song is accepted. When Eileen asks her fiancé if he doesn't love children, he replies, "No. I figure I'd get along better with other people's because they'd go home once in a while." Eileen makes Fred borrow heavily on his royalties for "June Moon"; Fred says Eileen wants a taxi even if she's only going in the other room. In Act 3, Fred's nostalgia for his money and for Edna make him renounce Eileen, and when it turns out that Eileen has been egging her sister, her married sister, into a love affair, Fred confronts her with: "Then I been going around all this time with a— bad woman?" And he decides to take Edna on the European honey-moon he had planned for Eileen. Fred speaks to Maxie: "I've still got the ticket for the boat and it says Frederick M. Stevens and wife. I wonder if the steamship people allow you to change your wife?" Maxie assures him: "Yes. If you don't do it in midstream."

During Act 2 we hear two songs written by someone else besides Fred. One is called "Hello, Tokio," and goes:

Girlie, you'll excuse it please, if I no spik Japanese.
This little call will leave me broke-e-o, but I simply had to say "I love
    you so!"
Believe me, dearie, it's no joke-e-o; I'd gladly fly through fire and
    smoke-e-o,
To share with you the marriage yoke-e-o, fairest flower of Toki-oki-okio.

Maxie's opinion of it is that it would sound better in Japanese.
The other number is "Give Our Child A Name":

> Should a father's carnal sins
> Blight the life of babykins?
> Mister, won't you give our child a name?
> I mean a last name.

In both cases, music and lyrics were by Ring Lardner.
Lardner started work on a second play with Kaufman, a play about
alcoholism, but the project was never completed.

Program notes written for the occasion by Ring Lardner:

WHO'S WHO IN THE CAST

LINDA WATKINS won instant recognition from the critics by her portrayal of Ibsen in the play of that name.

NORMAN FOSTER, who portrays the role of Fred Stevens, is well qualified to act the part of a song writer, as he is the stepfather of Stephen Foster. . . Norman (as you begin to call him after a while) is married to Claudette (Peaches) Colbert, who cannot be with us but sends regards.

FLORENCE D. RICE is the daughter of Grantland Rice, the taxidermist. Miss Rice's parents have no idea she is on the stage and every time she leaves the house to go to the theater she tells them she has to run down to the draper's to buy a stamp.

$\mathcal{A}$ Few Parodies

Ring Lardner had his own opinion of gossip columns of the 1920's. Some of the people he parodies here seem still to be with us.

Your Broadway, Beau, and You Can Have It

New York. . . . Guiseppe Verdi (Joe Green, as a Frank Adams contrib tagged him) seems to have penned another smash in "Aida," George Gershwin is Sullivan-Gilberting with his own brother, Ira.

Mrs. Palmer is anticipating a quadruply blessed event (the Marx Brothers). . . . Cal Coolidge is sealed to Grace Goodhue, a Burlington brunette.

A. Lincoln and Gen. McClellan are on the verge . . . Jimmy Madison and Dolly Payne Todd are THAT WAY. (Ed: This is the absolute Choynskie.)

Aleck Hamilton and Aaron Burr have phfft. . . . . . . The Geo. Washingtons (she was Martha Lorber of the Follies) have moved into their Valley Forge snuggery for the Old Man Shiver Days.

Naps Bonaparte has suggested Reno-vation to his femme, Josie . . . They say Jerry Kern was forced by the Society of Composers and Authors to auction his li-ber-ary, the other boys fearing it would smirch the industry's good name to have a song-writer own a book.

What writer on what paper is taking whose golf clubs to what Bahamas? . . . . . . Arthur Brisbane has signed up to do a daily colyum for William ("Randolph") Hearst.

An Exchange Place investment firm is recommending stock in a company that will convert hootch from liquid to solid form and thus be able to peddle it legally, perhaps as sandwiches. . . . . . You can order me a Scotch on rye.

Recommended to diversion seekers: The Florida East Coast R.R. timetable. . . . . The Lynn Fontannes. . . . . Iodine as a nose gargle to pfffend off the phffflu. . . . . A Madison Square Garden phfffight decision. . . . . A motor trip on Eighth Ave.

F. P. F. has quit the evemaily and is running a swell colyum on the world. . . . . . Heywood Broun and the last-named rag have phfft. . . . . The subway is going to install automat turnstiles which you can go through by dropping Anne Nichols in the slot.

Danny Deever is halter bound. . . . . What subscriber to the N.Y. telephone directory has got a cold? . . . . . .

Odd's Bodkins

Author's Note:

Each morn when the neighbors are through with our papers
And stealthily slide them beneath our front door,
I grab the *American,* knowing that there I can
Find O. O. McIntyre's column of lore.
You ask what it's like? I've no copy right here,
But p'rhaps I can give you some sort of idear.

Diary of a Modern New Yorker: Up and out five hours before dawn, and by scooter to the Hermitage Hotel, where the big Seminole Indian Chef, Gwladys, cooked me a flagon of my favorite breakfast dish, beet root and wrestler's knees. Hallooed to Lily Langtry and we fell to arguing over the origin of the word "breakfast," she contending that it was a combination of "break" and "fast," derived from a horse's instructions to a starter in a six-furlong race, and I maintaining that it was five furlongs. We decided to leave it to Percy Hammond, the philatelist, but his nurse told us he was out shoplifting.

Home for a moment to slit my mail and found invitations from Mussolini, Joan Blondell, Joan Crawford, Joan of Arc, President Buchanan, Joe Walcott, and Louisa M. Alcott. Then answered a pleasant long-distance call from Gwladys, the little French chef in the Café des Trois Outfielders in Sydney, her voice as plain as if she were in Melbourne. She had heard I had a cold, she said, and was worried. It was gratifying to hear her whimpers of relief when I assured her the crisis was past.

Breaking bread in the evening at the office of J. P. Morgan & Company and sat between Bernie Shaw, H. J. Wells, Charlie Dickens, Lizzie Barrett, Will Thackeray, Lottie Brontë, Paul Whiteman, and Bill Klem. Chatted for a moment after dinner with *Who's Who* and, finding a heavy rainstorm outside, dismissed my driver, Gwladys, and pirouetted to the lower West Side, where I sat on the New York Central tracks till dawn, watching the operations of a switch engine. I have always been a sucker for a New York Central switch engine in a heavy rainstorm.

Thingumabobs: I once motored around Vienna for two weeks thinking it was Vienna. When I chided the native jehu, Gwladys, he chirped: "Why, Massa, Ah done thought you knowed it was Vienna all de time." . . . If they did not wear identical hats, Jack Dempsey and Connie Bennett could easily pass for sisters. . . . Ellsworth Vines, the golf pro, is a dead ringer for Frank Crowninshield. . . . One-word description of Franklin Delano Roosevelt—President. . . . Otto Kahn always wears a union suit at first nights. . . . There is something about the name Babe Ruth that suggests rare old Dresden filigree work. . . . Mayor O'Brien is the image of Joan Crawford. . . . One of my favorite people—Senator Long. . . . Tallulah Bankhead and Jimmy Durante have profiles exactly alike. . . . Few ladies with as little money can act as grampous as Bernie Baruch. . . . Two of my favorite people—Senator Long.

Thoughts while strolling: Damon Runyan's feet. Kate Smith, a small-town girl who became nation-wide in a big city. Rosamond Pinchot and Theodore Dreiser could pass for twins. How did I get to thinking about "The Song of the Shirt"? Oh, yes; it started at tea when Fannie Hearst brought up Arthur Brisbane's quaint method of writing. His syndicated column averages close to 130,000 words a day, yet he writes it all in longhand on his shirt bosom, then forgets it and sends his shirt to the laundry. Damon Runyon's feet.

Mention of the name Rex Cole invariably reminds me of the Mother Goose rhyme, "Old King Cole," etc., and I never can figure out why. The surnames of two successful *Saturday Evening Post* writers, Samuel Blythe and Charles Francis Coe, begin with the second and third letters of the alphabet. Damon Runyon's feet. Personal nomination for the most thrilling of the summer's detective yarns—"Dracula." If you saw only the left side of Theodore Dreiser's face you would swear it was the right side of Ruth Etting's. Rube Goldberg, cover-designer for *Spalding's Base Ball Guide,* never wears a hat to bed. Damon Runyan's feet. One-word description of the Vice-President—Garner.

Insomniacs: While writing a novel "Red" (Socker) Lewis never eats anything but alphabet soup. . . . Irvin S. Cobb cannot eat before, during, or after 5 A.M. . . . Theodore Dreiser always dresses according to the time of day he happens to be writing about. Thus, if an incident in one of his novels takes place in the morning, he puts on a morning coat; if at noon, a noon coat, etc. . . . There is a striking resemblance between Damon Runyan's feet and Ethel Merman. . . . Theodore Dreiser often arises at 2 A.M. and walks for two hours steadily. I once knew a fellow in Gallipolis who often arose at 6 P.M., and at 2 A.M. walked for two hours unsteadily. No dog as cunning as the Cubanola Glide.

Miss Sawyer, Champion

The New Yorker
Sept. 10, 1927

In one of the closest and most irksome matches ever played on the Stadium courts of the West Side Tennis Club at Forest Hills, Miss Millicent Sawyer, the twenty-two-year-old Basque school girl from Astoria, yesterday won the United States Women's National Tennis championship from Mrs. Wallace Gruger Tuttle, the former Miss Dolly Atkinson of Americus, Georgia, until she married Joseph Hostetter from whom she was recently divorced owing to a tennis elbow on the Stadium courts of the West Side Tennis Club at Forest Hills, 6—0, 6—0, 6—0, 7—0.

This match, the final of the United States Women's National championship, was much closer than the score would indicate, Mrs. Tuttle giving the big gallery the thrill of its life by forcing the twelve-year-old Astorian to seven games in the last sett after dropping the first three at love. "Little Poker Face," so called because she is all aces, aces, aces, looked in bewilderment at Luke Darnell, who was in the umpire's chair until a woman with a nursing baby came in and he had to get up and hang onto a strap, when he called out, "Miss Sawyer leads in the final sett, seven-love," but she recovered her composure in time to claim her sweater and walk off the courts, leaving "Big Freckle Face" to get out of it the best way she could.

The streets surrounding the club are so bumpy and full of holes that it was suggested on the way home that the men who waste so much time rolling the courts with khaki shirts and blue neckties, which are already like a billiard table, leave the enclosure some day and roll the streets surrounding the club, which are bumpy and full of holes. This suggestion was made by Ken Quigley, the former Thomas Kitson. When Tom was in his first year in prep school, his father offered him one thousand dollars not to smoke until he was of age. Tom then changed his name to Ken Quigley and lighted one cigarette after another.

Yesterday's event was attended by the largest crowd of the season, attracted not only because it was the championship final, but also by the fact that the former Miss Stevens's birthplace in Portugal gave the match an international color.

It would be difficult to say too much in praise of Miss Sawyer's tennis progress since last January, when she took up the game. Her initial match resulted in a straight sett victory over little Irma Dugan, the two-year-old Los Angeles Basque. At this time, Millicent was only seven herself. Playing in an average of one tournament every two months, she conquered, in order, Miss Gertie Judson, the former Mrs. Graybar Kennison Prague; Miss Louise Tolliver, the stammering Wichita school girl; Mayor Thompson, of Chicago; the Wimbletonians, Mencken and Nathan (all Basques), and climaxed her first season's career yesterday with her hard-earned victory over the Hostetter divorcée. In addition to which, she has grown into blooming young womanhood and can play three musical instruments, all ukuleles.

There are two remarkable things about Miss Sawyer's triumph. One is her age. Very few women tennis players reach the peak of their game until they are well into their seventies. The other is the fact that she is a school girl. The large majority of successful net experts of the opposing sex are former laundresses.

Twenty-nine-year-old Mrs. Tuttle won the toss and elected to serve first, whereat Miss Sawyer cried:

"Youth will be——"

The gallery broke into uncontrollable laughter and it was necessary for Umpire Darnell to request that no demonstration be made until the jokes were completed.

It was while the former Miss Atkinson was serving the third game of the second sett that one of the judges called:

"Foot fault!"

An intermission had to be taken while attendants extricated the Portuguese girl from a pile of business cards thrown out of the stands by chiropodists.

"In Conference"

Harvey Hester entered the outer office of Kramer & Company, Efficiency Engineers. He approached the girl at the desk.

"I want to see Mr. Lansing," he said.

"A. M. or A. T.?" inquired the girl.

"Mr. A. T. Lansing," Hester replied.

"What is your name?"

"Harvey Hester."

The girl pressed a button and wrote something on a slip of paper. A boy appeared. She gave him the paper.

"For Mr. A. T. Lansing," she said.

The boy went away. Presently a young lady in mannish attire came out.

"I am Mr. Lansing's secretary," she said. "Did you want to see him personally?"

"I did and do," said Hester.

"Well, just now he's in conference," said the secretary. "Perhaps you would like to wait."

"Listen. This is pretty important——"

"I'm sorry, but it's against the rules to disturb any of the officers in conference."

"How long will the conference last?"

"It's hard to say," replied the secretary. "They just got through one conference and they're beginning another. It may be ten minutes and it may be an hour."

"But listen——"

"I'm sorry, but there's nothing for you to do but call again, or else wait."

"I'll wait," snapped Hester, "but I won't wait long!"

The conferees were sitting around the big table in the conference room. At the head of the table was J. H. Carlisle, president of the firm.

"Where is L. M.?" he inquired crossly. "This is the fifth conference he's been late to this morning. And we've had only six."

"Well, J. H. C.," said R. L. Jamieson, a vice-president, "I don't think we ought to wait for him. If we drag along this way we won't be able to get in a dozen conferences all day. And a dozen was the absolute minimum agreed on."

"That's all right, R. L.," said K. M. Dewey, another vice-president, "but it happens that L. M. is the one that asked for this conference, and he's the only one that knows what it's about. So we'd——"

At this moment the door opened and the tardy one entered. He was L. M. Croft, one of the vice-presidents.

"I'm sorry to be late," he apologized, addressing J. H. C.

"I was talking over the phone to J. P. The reason I asked for this conference," he continued, "was to get your thoughts on a proposition that came up about twenty minutes ago. There was a post-card in the mail addressed to the firm. It was from the main post-office. It says they are holding a letter for us which reached them unstamped. If we sign the card and send it to them, together with a two-cent stamp, they will forward us the letter. Otherwise they will send it to the Dead Letter Office. The question is, Is the letter worth the time and expense of sending for it?"

"Who is the letter from, L. M.?" The inquirer was S. P. Daniels, one of the vice-presidents.

"The card didn't say, S. P.," replied Croft.

"My suggestion, J. H. C. and gentlemen," said A. M. Lansing, a vice-president, "is to write to whoever is in charge of that office, authorize him to open the letter, see who it's from and what it's about, and if he thinks it important, to let us know, and then we can mail the required stamp."

"It's a mighty ticklish business, gentlemen," ventured Vice-President T. W. Havers. "I have a brother, G. K. Havers. He's a pharmaceutical dispenser at a drug store on upper Broadway. He received a card like this from a branch post-office. He signed the card and sent the stamp, and the letter turned out to be nothing but advertising matter from a realtor."

"Why, T. W.," said A. T. Lansing, "you never told any one of us you had a brother."

"Oh, yes, A. T.," replied Havers. "I've got two other brothers beside G. K. One of them, N. D., is a mortuary artisan and the other, V. F., is a garbage practitioner in Harrisburg."

"I'm one of a family of seven boys," put in Vice-President B. B. Nordyke.

"I was born in Michigan," said H. J. Milton, the firm's secretary, "in a little bit of town called Watervliet."

"I'm a Yankee myself," said S. P. Daniels, "born and raised in Hingham, Massachusetts."

"How far is that from North Attleboro?" asked K. M. Dewey.

"It's right near Boston, K. M.," answered S. P. "It's a suburb of Boston."

"Philadelphia has some mighty pretty suburbs," said A. M. Lansing. "Don't you think so, R. L.?"

"I haven't been there for fifteen years, A. M.," replied R. L. Jamieson. "Last time I was there was in 1909."

"That was fifteen years ago, R. L.," remarked T. W. Havers.

"That's what I say, T. W., fifteen years," said Jamieson.

"I thought you said fourteen years," rejoined Havers.

"Let's see," put in C. T. Miller, treasurer of the firm. "Where was I fifteen years ago? Oh, yes, I was a bibliopolistic actuary in southern Ohio. I was selling Balzac complete for twenty-six dollars."

"Did you read Jimmie Montague's poem in the Record this morning, Z. H.?" inquired F. X. Murphy of Z. H. Holt.

"No, F. X.," replied Holt. "I don't go in for that highbrow stuff and anyways, when I get through my day's work here, I'm too tired to read."

"What do you do with yourself evenings, Z. H.?" asked A. T., the younger of the Lansings.

"Oh, maybe play the player piano or go to a movie or go to bed," said Holt.

"I bet there's none of you spends your evenings like I do," said young Lansing. "Right after dinner, the wife and I sit down in the living room and I tell her everything that I've done down here during the day."

"Don't she get bored?" asked S. P. Daniels.

"I should say not, S. P.!" replied young Lansing. "She loves it!"

"My sister Minnie—she married L. F. Wilcox, the tire people—she was over to the house last night," announced L. M. Croft. "She was reading us a poem by this Amy Leslie, the woman that got up this free verse. I couldn't make much out of it."

"Gentlemen," said J. H. C. at this juncture, "have you any more suggestions in regards to this unstamped letter? How about you, Z. H.?" he added, turning to Holt.

"Well, I'll tell you, J. H. C.," replied Holt, "a thing like this has got to be handled mighty careful. It may be all right, and it may be a hoax, and it may be out and out blackmail. I remember a somewhat similar case that occurred in my home town, Marengo, Illinois."

"Did you know the Lundgrens there?" asked L. M. Croft.

"Yes, indeed, L. M.," answered Holt. "I used to go into Chicago to see Carl pitch. He was quite a card player, too. But this case I speak of, why, it seems that S. W. Kline—he was a grass truncater around town—why, he received an anonymous post-card with no named signed to it. It didn't even say who it was from. All it said was that if he would be at a certain corner at a certain hour on a certain day, he would find out something that he'd like to know."

"What?" interrupted the elder Lansing.

"I was saying," said Holt, "that in my home town, Marengo, Illinois, there was a man named S. W. Kline who got an anonymous post-card with no name signed to it, and it said that if he would be at a certain corner at a certain hour on a certain day, he would find out something that he'd like to know."

"What?" repeated the elder Lansing.

"Never mind, Z. H.," said J. H. C. "Tell us what happened."

"Nothing," said Holt. "Kline never went near the place."

"That reminds me," put in K. M. Dewey, "of a funny thing that came off in St. Louis. That's when I was with the P. D. advertising department. One afternoon the postman brought the mail to our house and my wife looked it over and found a letter addressed to some name like Jennings or Galt or something like that. It wasn't for us at all. So she laid for the postman next day and gave him back the letter. She said, 'Look here, here's a letter that don't belong to us at all. It's for somebody else.' I forget now just what the name was. Anyway, he took the letter and I guess he delivered it to the right people."

"I got some pretty good Scotch myself for fifty-six dollars a case," said S. P. Daniels. "It's old James Buchanan."

"Where did you get it, S. P.?" inquired Paul Sickles.

"I've got the phone number home," replied Daniels. "I'll bring it to you to-morrow, Paul."

Sickles was the only man in the outfit who was not an officer, so they called him Paul instead of by his initials.

"Prohibition's a joke!" said T. W. Havers.

"People drink now'days that never drank before," said S. P. Daniels.

"Even nice women are drinking," said L. M. Croft.

"I think you'll see light wines and beer before it's over," said K. M. Dewey.

J. H. C. spoke again.

"But what about this letter?"

"It seems funny to me," said A. T. Lansing, "that the people in the post-office don't open it and find out what it's all about. Why, my wife opens my personal mail, and when I'm home I open hers."

"Don't she care?" asked S. P. Daniels.

"No, S. P.," said the younger Lansing. "She thinks everything I do is all right."

"My wife got a letter last week with no stamp on it at all," said Sickles. "The stamp must have dropped off. All it was anyways was a circular about mah jongg sets."

"Do you play with flowers, Paul?" asked K. M. Dewey.

"Why——"

Harvey Hester, in the outer office, looked at his watch for the twentieth time; then got up and went to the girl at the desk.

"Please have Mr. Lansing's secretary come out here again," he said.

"A. M. or A. T.?" asked the girl.

"A. T.," said Hester.

The secretary came out.

"Listen," said Hester. "If I can't see Mr. Lansing right this minute it'll be too late."

"I'm sorry, but I can't interrupt him when he's in conference."

"All right," said Hester. "Will you please give him this message? You've got my name. Mr. Lansing and I were in school together and were more or less friendly. Well, I was tipped off this morning —I don't need to tell you how—I was tipped off that Mrs. Lansing is leaving for Chicago on the 12:05 train. And she isn't leaving alone. She's eloping. I thought Mr. Lansing might want to try to stop her."

"What time is it now?"

"Seven minutes of twelve," said Hester. "He can just make it."

"But he's still in conference," said the secretary.

$\mathcal{A}$ Close-up of Domba Splew

Not since the tardy, posthumous death of Agera Cholera has the American literati been so baffled toward a rising genius of letters than has been demonstrated in regards to the Italian poet, Domba Splew, who, just a year ago, sprang into world-wide indifference by the publication, in The Bookman, of his verse, "La battia fella inna base tuba" (The weasel fell into the bathtub).

It is a matter of history that in the month in which this poem appeared, the circulation of the magazine in which it was printed increased two copies. And the fame of the author on this side of the old pond, as I call it, spread as far west as North Attleboro, Mass. You could not wake up in the morning or any other time without either wife or kiddies yelping, "Sweet papa, did you see this poem of Domba Splew's, 'La battia fella inna base tuba' (The weasel fell into the bathtub)?"

It got so finely a person could not sleep at home at all and I for one rented one of the big New York hotels and slept outdoors, not being able to get a room. Everybody wondered what was the matter, but I laughed at them. Fincly the editor of Rickets Weekly caught me in an upright position in the gutter and made me the unheard-of offer of $5.00 and no hundreds dollars to go and interview this America-Italio sensation and find out something about his home life.

To locate a man as famous as him is what Ex-Attorney-General Daugherty would call "les arbeit tough" (a hard job). But the writer, an experienced interviewer, looked upon it as child's play and went to the nearest city ticket office where luckily I found a clerk who had not returned from lunch.

"Listen," I said, "where would a man be apt to run acrost a foreign literary genius, discovered only a year ago?"

"Listen," replied the clerk, "have you tried the artistic and bohemian mecca of American letters?"

"Where is that?" I coughed.

"Scranton, Pa.," was the clerk's reply.

So the writer bought a ticket to Scranton and arrived there only a half hour late.

To make a short story out of a risqué story, I found our hero living on the top floor of a six-story bungalow.

"If," he said, "I am away from the smoke and chimbley, I am at a lost. In other words, I am a gone gosling."

"Listen," he said: "I don't think you know much about Italy, but I will tell you. In the first place there is a military rule which provides that when a native born reaches the age of seven, they must spend the next three years in jail, or, as Oscar Wilde aptly named it, Reading Gaol. The reason I came over to America was on acct. of the fact that there is more words here. I need words."

In a little while he was supine.

"Now listen," I said: "I have been sent over here to Scranton to find out about your home life. Tell me what you do all day."

He went scarlet.

"I have got a set of rules," he said, pulling a fresh cucumber off the hatrack. "In the morning I get up and talk to my dromedaries. Oh, those dromedaries! I would walk a mile for one of them! I have got a collection of eighty of them and each one more laughable than the first one. Every morning somebody sends me a dromedary. After talking to my dromedaries, I sit down and read the telephone book from cover to cover charge. But now leave me go out and show you my garden."

The two of us strolled haltingly through his garden, which was an Italian garden with all the Italian dishes in bloom—ravioli, spaghetti, garlic, Aida, and citrous fruits.

"Is this your diversion?" I asked him.

"Yes," he said, toppling over a govvel sprig and breaking his ankle in two places.

"Tell me about your home life," I said with a sneer.

"I presume," he said, taking a pair of suspenders out of the nearest waste basket, "I presume you want to know my daily calendar. Well, I always make it a point to get up at six in the morning and eat my breakfast food."

I found out later that his breakfast food was ground-up quail feathers, the rest of the carcass being thrown outdoors.

"I," he continued, "spend my next ten minutes with my dromedaries. It is just a romp. Then I return to my own room, where an ostrich shaves me. Not too close.

"Then I sit down on a milk stool and begin my day's work. I aim to never write lest than one poem a day. For instance, look at this one I turned out this morning, just after the ostrich had shaved me."

And he read me the verse that was published by mistake in last month's Applejack—

> *Hail to thee, blithe owl!*
> *Bird thou never wantest to been.*
> *Queenly and efflorien,*
> *How did thou ever begin?*

"That," I said, "sounds like a steal on Kipling."

"Kipling yourself!" said the poet, and I loped over the nearest hedge.

"But listen," he said: "Have you heard my Gooseflesh, after the style of Alfred Geese?"

There was no use saying no:

> *Quiescent, a person sits heart and soul,*
> *Thinking of daytime and Amy Lowell.*
> *A couple came walking along the street;*
> *Neither of them had ever met.*

"That," said Mr. Splew, "is the verse I have worked on all winter."

"It's been a hard winter," I said. "We didn't have enough coal either."

With that, he climbed up on top of the pigeon house.

"I want to tell you about my wife," he said. "She has got what is called chronic paralysis. She has a stroke every day, but it is never quite enough."

With that, he led me into the beehive, where he and the dromedaries eat all their meals.

"Now, Mr. Splew," I said, "my editor wanted me to ask you how you got the name 'Domba.' He thought it might be a contraction of Dumbbell."

"Your editor is both wrong," said Mr. Splew. "I was named for my father, who gave the money to found the Kalter Aufschnitt (Cold High School) in Rome. And the children that attended the school said it must have been dumbfounded. Would you like to go into the pool?"

cA Visit to the Garrisons

For the benefit of folks that is planning or building new homes, or nests as I call them, or have moved into homes all ready built and don't know what to do with all their space, I will try and describe something I seen the other night which it strikes me like it will solve a problem for a big majority of families besides adding to the gen. appearance and comfort of the home (nest).

A couple named Garrison who we met them a couple times at different parties asked us to come over and play mah jongg some evening so we went over to their house which they had just finished building it and Mrs. Garrison says did we want to see the house so of course we says yes and they showed us over it and the most of it was a good deal like other houses but they was one room which was in the way of a novelty and that is what I am going to try and describe.

This room was a kind of a small room next to the living room.

"I don't dast come in here unless I am invited," said Mrs. Garrison. "It is Mr. Garrison's den."

"His what?" I asked her.

"His den," says Mrs. Garrison.

The Mrs. and I was both obliged to laugh at the quaint idear of calling a room a den.

"Mr. Garrison comes in here when he doesn't want to be disturbed," says Mrs. Garrison. "Not even I or Junior dast disturb him."

"Junior!" I says. "Who is Junior?"

"Junior is our son," says Mrs. Garrison. "His real name is Ralph, after his daddy, but we thought if they was two Ralphs in the house, we would get all mixed up. So we call little Ralph Junior."

"A good idear," I could not help from saying.

Well, the den, as they call it, was furnished with one easy chair, a couch, a straight chair and a desk. They was two pillows on the couch and one of them red and blue and had the word Pennsylvania worked on it.

"Oh, is your husband a railroad man?" asked my Mrs. who is kind of ignorant.

"You mean the pillow?" says Mrs. Garrison. "No, that's for the University of Pennsylvania, where he attended."

Everybody laughed at my wife's mistake.

The other pillow was maroon and gold and had a big M in the middle of it. Mrs. Garrison exclaimed that this was for Minnesota where her brother attended the university.

"What did he study?" I asked her.

"Pharmacy," said Mrs. Garrison with a smile.

But what I want to describe mostly is the ornaments with which the den, as they call it, was decorated. On one side of the door as you went in was a giant pine cone.

"My goodness, is that a real pine cone?" asked my wife.

"Yes," said Mr. Garrison, speaking for the first time in several moments.

On the walls on either side of the window was a pair of antlers.

"What pretty antlers," says my wife.

"Ralph shot them himself," said Mrs. Garrison. "I mean he shot the deer they belonged to."

"That was up in Wisconsin, in 1903," says Mr. Garrison. "No, it was 1904."

Another wall was adorned with a mounted tarpon and a sail-fish.

"Ralph caught those himself," said Mrs. Garrison. "He caught them a little way out from Palm Beach."

"What year?" asked my Mrs.

"1919," said Mr. Garrison.

Leaning up against one corner of the den was a mandolin in a case. Mr. Garrison exclaimed laughingly that he had not played it for several years. Other decorations in the room was two shot guns, several pieces of fishing tackle, kodak pictures of the time the Garrisons drove from Chicago to the Coast, a pair of foils, pennants of all the big colleges and last but not least a rather risky picture called September Morn.

"I am always threatening to tear that down and throw it away," says Mrs. Garrison.

"You better not!" says her husband.

"Aren't you terrible!" says Mrs. Garrison.

The laughter was general.

That is about all I remember in regards to the den, but it seems to me like it strikes a new cord in the matter of hominess.

After we was through admiring the den we went in the living room and Mrs. Garrison got out the mah jongg set and we played till after ten o'clock. During the evening Mr. Garrison served us a couple of drinks of gin and ginger ale.

"I call it a squirrel rickey," said Mr. Garrison and the laughter was general.

"I bet you would never know that Ralph made this gin himself," says Mrs. Garrison.

The Mrs. and I nudged each other.

Business Is Business

I won't give no hint as to the identity of the town where the scene of this little article is laid only to say that it is a suburb of the largest city east of Green River, Wyoming, and can be reached by motor from the midst of the large city referred to in 35 minutes.

Well, like practically every town of a population of 12 and upwards this town has got a fire dept. and like a whole lot of them, this fire dept. is what is known as a volunteer fire dept. which means that the members ain't supposed to get nothing but glory. Well, they's a man living in this town who is in the theatrical business in one way and another and one day the chief of the fire dept. asked him would he join the fire dept. and he says yes on acct. of being public spirited. So he bought himself a rubber coat and a helmet and a pair of rubber boots and staid home several nights with the windows open so as he would sure and hear what is known in the town as the sireen.

Well, the sireen did not blow and did not blow and finely our hero, who we will call Mr. Kloot, recd. a card saying they would be a meeting of the dept. at the fire house the following night and would he please try and attend. The dept. meets once every 2 weeks to disgust prohibition. Well, Mr. Kloot attended the meeting and pretty near all the members was there and he knowed the most of them. The chief is a building contractor and the asst. chief is the town's most prominent plumber. Others who he recognized was all well known citizens in various walks of life. Amongst them was a dentist, the supt. of the gas company, a plasterer, a painter, a mason, a paper hanger, an insurance man and etc.

Well, they set around the whole evening and disgusted prohibition and the sireen did not blow, but the meeting could not of been adjourned more than 5 or 10 minutes when it did blow and the firemen rushed back to the fire house and clumb aboard the 3 vehicles with which the dept. is equipped.

Mr. Kloot happened to board the same vehicle as the chief and the both of them was right close to the driver. "Whose place is it?" shouted the chief as the vehicle tore recklessly down —— Boulevard. "L. M. Taylor's," the driver shouted back. L. M. Taylor being the town's millionaire, worth more than $150,000. "Well, what's your hurry?" shouted the chief and the driver slowed down a little, wile Mr. Kloot did not know what to think.

Well, they got to the fire and it did not look like a very big fire for such a big house and in fact Mr. Taylor's Chinese help had just about put it out with the aid of a few seltzer bottles, but the fire dept. seemed to think the danger was nowheres near over and wile some of them connected a couple of sections of hose with the nearest hydrants, others entered the house through the front and back doors and up ladders through the 2d story windows and begin wielding their axes vs. walls, closets and etc. to see if maybe they wasn't some concealed tongues of flame that would burst forth after the family had went back to sleep. One stream of water was turned on the entire upstairs and another on the ground floor and in a few minutes the family and the servants and the firemen moving hither and thither was instinctively shouting ship ahoy.

Mr. Kloot strayed into the bathroom and found the asst. chief cutting holes in the different pipes. "Safety first," said the asst. chief. "Many a home has burned to the ground on acct. of hidden flames in the plumbing."

Mr. Kloot walked into a master bedroom on the 2d floor and seen 2 firemen with axes excavating the floor. "Safety first," said one of them. "If we should all half to go downstairs in a hurry, they'd be a panic on the stairs so it is best to have a place big enough to drop through."

Mr. Kloot encountered Mr. Taylor, the owner of the house. A couple of firemen was talking to him. "Was you covered by insurance?" asked one of them. "Not fully," says Mr. Taylor. "Well," says the fireman, "this should ought to learn you a lesson."

"This fire," said the other fireman to Mr. Taylor, "was caused by defective wiring. If you would use gas for light a thing like this could not happen."

Mr. Kloot next met Mrs. Taylor and her two kids in company with still another fireman. The lady and the kids was open mouthed with horror, and the fireman was looking into their mouths. "Madam," he says, "you have got a advanced case of pyorrhea and your kinds has got cavities that makes the Grand Canyon look like a dimple. It is a good thing I happened to drop in."

In the early hours of the morning the firemen decided they was nothing more to be done and left what might now be laughingly referred to as the house. Mr. Kloot was the last to leave and Mr. Taylor accompanied him to what had formerly been the front door.

"I feel like I had been giving a old-fashioned at-home," said Mr. Taylor and pulled out of his pocket a small pack of cards, the business cards of the town's volunteer fire dept.

Next morning Mr. Kloot called up the chief and submitted his resignation.

"But what's the idear?" asked the chief.

"Nothing special," replied Mr. Kloot, "only that I'm in the theatrical business."

Here's Ring Lardner's
Autobiography ...

Hardly a man is now alive
Who cares that in March, 1885,
I was born in the city of Niles,
Michigan, which is 94 miles
From Chicago, a city of Illinois.
Sixteen years later, still only a boy,
I graduated from the Niles High School
With a general knowledge of rotation pool.
After my schooling, I thought it best
To give my soul and body a rest.
In 1905 this came to an end,
When I went to work on The Times in Souse Bend.
Thence to Chi, where I labored first
On the Inter-Ocean and then for Hearst,

Then for the Tribune and then to St. Lews,
Where I was editor of Sporting News.
And thence to Boston, where later a can
Was tied to me by the manager man.
1919 was the year
When, in Chicago, I finished my daily newspaper career.
In those 14 years—just a horse's age—
My stuff was all on the sporting page.
In the last nine years (since it became illegal to drink),
I've been connected with The Bell Syndicate, Inc.,
I have four children as well as one Missus,
None of whom can write a poem as good as this is.
                                        Ring Lardner.

The Perfect Woman
"Vanity Fair" 1926

Among the gentlemen asked by Mr. Crowninshield to list their quali-
fications for the Ideal Woman were Charles Chaplin—who demanded
devotion, on the whole; George Jean Nathan—who asked that she be
described in prose by Cabell, Cather and Anatole France; Florenz
Ziegfeld—who came across with a list of practical physical dimensions;
Rudolph Valentino—who wanted fidelity, intelligence, beauty, a sense
of humor, etc. etc. Mr. Lardner's contribution runs as follows:

THE PERFECT WOMAN

1—Lockjaw.
2—Hereditary obesity.
3—Shortness of breath.
4—Falling arches.
5—Mechanical Engineering.
6—Draftsmanship.
7—Absolutely Fireproof.
8—Day and Night elevator Service.
9—Laundry sent out before 8:30 A.M. will be returned the same
    day.
10—Please report to the management any incivility on part of em-
    ployees.

Over the Waves

Ring Lardner was in Doctors Hospital in May of 1932 when he asked Harold Ross if he might try some radio columns for The New Yorker. The last of these was written shortly before Lardner's death on September 25, 1933. The columns reflect his irritation with idiocy, sentimentality and bad taste. He became during this enforced idleness somewhat over-concerned with the dubious lyrics of current songs (the lyrics were so much more often insane than insanitary). But there are gems in the columns, even though some of the references to forgotten radio stations and mislaid performers will mystify those born after 1960.

No Visitors, N. Y.,
June 4, 1932

To the Editor:

In this Home for Disabled World's Series Experts they give you a *New Yorker* once a week as part of the treatment for insomnia, and in skimming over recent issues I have noticed that the publication always contains reviews of new productions on stage and screen, but hardly ever a mention of dat new davil radio which is largely responsible for the fact that there ain't more stage and screen productions to review. Now I am not a charity patient in this institution, and a man named Mr. Pest who works down in the front office claims I owe him three weeks' back rental for a concrete mattress, so I wonder how would it be if you took me on your staff as a radio critic and perhaps you would pay enough to keep Mr. Pest from running a temperature and I could do the work in my spare time which begins at seven o'clock in the morning and ends at eight o'clock the following forenoon.

You will want to know what are my qualifications. Well, for the last two months I have been a faithful listen-inner, leaving the thing run day and night with the exception of a few minutes during and after breakfast whilst I wanted to concentrate on the Seabury testimony, and am fortunate in having as special night nurse a hopeless radio addict who knows such inside details as that the Street Singer's real name ain't Arthur Tracy, that Bing Crosby resents Russ Columbo, or vice versa—in fact, everything save (and this is a universal feminine failing) who wrote what song and why. The latter item doesn't make so much difference to me because lots of times I can guess. When I can't, I call up Gene Buck and find out. I guessed Walter Donaldson for both words and music of "My Mom" the first time I heard it. The nurse insisted on verification and got it, but she still thinks I cheated in some way.

Before we leave the subject ("Mom"), here is a little parody I tore off while she was looking under the bed for my pulse:

> "My nurse, I love her;
> My nurse, you'd love her;—
> Who wouldn't love her, my nurse!
> She's on night duty,
> But never snooty,
> My chum, my cutie, my nurse.
> When I sleep a wink, which is almost seldom never,
> I can hear her think, 'Must I dwell in hell forever!'
> At sev-en a.m.
> She sings, 'Te Deum!'
> She's my Miss Graham, my nurse."

The lady referred to promised a reply in kind, but so far has thought only of a title—"Lard, You Make the Night Too Long."

You may observe that once in a while I write ungrammatically. Kindly charge this to the influence of the Seabury witnesses and the present-day lyric writers, who say, "Somebody loves you, and that somebody is me," and "I reach for you like I'd reach for a star," and have taken to their unanimous bosoms the phrase "For you and I."

Miss Graham now insists that I make a confession: We can't get WJZ. Somewhere between this asylum and the knoll from which that important NBC branch's programs are distributed, there is, we are told, permanent interference. A repair man gave me a long technical explanation of this. Please don't ask me to repeat a word of it.

The honest Miss Graham's point is, am I competent to review the events of the air when I can get WEAF, the red network, but can't get WJZ, the blue (so far as I am concerned) notwork? It all depends, I think, on what I miss and what I miss. I miss "Beautiful Thoughts," "Clara, Lu and Em," "Lum and Abner," "Household Hour;" "Edgar A. Guest," "Lowell Thomas," and "Death Valley Days." And then again I miss Paul Whiteman, most of George Olsen, the Pickens Sisters, and Amos 'n' Andy. (Mention of the last named reminds me of a suggestion I have been intending to make as soon as I mustered sufficient courage: Let's fling caution to the winds, come out in the open and program these two fellows as Amos *and* Andy, which, I may as well confide to their sponsors, is the way they are spoken of by the great invisible, not to say insensible, audience.)

The stations we can and do get, in addition to WEAF, are WOR, WABC and WNYC. I insist on WNYC at seven-thirty every evening because it gives the baseball scores and I, having backed the Giants to win the pennant, can't wait for the morning papers to tell me whether they lost two games or only one or held their ground on account of rain. (Note: This is written at noon, June 4.) Even if you are not interested in baseball, I advise that you tune in on this station at the hour named; the scores are preceded by the police department's list of missing persons, a fascinating broadcast as the following sample will show: "Missing since May 28—Antonia Demartino, 322 New York Avenue, Brooklyn; sixteen years, five feet two inches, ninety-eight pounds, black eyes, black hair, black shoes, tan stockings, black hat, short brown coat, green dress. She is poor mentally." There are about five of these on each evening's list, and four out of five are missing from Brooklyn. So the "poor mentally" may be taken with a grain of garlic.

Some time in May I had Miss Graham days instead of nights. It was an experiment and lasted less than a week. But while it did last, I found that a person who is too tired or lazy to reach out and turn knobs will get best results by setting the thing at WABC and leaving it lay. WEAF and WOR have their moments (particularly WEAF since Texaco grabbed Ed Wynn), but day in and day out, Columbia is, to me at least, the gem of the atmosphere. Prior to the engagement of Mr. Wynn, WEAF provided no real opposition in a comedy way unless you except Ely Culbertson, and Ely's gags, in dialect, were more than balanced when Flo Ziegfeld took the air Sunday nights on WABC. Even the Columbia's singing is funnier, and its conscious comics, such as Col. Stoopnagle and Budd, Burns and Allen, and Ben Bernie (an orchestra leader with a real sense of humor), are so good that they ought to be perfect, and would be if they would take advice.

For several reasons I wish I had applied for this job a few weeks ago. The principal one is that a flock of big sponsors recently woke up out of a deep slumber and discovered that some of their thousand-dollars-a-minute stars were being slightly overpaid. The result was a wholesale cancellation of contracts, or maybe just a refusal to renew contracts that had expired. In some cases the butter and egg men were right; in others they were wrong. I ain't saying which was whom, but I am saying that my evenings were pretty well spoiled when the Camel combination of Downey and Wons took the count, and my Thursdays ruined when La Palina cut Kate Smith's mountain climbing from four times a week to three.

I had just got to a point where I could distinguish, without looking at my watch, whether the vocalist at the mike was Mr. Downey or Miss Smith when the Depression or something hit the tobacco game and messed up my continuity. The popularity of Mr. Downey is evidenced by the fact that WABC keeps him going three times weekly Camels or no Camels, but to me he can never be the same when deprived of his sweet-toned side-kick, Tony Wons, on whom I was developing such a crush that I started to write him a special cheer:

> "Tony Wons! Tony Twice!
> Holy, jumping—"

And that was as far as I had progressed when the flash came that he was temporarily through and at present reciting Edgar Guest's poetry to an audience of helpless Wisconsin pickerel.

Whether or not you accept the theory that Mr. Downey is a tenor, as the programs and Miss Graham's radio publications say, he is worth listening to if you want to keep up with the popular songs of the day. I firmly believe that his voice was the inspiration for Walter's "Mom." Just as firmly I believe that Vince Youmans had someone else in mind when he composed "Drums in My Heart." (The latter, by the way, was written, or at least published, in the key of C by a composer whose exclusive right to three flats is challenged only by Jerry Kern. Speaking of Vince, I am told that a posse of his lyric writers are at work on a logical successor to "Time on My Hands" and "Drums in My Heart." The title is "Water on My Knees.")

When I first became Kate Smith conscious, the young lady was through with her part of the entertainment and on her way out of the studio one night when the announcer, Bill, said something rather sweeping about La Palina cigars. The Songbird of the South was still close enough to the mike to be heard remarking, "You're right, Bill. Most every man I know smokes them." And ever since then I have thought she must read lots of books.

Well, before this sees print, if it sees print, we will know who won the $2500.00 first prize in the Blue Ribbon Malt limerick contest. Ben Bernie first announced this contest several weeks ago. I was interested when he said that all you had to do was write a twenty-five word opinion of the Malt program and supply a last line for the limerick. Being a born last liner and a cheer leader for Ben's stuff (when he doesn't "imitate" Bert Williams by talking a refrain in a low voice and saying "Yes, suh" every little while), I thought to myself, "Here is where I combine pleasure with $2500.00, and though of course I will give the $2500.00 to some hospital—" I thought that until I heard the first four lines of the "limerick," which I now repeat:

> *"There was a young fellow from Broadway,*
> *Whose friends told him, 'Here's what we all say:*
> *When malt's put to test,*
> *Blue Ribbon is best—' "*

"And," explained Ben, "all you have to do is rhyme with Broadway and say."

Oh! Is that all you have to do? Well, it sounded so simple that I scratched my entry, and now I am dying to hear the winning last line. It speaks volumes for whoever thought up, and whoever edited and approved, those first four lines, that in less than a month after the first announcement, they, or somebody, realized that *something* was wrong, and the last three or four times Ben gave it to you, he said you had to rhyme with way (not Broadway) and say.

My suggestion is that we start the contest all over and the malt people can give me $2500.00 to start it right:

> *"There was a young fellow from Broadway,*
> *Who said in a thoroughly awed way:*
> *'When malt's put to test,*
> *Blue Ribbon is best;*
> *Ja, best in an honest to God way.'"*

You see, I would go the whole hog and give them their last line, and all they'd have to do would be to write twenty-five words about Ben Bernie. Which isn't so tough.

A few paragraphs ago I said that WEAF and WOR had their moments. To be perfectly fair I ought to say that they have, or did have, moments and half hours and hours (not even counting Mr. Wynn's) that were as well worth listening to as anything WABC can boast—and a few, such as the ones that featured Lawrence Tibbett and Grace Moore, which would have been marvelous if the stars or their sponsors or somebody hadn't got the quaint idea that they ought to sing request numbers instead of decent stuff. There is nothing better to my "mind" than the WOR Minstrels, who advertise, in a unique way, Macy's store. WEAF had a swell combination, sponsored by Coca-Cola, made up of Gus Haenschen's all-string orchestra, Ohman and Arden, the Revelers (who by any other name can sing as sweet), James Melton, tenor soloist, and an interview by Grant Rice with someone prominent, usually, in the world of sport, all arranged by Frank Black, excepting Grant and his guest, who arranged themselves. And the Cities Service Cavaliers, with Jessica Dragonette. And the Sacred Cow, or Do You Inhale, hour, especially when Walter Winchell was exhaling with no inhibitions or sacred cows to cramp his style. Then there is Cab Calloway and his orchestra, far and away the class of the Afro-American contributions to the air. Cab is generally scheduled on our unobtainable station, WJZ, but is likely to pop up on WEAF as a pleasant surprise.

Well, it is still June 4, but it's long past seven-thirty, four more alleged mental paupers have snuck out of Brooklyn, and the Giants have *won* a double-header. And Miss Graham says I *look* sleepy.

JUNE 8—Bulletin: WEAF, thanks to General Electric and Bayer Aspirin, made this tentative critic feel kind of foolish Sunday evening by giving us a half hour of Paul Robeson in a program of perfect selections (*not* requests) and a half hour of Ohman and Arden at their best, Haenschen's orchestra, an anonymous male quartet (I believe I could disclose one of its aliases), a tenor billed as "Frank Munn" (and maybe he is) and that rara avis, a female soprano, her name being Veronica Wiggins.

Mr. Robeson sang a flock of swell spirituals, one love song (not "Is I in Love? I Is"), and "Old Man River," words and music by, respectively, Oscar Hammerstein and a promising fellow named Kern of Cedar Knolls, Bronxville. By "promising," I mean a fellow who promises to come and see you, but doesn't. In other words, a composer. Phil and Vic, as I call them, played those two pianos as they used to play them before they thought they needed orchestral assistance, and what they played was grand stuff from "Lady, Be Good!," score by G. Gershwin in the days when he wasn't so Gershwinesque.

Came last night and Ben Bernie, better than I had ever heard him. But no announcement of the "limerick" prize winner, the alibi being that there were so many hundreds of thousands of contestants that the judges would require more time. You bet they will, and I bet they won't dast say the winning last line out loud.

Heavy Da-Dee-Dough Boys

No Visitors, N. Y.
June 25, 1932

My nurse, Miss Graham, who seems to know more about radio than most of the people financially interested in same (and when I say this I am not handing the young lady a Phi Beta Kappa key), is a chum of a chum of a cousin of one Bing Crosby, and several weeks ago she (Miss Graham) told me a story about Mr. Crosby which came from the chum-cousin via the chum.

Bing was a featured singer at a night club or something in California. A scout for one of the big broadcasting companies heard him sing and thought he was good. This sounds like a knock at Bing, but isn't intended that way; the big broadcasting companies have had a few good pickers in their employ, hired, perhaps, through some misunderstanding. (And that reminds me that in the recent retrenchment exercises, Reinald Werrenrath, who certainly was no sap about arranging worth-while musical programs or recommending good new talent, received his notice of unconditional release, or was permitted to resign, from the N.B.C., and as soon as this news reached the ears of New York University, the latter made him a Doctor of Music.)

Well, anyway, Bing was engaged, brought east and given a good spot in the WABC schedule. His style and his programs were extremely popular, particularly with the ladies GBT (God Bless Them), and when it was announced not long ago that he was going to quit and do some pictures in Hollywood, hundreds of thousands of fair radio addicts simply swooned.

Bing's departure from the California night club left the club's proprietors and clients in a tearful mood and they remained so until Russ Columbo was engaged to replace him and instructed (according to Bing's cousin's report) to copy as closely as possible the Crosby method and style of singing.

So long as Russ remained in the night club, Bing had no objec-

234

tion to being imitated, but when Russ carried the alleged imitation to the point of coming east and getting himself a radio job, Mr. Crosby (Cousin to Chum to Nurse to Me) squawked. The squawk wasn't a loud one; merely an outspoken expression of opinion that Mr. Columbo's whole method and style of singing were based on his own.

Now this got me kind of interested and I, a neophyte in radio criticism, but (he said shyly) a person who knows music, even the quaint sort that usually is miked onto the defenseless air, decided I would eavesdrop on both of the boys over a period of weeks and find out for myself and my own invisible audience whether Mr. Crosby's plaint was justified.

Well, the first time I listened, it occurred to me that if I had originated the Capone system of depopulating Chicago and Brooklyn, I wouldn't brag of it and hint at plagiarism on the part of Scarface Al. (And I wouldn't be calling him Scarface if he weren't summering in Georgia behind reliable bars.) It also occurred to me that at least one thing could be said in favor of both Bing and Russ: When you hear either of them, you don't think, "Why, that's Connie Boswell!"

Analyzing their similarities and differences that first time and many other times, expertly and with great care, I have reached the following conclusions, which will be incorporated in my charge to the invisible jury:

Both are extremely proficient in the art of not hitting a tone on the nose. They sneak up on it or slide down to it or miss it entirely.

Another thing they have in common is a talent, amounting to genius, for being left at the post by the orchestra or other accompaniment. They usually start from two to six or seven beats behind and as a rule frighten those who have bet on them by seeming hopelessly out of the race until they are right at the wire.

For the benefit of the untutored I must explain that in the days before the Musical Depression, a singer ordinarily ended a song on the keynote, or tonic. If a song is in the key of F, F is the tonic. The "third" is A natural and the "fifth" is C. (Am I educated!) In those days it was the exception when a number was wound up on a third, and even more so when the vocalist fifthed at the finish. Bing and Russ use the fifth nine times out of ten, or at least, they nibble all around it. It must be part of the Crosby system, but I hope Bing doesn't claim it as original. If he does, he should accuse not only Russ, but also Ruthie Etting, Artie Jarrett, Streetie Singer, Katie Smith, and, countless others of stealing his stuff, and among the countless others is the late Giacomo Puccini, who put it in the script of an important tenor aria in "La Bohème," which was composed before the invention of static. At any rate, the "trick" has become more or less familiar and I have been tempted to write to both of the boys and say, "Take a tonic." ("Oh, dear!" as Harry Richman remarks after his gags on the Chase & Sanborn Oh Dear hour, taking the words out of the indestructible audience's mouth.)

It is just about a toss-up between the lads in the matter of putting lyrics across. My favorite melody of the current supply is "Dancing on the Ceiling," Dick Rodgers' best piece since "My Heart Stood Still"—a better piece than the last-named if you're asking me. I presumed that the lyric was by Mr. Rodgers' regular collaborator, Lorenz Hart, and wondered what it was about. Mr. Columbo sang it one evening. I am still wondering what it's about. Russ can outsyllable Bing over a distance; for example, Russ, without apparent effort, sings, "Na-hight shall be fa-fa-filled with mee-hew-hew-sic, na-hight shall be fa-fa-filled with luh-uh-uh-uhv," or whatever it is. Bing, however, is unbeatable in a sprint, such as the word "you," which he nurses along till you would swear it was spelled yoohoohoohoohoohoo-oo. When Russ repeats a refrain whose lyric bores him, he usually substitutes dee-dee-dee-dum, whereas, in like circumstances, Bing uses da-dee-dee-do. Occasionally Bing even improves the song a lot by whistling eight or twelve or sixteen bars.

So far as I know, Russ is innocent of song-writing. Bing is a part author or part composer of at least two numbers, one of them his own theme song, "Tit-Willow," done in collaboration with John Gilbert and Mike (Twin) Sullivan. No, no. I must be getting confused. The song I mean starts:

"Where the blue of the night meets the gold of the day,
Someone waits for me."

Probably the someone is the orchestra leader. I haven't heard the latest Crosby product, but it is boosted in Rudy Vallée's "Tuneful

Topics," which he writes for *Radio Digest*, one of the publications subscribed for by Nurse. The title of the number is "My Woman" and Rudy says "I am sure you will like it," "Its minor vein makes one think of 'Deep Night,'" and "The first syllable of the word 'Woman' gives Bing on the record an excellent chance to utilize his exaggerated glissando." When Rudy plugs a song, it is praise from Caesar, and very high praise in this case because Rudy himself co-authored "Deep Night," of which the minor vein of "My Woman" makes one think. Recent blood tests in my own minor veins didn't show any glissando and I had to call for a dictionary. Well, it's a gliding effect, as the playing of a run on the pianoforte by sliding the fingers over the keys. O.K! Funk & Wagnalls! You may call it gliding, but I calls it da-dee-dee-do-dee-dee-da-dee-dee-do-dee-dee-Dumb.

The mention of Caesar reminds me of another Shakespearean creation, Romeo. Mr. Columbo's sub-title, as you doubtless know, is "The Romeo of Song." Miss Graham doesn't think Bing has an intriguing alias, and though she shares her sex's devotion to Mr. Crosby and grief at his projected desertion of the air, she admits that Russ is the more beautiful of this exciting da-dee-dee-dee-do-dum duo and wants to wager that he could give conclusive evidence to support the truth of the old saw, "There's Always Juliet."

Jury, the case is in your hands. You have read the testimony and my clarifying analysis of same. It is my honest and expert opinion that the boys are pretty evenly matched, that any decision save a draw would be unfair to one or the other. But don't let me influence yoohoohoohoohoohoo-oo.

The big event of the period covered in this report was the smashing up of the interference between WJZ and I (as the lyricists would say), making it possible for me to take, or to leave alone, Amos and ('n') Andy; Household Hour (with Edgar A. Guest); Little Orphan Annie (possibly too orphan. Oh, dear!); Mouth Health; Clara, Lu and Em; Just Willie (Stevens?); Lady Bugs, piano duo; Biblical Drama; Beauty Talk, tenor (is it by him or about him?); Celebrated Sayings (maybe they will include "But now even young girls get drunk"); Rin Tin Tin Thriller; and all I want (which is a great deal) of Grace said: "Were you listening, mother dear?" I couldn't get Jellico in time to hear the reply. Almost immediately afterwards, who should walk into the studio where Grace was singing but her father! This gave Grace a big thrill, she said, but he got one right back when she sang *his* favorite song, an Irish ballad. It was uncanny that the musicians had the orchestrations right there on their easels. Just the same I hope to hear Grace again before the end of summer, and I don't care what she sings just so she sings.

Does Ben's face Bernie! (Oh, dear!) The old Maestro, back in New York for an engagement at the Palace, was up to his high standard in the Tuesday eve broadcast, but there was no chance for him to avoid mention of dat ole davil limerick contest, which must make him blush. His mention was brief. "Everybody will get a square deal." "There were so many hundreds of thousands of contestants." "Everyone [presumably everyone connected with Blue Ribbon Malt] is working day and night." But not even an approximate date for an announcement of the winners.

I harp on this contest because it is radio personified. Some big Malt man said, "Leave us have a limerick contest." Another big Malt man said, "Who can we hire to write a limerick?" "Hire!" said the first Malter disgustedly. "Why anybody can write a limerick!" But only God can make Blue Ribbon Malt.

So anybody wrote the first four lines of a limerick, making it impossible for Edmund Lear, or Edgar Guest, to supply a fifth, as required. And for $1.50 any literate child (my thirteen-year-old David, for instance) would have been glad to do a decent job of it.

I must refresh your memory of the first four lines as written, and then you won't wonder why the announcement is postponed:

> *"There was a young fellow from Broadway,*
> *Whose friends told him, 'Here's what we all say:*
> *When malt's put to test,*
> *Blue Ribbon is best,*
> *Da-da-da, da-da-da, da-da-da.' "*

Ed Wynn's performance for Texaco on the same eve was Ed at his best. It was even better than his best because: he had four (4) new jokes. When he has no (o) new jokes, he still leagues the league.

Life of the Boswells

Hardly a man is now alive
Who recalls that in 1795
Occurred the death of a Mr. James Boswell;
A joke on his doctor, who'd thought that he was well.

I could go on in this manner for a week [Yes you could—Ed. Yes
I could—Auth.] but the result would be as disgusting to reader,
editor, and author as was this department a fortnight since, when
I started out by trying to please a worshipper in Danbury, Conn.,
who wanted a few facts concerning Paul Whiteman and his self-
styled musicians, and wound up by creating the dismal impression
that *The New Yorker* was Mons. Whiteman's house organ and I
his general press representative, whereas neither I nor any other
copyboy even faintly connected with *The New Yorker*'s staff (its
what!) has willingly talked to Mons. Gershwin's floor leader since
California got too hot for him.

The purpose of part of this piece is to show a bit of appreciation
for Ol' Marse Boswell's kindness in that six-volume eulogy of my
International, All-Time Literary Hero, Dr. Samuel Johnson, who
won himself eternal fame by virtue of his notorious indolence, by
bragging that he had "lounged" from the age of eighteen to the
age of twenty-one, and by getting himself nicknamed The Great
Lexicographer by writing a dictionary and misspelling forty-eight
of the seventy words he knew, being, no doubt, a radio announcer.

Whether he was Mr. Boswell's own doctor I am not sure; in sooth,
I faked that line about the doctor. Doc Johnson outdied Jim by
eleven years, but that's no sign he didn't lay the groundwork for
Bozzy's extinction, though the percentage of leeches who pass on
while you still owe them for even one visit would just about pay

the next quarterly dividend on Fisk Rubber. However, if there hadn't been a close friendship between some doctor and James Boswell, why should one of the latter's three sisters be called Vet?

When I asked my Latvian swineherd how I might repay in a measure the debt we Johnson disciples owe the Boswell family, he suggested that I give some publicity to the Boswell Sisters in one of the magazines that are under my thumb. They are radio artists and, while he had heard that their work (they sing) had real merit, they were unlikely to "get anywhere" (he picks up slang as if it were so much slang) unless they were "plugged" in the "public prints." Just at this time I began receiving the Columbia Broadcasting System's daily reports on its plans and interesting items regarding the personal habits, tastes, modes of life, etc., of its artists —the regular press matter sent out to radio reviewers employed by the newspapers, but to print which in full they unfortunately lack space. From these reports, Latvy and I have been able to clip thousands of words of Boswelliana as well as human-interest details concerning other Columbia stars. Today I feed you a little fanfare about the Boswells and, to prevent a recurrence of the embarrassing Whiteman scandal, will try to serve you also small tidbits designed to tickle the palates of Etting, Downey, and Mills Brothers admirers, together with delicate morsels from the menus of N.B.C., which, I grieve to say, doesn't send me its publicity.

In the case of Columbia, I will add brief comments of my own so that the boys who pay for my stuff will not think that I do all my work with shears and glue. Editors and readers can spot what I have written by the absence of quotation marks—" ". What I have lifted from Columbia's press man will carry quotation marks—" ". When I mention an N.B.C. hero or heroine, quotation marks—" " —will be unnecessary because, as I save said, the N.B.C. press bureau treats me as if I were Col. Crater Q. Park. They sing in muted voices and Martha taps out the accompaniment in pianissimo. Connie tries out the 'hot licks.' Even at this time of year, those Southerners would suffer in New York without huddling around a big open piano in heavily draped pajama suites, sipping New Orleans hot licks such as only Connie knows how to mix and serve at the proper temperature.

"Sometimes, when they strike a snare or seek variety, they start in at the end of a song and work backwards." And sometimes, believe it or not, the Insensible Audience doesn't know the difference. "Often an improvisation comes to them suddenly." Whereas, you take most other Boswells and they'll testify that their improvisations call up ahead and give them a chance to order a couple mo' po'k chops. "Occasionally they work in a dish of harmonious 'pig Latin' —lyrics arranged in the gibberish of school days. It comes out 'hot.' If work reaches an impasse, they relax for a moment at other things. Connie, who paints, may swish a brush. Martha, a cook by hobby, stirs up some of her famous southern dishes. Vet curls up around a book. But not for long."

Probably we all ought to be satisfied with finally knowing what pig Latin really is and that it comes out hot, but I, for one, am just longing to improvise myself into that heavily draped suite during an impasse and catch Connie swishing, Martha stirring up dishes that must be famous, perhaps notorious, by now, and Vet curling and curling herself around a book until, in record-breaking time, she finds out which is the top and which the bottom.

Here I've pulled another Whiteman. I haven't even got started on the Boswells, let alone mentioning anyone else, and they tell me I've already run out of bounds. The best way to do, I think, is to beg pardon for neglecting the others this time and to finish as briefly as possible, much more briefly than I want to, on the fascinating subjects who have been most prominent in this essay, subjects to whom I will revert as soon as I can dig up another excuse. Well, then:

"In such times [days when they can snatch only an hour or two of sleep] Connie describes the three as 'Winkin, Blinkin and Nod.'" She ought to have been a poetess instead of a swisher. That New Orleans attic contains two letters that money couldn't buy, "one from the first couple who named their baby 'Connie' and one from a lady in Brooklyn who prays for them every night." The Boswells or the couple?

"When on the road, the Boswells have singled out their correspondents and amazed them with a phone call or an invitation to tea. Connie's idea of a vacation would be a motor tour of the towns where such favored fans live." Me, I would rather borrow a machine gun and visit the place where they make Waterman fountain pens.

"The Boswells are gregarious. They like people." That, you must bear in mind, is what the Columbia press man testifies, and he is naturally biased. Friends of mine on the inside tell me that actually they are sociable, jolly, chatty, hail-fellow-well-met, and quite easy to know.

"It amuses them if a pompous tuba player drops his horn.

" 'We keep going with a sense of humor and a liking for people,' is the way Connie sums it up. 'But most of all, I guess we just like to sing.' "

There is a bare possibility that we can squeeze in one small non-Boswell item. Sure it's worth it:

"Jacques Fray and Mario Braggiotti, C.B.S. international pianists, combined business and pleasure with a trip to Newport. After a recital, they visited St. George's School which Braggiotti once attended."

And chances are that all the students, in order to amuse the famous alumnus, posed as pompous tuba players and went around dropping horns.

"Pu-leeze! Mister Hemingway!"

No Visitors, N.Y.
Oct. 1, 1932

Well, it seems that N.B.C. got cross at this dept. because this dept.
was giving a lot more mention to C.B.S. than to N.B.C. Mutual or
neutral or some other kind of friends asked why. The explanation
was just like the people in charge of radio business—simplicity itself. Right after the appearance of the first installment of these con-
structive criticisms, C.B.S. began sending the undersigned its daily
press stuff, the stuff it sends to radio reviewers on newspapers. The
latter can't begin to use all of it. For one reason, they are supposed
to work for a living; not just clip and paste. They are young. For
another reason, the stuff reads like advertising, and newspapers are
not supposed to use advertising in reading matter devoted to alleged
amusements, excepting baseball, boxing, football, wrestling, track,
hockey—Golly knows why. Everybody in the world may be perfectly
sure that a boxing bout between two housewives like Sharkey and
Schmeling is bound to bore you to death, but it is oke for the boxing writers to ballyhoo it for weeks in advance and then, when it
turns out to be just what it was never anything else than—

Where was we, as Paul Waner once said? Oh, yes! N.B.C. took the
hint and finally started sending the old man its press stuff, and I
wishes some of you able-bodied kids would romp up to No Visitors
and help the maids relieve the situation before I am compelled to
lease the Manhattan Storage & Warehouse or the East River.

Once upon a midnight dreary—'tis some ice water, I muttered—
only this and nothing more. I wished you could see it. It starts out
with a three-pound biography of Paul Whiteman (as if I had never
given him a line) and goes on with tons of details of what Rudy
Vallée, Joe White, The Three Keys, "Ward" Wilson, The Jesters,
Madame Sylvia, Cesare Sodero, Julia Sanderson and Frank Crumit,
David Rubinoff, Gladys Rice, Erno Rapee, Ray Perkins, Jack

Benny, Olsen and Johnson, Walter O'Keefe, Ohman and Arden (I hate to mention them), Frank Munn, Frank Luther, Billy Jones and Ernie Hare, William Hard, Frank Black, Gene and Glenn, Walter Damrosch, Russ Columbo, and Sigmund Spaeth eat, wear, sleep in, talk about, look like, feel like, comb their hair with, ride, read, write, buy, sell, brush their teeth with, reduce with, stay fat with, get, write with, and help yourself. Boys, if you think this publication has got room for all that in a lump— Well, let's get back to Columbia for a while.

"From northern Wisconsin came word that Tony Wons was spending his vacation in the lake district fishing and making friends with the Chippewa Indians. The tribal chieftains have taken a fancy to Tony's philosophizing and are considering making him a member of their clan. Although he hasn't been formally initiated, the Chippewa already have given him a name. It is Meshkaegegit and means 'sending big voice over the air.' " From private Wisconsin sources, this dept. learns that the Chippewa chief's name in that region is "Heap Big Cream Puff."

"Kate Smith's grandparents, Mr. and Mrs. B. I. Hanby of Riverdale, Md., attended her broadcast for the first time when 'The Songbird of the South' brought them to the Columbia studios to watch her in action. Kate warned her visitors not to utter a sound while in the broadcast room. So literally was the warning taken that they continued to sit silently for ten minutes after the broadcast was over." No chance that old people occasionally doze.

"Jay C. Flippen, Columbia's newest comedian and master of ceremonies, one of the least self-conscious persons who ever faced a microphone, is constantly on the go while in the studio and speaks his lines into the microphone nearest him at the moment." That's where that old Friar differs from me. In my two broadcasts with Mr. Grantland Rice, why, when he would ask me a question, I would rush out of the building and ask different policemen the location of the most distant mike.

Now this is not Columbia, but just a rumor. They tell me that Mr. Gatti-Casazza, trying to supplant Gigli and Jeritza, has hit on the idea of engaging either Mr. Downey or Mr. Donald Novis to take the place of both.

Finally, here is a letter from Abner Silver, author of a song called
(appropriately) "Pu-leeze! Mister Hemingway!" He says: "Being a
steady reader of your column, etc., I thought I would send you a
copy of my latest mental cloud-burst, 'Pu-leeze! Mister Hemingway!'
The song seems to be catching on and would appreciate your criticism, be it favorable or otherwise."

One verse and a refrain is all you get:

Girl:

You'll find that I'm the sort
That likes a little sport,
But there's a limit nevertheless.
There's something in your eye
That seems to warn me I
Had better beware of your finesse.

Refrain:

I can understand when you hold my hand,
That it's love finding a way.
I don't mind your feeling thrilly, but when you start acting silly
Pu-leeze! Mister Hemingway!
It's so plain to see, you appeal to me;
When you're near my heart must obey.
You're so sweet and so delicious, but when you get ambitious,
Pu-leeze! Mister Hemingway!
I love affection, but we're all alone.
There's one objection, if we only had a chaperon.
I don't mind the park when it's nice and dark;
'Neath the moonlight I love to stay.
I adore you when you're gentle, but when you get sentimental—
Pu-leeze! Mister Hemingway!

No criticism at all, Mr. Silver. But if I were that old goofer,
Ernest, I would certainly sue.

The Crucial Game

No Visitors, N.Y.

Oct. 22, 1932

One of the grand ideas of the autumn is that of the Columbia Broadcasting System—and maybe the National as well—to have its football reporters scout the teams that are to be involved in forthcoming broadcasts, in order to familiarize themselves with the coaches, captains, athletes, plays, and systems, to say nothing of the songs, cheers, and laundry marks of the rival warriors. While the World Series was in progress, some of the larger universities were visited by Ted Husing's spies. They announced their presence, were cordially received by the athletic directors and coaches in charge, given copies of the signals, and in some cases even told what towns they were in.

The result was noticeable in the first broadcast to which these old lop ears listened, that of the Michigan-Northwestern game. Michigan is where I helled from, deny it though they may, and so I was in a position to detect the improvement evolved by the new scheme. Mr. Husing was warned in advance that the word "putrid" was obsolete in my native state, so he merely called Pug Rentner's handling of the ball sloppy. I think this was either just before or after he had announced that he and his associates were reporters, not critics.

Columbia didn't economize on this stunt. Mr. Quailey or Bronson or some such name sleuthed at Ann Arbor and Evanston in advance and was on the job to assist Mr. Husing during the game. The latter, for the second time this year, called Louis Elbel's "The Victors" Northwestern's "Alma Mater," but nearly everything else was perfect. As is now a matter of history, Michigan scored an early touchdown and Northwestern soon afterwards tied it up. Then there was a discussion about who would kick-off. The broadcasters thought

246

that the Wildcats had shown an offensive strength that made it dangerous to give the ball right back to them and predicted Michigan would receive. Mr. Lardner, having an acquaintance with Mr. Yost, thought not. The broadcasters were wrong this time and attributed it to Northwestern strategy, though personally I attributed it to the football rules for 1932.

Unless you came from Michigan yourself, you would have no idea how much of a surprise this game turned out to be. To begin with, this old eavesdropper discovered that even though it was an early-season game, the Michigan-Northwestern game was always the big game of the Middle West and they hadn't played each other for six or seven years, that's how big a game it is. Well, folks, when I lived back there on the farm, Michigan didn't even know where Northwestern was located at; it only knew that Northwestern was a practice game on Chicago's schedule, excepting for a couple of years when it had two fellows named Potter and Van Doozer. Another news item was that Coach Harry Kipke was not only a grand kicker in his day, but maybe the greatest all-around athlete ever developed at Ann Arbor. As my failing memory tells me, all he ever did besides kick and play football was throw a left-handed javelin through the high hurdles, put the shot sideways, and high-jump backwards. I do recall a man named Neil Snow and another named Johnny Garrels who had some kind of specialty on the side.

There was quite a novelty between halves. The Northwestern band of three pieces marched out on the field and formed a "Z." The Michigan band of a piece and two-thirds (the drummer fell down) repaid the compliment by forming an "H." Which is perhaps the part I slept through. Anyway, some day I want to be in charge of the pep stunts at a big crucial game and form a letter that doesn't belong to either college—possibly an "N," for Neither.

Speaking of Michigan and bands, this dept. was in receipt of a letter the other day from none other than George Olsen (not to mention Paul Whiteman, Bing Crosby, and the Boswell Sisters, honestly) which reminded us that George was drum major of the Michigan band back in 1776 or 1902, when Boss Weeks was quarterback. George was merely writing a friendly letter about nothing, but once he told me that when he went to Michigan he was given the choice of playing quarterback or being drum major. I congratulated him on choosing the drum major's rôle because otherwise his position might have been contested by Boss Weeks, who didn't want to be drum major.

The dept. continues to get publicity stuff from the two major networks (the National still sending it to the wrong address) and I wish we had room to print it all, because it's fascinating. A magazine of any size could be filled with items about the Boswell Sisters and their recent, or current, vacation in New Orleans. These items and the overwhelming thrill of getting a letter from them have gone to the head, so the other night poor Nurse had to take this dictation:

> *Which is most blithesome and bonnie,*
> *Vet or Martha or Connie?*
>
> *Which would you like to get,*
> *Martha or Connie or Vet?*
>
> *For which would you go the farther,*
> *Connie or Vet or Martha?*

The warden in charge says that a person can get permanently deranged on the Boswell Sisters and orders that the patient be restrained from reading about them or listening to them until they are back from their vacation in New Orleans. (They have been, or are, on a vacation in New Orleans.)

Herb and Frank Panic 'Em

No Visitors, N.Y.

Nov. 5, 1932

The rival Presidential candidates have very few hours left for their frantic efforts to elect one another by broadcasting, and this department strongly advises both Mr. Hoover and Mr. Roosevelt to take full advantage of their final opportunities to impress the networks, the manufacturers, the advertising agencies, and the radio fans with the subject matter of their talks and their novel methods of delivery. The man who succeeds in throwing the campaign will soon be out of a job, but both he and the man who wins can increase their incomes two or three hundred per cent by accepting offers of radio work that are bound to follow the splendid auditions of the past three weeks, unless they go stale in the stretch.

It seems to me that both men are eminently qualified to report baseball, football, boxing, and boat races. They appear able, with very little effort, to get all balled up. Mr. Hoover's Detroit speech was a masterpiece of wait-a-minutes. You could shut your eyes and imagine you were hearing one of the regulars describe that play in the 1931 World's Series when Jimmy Wilson caught a third strike on the hop and flung it to third base. But Mr. Hoover, and Roosevelt, too, would be foolish to take that kind of job. It is tough going and doesn't pay nearly as much as either man could earn if he worked for a sponsor one night a week.

In my first radio review, early this summer, I think I said that Columbia consistently provided better entertainment than National, and particularly so far as comedy was concerned. Since that time, conditions have altered. With Eddie Cantor back, Ed Wynn hitting way up in the thousands, and Jack Pearl, who must have thrown precedent to the winds and hired a writer, setting all the boys a dizzy pace, N.B.C. has stepped out in front as a mirth-provoker, and that gives Herbert and Franklin their golden chance. Neither of the two big broadcasting companies likes to see its rival run ahead of it in any respect and you can bet that Columbia will make a tremendous effort to land one of the candidates or both. It will try hard to sell them to one of the rich sponsors, and N.B.C. will try just as hard to land them for itself. There will be merry bidding and a contract that will probably top Ed Wynn's. If I were a big gargle-and-spray man, I wouldn't hesitate an instant to offer either gent ten thousand dollars a performance, engage a good straight to play with him, cast him as a male Gracie Allen, and let him ad-lib.

And it is possible that one or both can croon. It looked for a time as if the bleaters were out of luck, but the continuing popularity of Donald Novis and the triumphal comeback of Morton Downey, God's greatest gift to the treble clef, indicate that whimpering still has its appeal and that ladies like Miss Ponselle and Miss Moore are not yet safe from the competition of the opposing sex. Well, Mr. Hoover, for instance, bears a striking resemblance to Mr. Downey (and the full moon) and his speaking voice suggests that he could coo if he tried. Imagine that combination of talents—ability to mimic a mourning dove and to prattle Gracie Allen's brand of naïve inanities with or without preparation! Why, a guy could grab twenty thousand for a half-hour a night and balance the budget out of his own change purse before you could say Senator Robinson.

I have mentioned Mr. Downey a couple of times and Nurse says I wake her up screaming his name the moment I start on my hour's sleep. (She sleeps the other twenty-three.) This has been going on since I read of his contract with the Woodbury people and some intimate details about him in a recent *Radio and Amusement Guide*. As you doubtless know, the Camels gave him thirty-five hundred for six quarter-hours of whinnying per week. That agreement ended this summer and was not renewed. One party or the other was dissatisfied—I can't believe it was the Camels. Mr. Downey's ill-wishers, consisting chiefly of gents with gents' voices, said he was through and hoped so. But here is how through he was: Woodbury Soap took him on for two thousand a week, the week consisting of *thirty minutes* every Friday night.

From the *Guide* I learn that "He punctuates every sentence by knocking wood, favors a slouch hat and turned-up coat collar, carries good luck charms on both ends of a watchless watch chain, bites the thumb nail of his right hand when excited, and gets nervous when anyone drives his roadster. When he's driving, everyone else gets nervous. He can memorize the words and music of a song at a glance, is TICKLISH, LOVES TO TELL IRISH STORIES, and CONTINUALLY JINGLES COINS IN HIS POCKETS. He calls his wife 'LOVER.' "

Well, when you consider that I go through two months of heck to turn out an acceptable story and that they pay me for it in loose stamps, all because Golly made me a bass singer, do you blame me for screaming in my sleep, or out of it? Or for switching to Palmolive Soap? At an auction a little while ago, he bought a Gainsborough for a thousand dollars. That's the way he throws his money around —fifteen minutes' pay shot to heck for one Gainsborough, though he may have thought they said it was a Ginsberg.

There is a whole lot of news to tell you this week and no room in which to tell it. One must select the most important items and I guess that includes the fact that Jack Benny and George Olsen's band are separating and the Canada Dry "humorist" will from now on be supported by musicians under the direction of Ted Weems. Ted will, they say, have his band on hand the afternoon of the broadcast for laugh rehearsal. It seems that George's boys laughed occasionally at the wrong time. I played it safe.

From the indefatigable Columbia publicity man comes word that Singin' Sam never received musical training of any sort. I believe this is given out in a spirit of boastfulness. Well, listen, Sam. If you'll take a very brief music lesson, really just a hint, it won't hurt your singin'. Do you know that when you sing a song such as "When Day Is Done," in which so many lines start on a low fifth and then jump up an interval of three tones, or two tones, or any number of tones, you never by any chance come close to that low fifth, your proper takeoff? Try once to sock it right on the button. It will be a great relief to people who have received a little musical training of some sort, and it's at least as easy as shaving with Barbasol.

Lyricists Strike Pay Dirt

You can count on the fingers of one thumb the present-day writers of song words who could wear becomingly the mantle of W. S. Gilbert, or even the squirrel neckpiece of Ira Gershwin. Some of them should be fitted out with rompers, the costume for which their birth, bringing-up, and education qualify them; some with sturdy boys' suits appropriate for children belonging in the third, fourth, and fifth grades. Some ought to be garbed in the night-gowns, pajamas, and lounging robes provided for rest cases at Belle-vue. And a few, I am afraid, would feel at home only in strait-jackets.

This department has been laughed at for prudishness, but has not been laughed out of it. This department has reached a stage where it almost doesn't mind a song whose only faults are inanity, terrible rhyming, and glaring infractions of simple grammatical rules. Unfortunately, the "lyricists," the singers, and the whimperers are not satisfied with that comparatively harmless kind. They are polluting the once-pure air of Golly's great out-of-doors with a gas barrage of the most suggestive songs ever conceived, published, and plugged in one year.

Weeks ago in these fascinating columns, I wrote to the effect that it seemed silly for radio to bar words like God, Hell, and damn and to permit the "comedians" to get by with gags running the gamut from vulgar to vile, and the singers to use the unmistakably off-color "Paradise" and the flagrantly immoral "As You Desire Me." In that piece, I charged Ray Perkins with unnecessary roughness, and a more or less amicable correspondence between us left him unconvinced and me pretty sad. N.B.C. asked Allie Wrubel, author of "As You Desire Me," to rewrite his refrain, cleaning it up. The rewritten version means absolutely nothing, but surely we can't complain of that. Mr. Wrubel charged me good-naturedly with responsibility for the N.B.C. edict. I hope I was guilty. But the boys in the Columbia studios didn't read my stuff that week and their singers (notably Charles Carlile, who ought to know better) still stick to the original mess. The melody, also by Mr. Wrubel, is pretty enough to deserve what it is getting: a much longer life than is usual under the radio régime.

Perhaps you wonder why I revive this tedious subject when there is so little chance of a queasy crusader making headway. There are several reasons, and one is that Mr. Wrubel and the authors of "Paradise" ought not to be the only boys criticized when scores of their fellow-geniuses are trying their worst (and with ever-increasing signs of ultimate success) to out-smut them. Another reason is that, queer as it may seem, I don't like indecency in song or story, and sex appeal employed for financial gain in this manner makes me madder than anything except fruit salad. Reason 3: A large percentage of the invisible audience is composed of old people who retain the faculty of being shocked and of children between the ages of nine and sixteen who are not morally damaged by the words Hell, damn, and God, but can't help wondering what the heck when they hear songs that glorify defiance of the seventh amendment to Moses' constitution. Reason 4: A curiosity as to whether there is such a thing as radio censorship, and if so, whether those in charge of it are morons themselves or simply don't know what is what and what is not; and whether they will take the hint lying down when their attention is called to this squawk, as it shall be. Reason 5: A curiosity as to whether the sponsors and their advertising agencies are just plain dumb or as broad as the ocean and as lewd as the sky. Reason 6: Something happened on a very recent Sunday night which rekindled the smoldering ashes of offended prudery and forced me to mention the six-letter surname of a New Testament character with such volume that even the nurse woke up.

The stations I usually play are WEAF, WOR, WJZ, and WABC. Tuning in first on WABC, I found myself listening to a risqué song. Tuning in on WJZ, I heard another one. Similar thrills were waiting on WOR, and WEAF, and it was then that I lost control of my tongue and frightened poor Miss Graham out of her nap and her cap. An apology and an explanation were in order.

"Well," she said, "it's Sunday. They probably thought of that and now they're celebrating the Fourth Commandment, which begins [she whisked out the midget Bible that she carries in her hypo case]: 'Remember that thou keep holy the Sabbath Day' and ends: 'Wherefore the Lord blessed the Sabbath Day and hallowed it.' "

Now, I won't put your credulity to a test by averring that there was nothing except risqué songs on the four stations that night, but between speeches and risqué jokes, the boys and girls managed to crowd in a flock of numbers that were "questionable" in title, or in one or more lines, or in toto. I took down a few titles and print them here so that when you go Christmas shopping, you can visit your favorite music store and buy something educational to read aloud or sing to the baby. Some of them may be classified as bedtime stories, as you will see when you get them. Ready?

"I'll Never Have to Dream Again," "You're Telling Me," "Good Night, My Lady Love," "Pu-leeze! Mister Hemingway!" (a swell tune and a good idea, marred by two or three words), "You Little So-and-So," "Forbidden Love," "Let's Put Out the Lights and Go to Sleep" (just on the border. They say that in the original lyric, the last word was not "sleep"), "Love Me Tonight," "I'm Yours for Tonight," "Horses Carry Tales" (sung by what I thought was a new Negro quartet which could make "Rock of Ages" sound nasty), "Bring 'Em Back Alive," "And So to Bed" (an ingenious finishing touch), "Please," "Take Me in Your Arms," "Here Lies Love," and "What Did I Get in Return?"

Others you might buy, if the kid is bored by those I have named, are "Ain'tcha Kinda Sorry Now?" and "Thrill Me!" The latter I have not yet heard on the air, but I expect to, for it probably touches a new low for the year. A copy of this number ought to be in every right-thinking, kiddy-loving American home. Why, the refrain goes: "Thrill me with a kiss that's vicious with love delicious . . ." No, I won't spoil a sale. And I'll try hard not to feel so comstocky next time.

Announcers' Prep School

NO VISITORS, N. Y.
DEC. 3, 1932

This red-hot crusader against immorality would keep the following episode *sub disney* (unter sein' Hut) if (1) he were unable to preface it with the confession that he has begun to doubt his infallibility as a critic and (2) if it didn't solve the riddle which has had him, along with thousands of other ether addicts, completely mystified these many a moon; viz., where do announcers come from?

(Time out. Capital I goes in at quarterback for Waves, replacing Third Person Singular.)

Four weeks ago I pulled two boners in one paragraph. I was trying to say something sweet about the Thursday Maxwell House program and I referred to it as Uncle Henry's Show Boat—a trivial mistake, but one for which I expected a good booing. I didn't get it and I hope you people were just being kind, though I suspect that you didn't know where a boo would reach me. The other blunder was so serious that when it was called to my attention, I swooned for the first time since Tony Wons sent me his autograph.

The attention-caller was a lady connected with the advertising agency which handles the Maxwell account. She wrote to thank me for my blurb, casually added that Henry was a Captain, not a relative, and wondered why, in listing the show's great cast, I had omitted the name of the head man, the man who plays Captain Henry, the man who in private life is known from Wisconsin to Russia as Charles Winninger.

Well, I died, as Mr. Wynn would say. For this same Charles Winninger became the ideal of my dreams when I lived eight miles north of old St. Mary's and he went to Notre Dame, and nothing has happened since then to alienate my affection for the old galoot, either as performer or friend. He would undoubtedly hear about my apparent perfidy even if he didn't read the piece himself, and he would think the only thing there was for him to think: that I was deliberately trying to clip him from behind.

You will be spared the details of my frantic and finally successful attempts to learn his unlisted telephone number, but you will have to hear my excuse, which he heard, and believed because it was true. On the two occasions when I had listened, I had missed the first two minutes of the broadcast. Therefore I had missed the only spot in the program in which his name was mentioned. That I failed to recognize his chatter is understandable because in our offstage conversations he always talked in his Wisconsin brogue. But I certainly ought to have known that inimitable giggle. Just the same, if I were sponsoring a program on which Charles Winninger was master of ceremonies and at least co-star, I wouldn't try to keep him a secret from people who tuned in a couple of minutes late.

Now, what makes this story immoral is the fact that I was rewarded instead of punished for my mistakes. "To err is human but profitable" seems to be the lesson taught. Not satisfied with my telephonic apology, I reinforced it with a note. At the bottom of the note I asked him to persuade Lanny Ross and Miss Hanshaw to substitute decent songs for the ones selected for the next program. A trusty friend delivered the note at rehearsal and Mr. Winninger read my request aloud. The trusty friend, in show business himself, heard him read it and heard the announcer say: "Who the hell is L–dn-r?" And when this was reported to me by telephone, I came right back with "Who the hell is the announcer?" "Tiny Ruffner," said the trusty. "He was a chorus boy in 'Princess Flavia.'"

Well, Miss Hanshaw came clean and substituted respectable songs for the ones she had planned to sing. Mr. Ross met me halfway by using the decent version of "Desire," but sticking to the questionable "Please." Let's pretend that the concessions made were made for me even if they weren't. There is quite a kick in feeling that your crusade is getting somewhere. And when the self-effacing Mr. Winninger speaks his forgiveness with a brace of partridge—oh, let's admit that WEAF on Thursday nights from nine to ten o'clock is the best hour radio can give you, and those who disagree are referred to the first paragraph of this piece, wherein the undersigned admits that he may not be an infallible critic.

The reason for my loss of confidence is a difference of opinion between Mr. Louis Reid, of the New York *American,* and me re-

garding Al Jolson's début. It makes me feel good when I am in ac-
cord with a good critic, and it makes me feel good when I am at
odds with a bad one. Mr. Reid is a good critic, one whose opinion
I respect. He thinks Al got off to a bad start and I think he got off
promisingly. If he heard Ed Wynn's opening, he must recall that the
Perfect Fool was nervous and not himself. And if he heard Jack
Pearl on the Ziegfeld-Dowling hour, he must know that Jack wasn't
so hot. Ed and Jack are now in stride and maintaining a fast pace.
I mention them because Mr. Reid says that Mr. Jolson must not
be himself but must submerge his personality in the character he
is playing, as Ed has submerged his personality in his fireman and
Jack in his Baron Munchausen. Well, when I listen in on Ed, I
don't know whether he's a fireman or an architect, but I do know
that he is Ed Wynn. And I am always conscious that Jack Pearl is
Jack Pearl and not a Baron. It is my belief that Al Jolson's personality got him his job, and if he attempts to portray a laundress,
he won't have his job very long.

Some Short-Selling

No Visitors, N. Y.

Dec. 17, 1932

In order not to frighten you away, I am announcing at the out-
set of this broadcast that it will not be devoted exclusively to suggestive songs, suggestive jokes, or suggestive anything else, though
I simply can't resist bragging of the fact that the people who scoff
at my crusade are people who are exhausted by the effort of spelling
their own names, while the heartening words of praise have come
from people who have made a good living by using their minds and
whose worst enemies could scarcely accuse them of illiteracy. I shall
mention three as representative of the latter class: Mr. Franklin P.
Adams, Mr. Quinn Martin, and Mr. Julian Street. A threesome of
the hostile group—well, perhaps you can amuse yourselves guessing
who they are from this hint: One of them calls a piano-player a
pee'-an-ist. So do the other two.

Now, before the limit of space looms, I want to speak of a few
quarter-hour programs which have been on the tips of my two
working fingers for a month or more. Get an earful, some time, of
Heywood Broun's General Electric News, on WEAF at 6:45 every
evening save Tuesday and Sunday. Also Eddie Dooley's Football
Dope, on WABC at 6:30 P.M. Thursday, Friday, and Saturday. Try
Harry Hershfield's monologues on WOR at 7:15 P.M. Mondays,
Wednesdays, and Saturdays, and Ford Frick's Sport Talk on the
same station at 7:00 each P.M. excepting Sunday.

Probably I am too late blurbing Eddie Dooley. If so, I hope they
get him back next year and that his sponsor, Shell Gasoline, will
give him a better chance to disseminate his football knowledge by
not throwing the "Directory of American Colleges, Prep Schools,
Nursing Homes, and Hand Laundries" at his head and asking him
to pronounce as many names as possible in fifteen minutes. Ford
Frick, or an understudy, talks authoritatively and entertainingly of

all kinds of sports, but this department can't solve the riddle of why they make him give race results and prices. When you, Mister, are betting on a horse, or what you think is a horse, you ain't likely to wait for seven o'clock and Ford Frick to tell you whether he win or lose. And when you ain't betting, you don't care a four-letter word if the old cayuse finished behind Hoover. Harry Hershfield always discourses on one subject—Nothing—and in three talks or less he can convince anybody that he's wrong.

The General Electric idea is new, at least to this hermit. It's an oral evening paper, with a front page, a sports page, an editorial page, an advertising section, a comic section, etc. Editor Broun selects, from the regular evening papers and from late press dispatches, the most striking and amusing happenings of the day and reads them to you either straight or with editorial (sometimes very witty) embellishment. There is usually a special story on cosmic events, crime, or dogs, written and recited to you by one of four contributing editors: John Erskine, Hendrik Van Loon, Emily Post, and Albert Payson Terhune. But the added de-luxe feature, unique in "journalism," is an audible music section in the form of one Theodore Webb, a he-blooded, male-gendered, adenoidless American baritone, engaged for radio by mistake and probably drugged before each performance so he won't find out what he's doing and insist on having his voice lifted.

Piled knee-deep on my table is a month's accumulation of literature concerning your idols and mine: reams of publicity from the Columbia and National offices and a dozen radio magazines that I have been too busy or lazy to look at. No doubt most of the stuff is old by this time, but I won't feel comfortable till I have reprinted what seems important, so here you are:

Early in the new year, Col. Stoopnagle and Budd will be featured by the Pontiac division of General Motors. The program will run half an hour and the accessories will include André Kostelanetz' orchestra and a songbird. Along about the same time, "Music That Satisfies" will cease to do so by taking my Boswells out of the lineup and substituting Tom Howard, a comic who is funny when he has good material (as who ain't?), and, possibly, a Personality Songstress. Bing Crosby will supplant the Street Singer, or Nurses' Delight, and you won't hear any squawk from me on that account, but I refuse to believe that even a Personality Songstress, brought back alive despite tremendous difficulties, can sell more cigarettes than Connie, Vet, and Martha. The only member of its present troupe to whom Chesterfield will cling is Ruthie Etting—even a thriving tobacco concern would know enough to keep her. And of course Norman Ah-Ruth-You-Are-So-Beautiful-Tonight Brokenshire will continue as announcer, so don't throw away that bottle of rhubarb and soda just yet.

Speaking of which, it seems to me that the American Academy of Arts and Letters established an almost fatal precedent when it crowned David Ross king of announcers for 1932 and gave him a medal for clarity of diction. When it penetrates other announcers' skulls that they will be rewarded for talking plain, they will all try it, and the day will come when you can't help understanding every word an announcer says. But you can still enjoy the excitement of wondering what the hell he means.

Mr. Ross can be heard these Friday evenings doing a Tony Wons between M. Downey's twitterings on the Woodbury hour. To be sure, you can't compare Dave with Tony; who is all by himself. In fact, the legend goes that when Gosh had finished Tony and sold him, no one would even bid for any of His other creations, but kept clamoring: "Give us the Wons over!" State troopers, however, ordered the mold destroyed.

A recent issue of *Radio Guide* more than hinted that Don Novis would soon be performing for Woodbury. Panicky at the thought that Morton was going to lose out, your indefatigable reporter telephoned the advertising agency which has the soap account and was referred to a young lady who spoke with authority and considerable accent. "We do not confirm the rumor," she said. "Do you deny it?" says I. "Rawther!" says she. But she left me rawther suspecting that both Mr. Novis and Mr. Downey were engaged to bleat for dear old Woodbury, putting on two hebdomadal cooing carnivals instead of one.

Rudy in Irate Mood

No VISITORS, N. Y.

FEB. 4, 1933

The following is For Men Only, because the main topics to be discussed are Rudy Vallée and (am I versatile!) suggestive songs. Ladies naturally shrink from the latter as comedians from a stolen joke, and my encomium of Rudy may not be enthusiastic enough to satisfy those of his adorers who can read print.

Before you gents doze off, let me remind you that the Fleischmann Yeast Hour (Thursday nights on WEAF, eight to nine) seldom runs worse than one-two-three in the week's radio derby, and twice during January was clearly entitled to first place, not only in my opinion but in that of two literate persons with whom I got acquainted by mistake.

The Hour is planned, rehearsed, and directed by Mr. Vallée. His orchestra plays popular melodies, he sings popular songs (few of which would be passed as one-hundred-per-cent O.K. by prude, grammarian, the late W. S. Gilbert, Tune Detective Sig Spaeth, or, in fact, anybody in his right mind), and he offers really worthwhile entertainment by guest artists with Names: Eva Le Gallienne and Joseph Schildkraut, Beatrice Lillie, George Gershwin, Victor Moore, Frieda Inescort and Selena Royle, Sophie Tucker, Marie Dressler, June Walker and Geoffrey Kerr, Milton Berle, Gracie Allen (charge an error to the N.B.C.), Ken Murray, Colin Keith-Johnston, Fannie Brice. There is always a good balance of comedy, drama, and song, and the care Rudy takes to maintain this balance was demonstrated as recently as four Thursdays ago, when Dr. R. E. Lee was too sick to appear and Gracie Allen, a Columbia networker, batted for him and virtually stole the show. I don't mean that Gracie imitated the Doc; she was herself, and she was so funny that you didn't miss him.

Dr. Lee, if you don't know, is the only regular on Rudy's program excepting Rudy and his orchestra and James Wallington, the announcer. The Doc extols fresh yeast as a promoter of health, and on Sunday nights he pops up in Eddie Cantor's Hour and says it's all right to drink large quantities of coffee if the coffee is dated. I am not a yeast-bibber, but I tried to sell Doc Lee's coffee talk to my own doc, Dr. Tyson, and didn't get halfway to first base. Dr. Tyson is a joiner and belongs to the American Medical Association. Dr. Lee doesn't even belong to the Coffee House. My doc gave me a copy of the Association's *Journal,* and what it said— Well, Dr. Lee may have seen a copy himself. It may have been what made him sick.

Miss Graham, reading my stuff while I drink undated cocoa, remarks that I seem to have strayed from the threatened topics: Rudy and suggestive songs. Before I return to them, allow me to establish by Rudy's own words that his judgment isn't always infallible. In introducing Ken Murray, he said that the latter was to vaudeville what Charlie Chaplin was to pictures. Let's reply to that with a couple of questions: If Chaplin (Golly forbid!) were to die a natural death tonight, on what page would you find the news in tomorrow morning's paper? If Ken Murray (Golly forbid!) were, etc? Example 2: In speaking of "Lullaby of the Leaves" as one of the outstanding songs of 1932, he called attention to the blending of a beautiful tune, which it certainly is, whether the lady consulted with Brahms or not, and a great lyric, which—Well, listen:

> "I'm breezing along, along with the breeze,
> I'm hearing a song, a song thru the trees,
> Ooh ooh ooh ooh ooh ooh.
> That pine melody caressing the shore
> Familiar to me, I've heard it before,
> Ooh ooh ooh ooh."

Now then, on a Thursday night not so long ago ooh ooh, I was tuned in on Rudy's program, as is customary with me and other discerning radio addicts, when suddenly it dawned on me that the young man had lost his temper; he was quite ooh ooh ooh because someone had impugned the modesty of "Let's Put Out the Lights and Go to Sleep," *née* "Bed." The title was familiar to me or possibly I had heard it before; possibly I had heard the song itself, and blushed over it in these very columns, and here was Rudy all hot and bothered, saying it was perfectly decent, having been written by a friend of his, and that he (Rudy) was about to sing it, presumably as incontrovertible evidence of its purity, or perhaps to purge it with the hyssop of his immaculate larynx.

Mr. Vallée, let's put out the fire and go to midyear exams. (1) Did you ever sing "Paradise" before comparatively harmless words were put in where Mms and Whistles made the number charmingly suggestive, and if so, did you give a damn? (2) Arthur Ruhl, writing in *The Herald Tribune* under the name of Percy Hammond, commented as follows on your friend's spotless number: "The favorite song of the 'Music Hall Varieties' is an idyll entitled 'Let's Put Out the Lights and Go to Bed.' Sung expressively by Mr. Lahr, Mr. Richman, and the blushing Miss Damita, it leaves none of its innocent hearers in doubt about the facts of creation and recreation." And an anonymous contributor to the publication you are now reading told this story: "A frantic little niece of ours went into a music store on Broadway the other day to buy a song she had heard over the radio. (There is a touch of the pixie in her.) When she got to the counter, she hesitated. Immediately the clerk handed her 'Let's Put Out the Lights and Go to Sleep.' 'How did you know that was what I wanted?' she asked, piqued. 'You hesitated,' he said. 'They all do.'" Is alias Mr. Hammond dumb? Does the anonymous uncle sound as if he were half-witted? (3) In the middle of the refrain occur four sentimental lines beginning, as I recall them, "I'm waiting now for you to say," and ending "You never were as sweet before, dear." Considering these lines, spotted as they are, is your friend c-c-razy or is he hinting at romance? (4) Did you really go to Yale?

Anyway, Rudy, neither you nor your friend ought to be mad at Hammond or the uncle or the undersigned for hinting that "Lights" was low. The lady who runs the music store in Wellesley (that's near Boston, and a girls' school is located there ooh ooh) wrote and thanked me, at least, for my pressagentry, saying that more prospective customers than she thought existed had overwhelmed her with orders for the sheet music and pornograph records. Is the author of "Sitting in the Dark" another pal? Good night, Ohman and Arden dear.

The Old Man Shows His Air Mail

NOWHERES, CALIF.
APRIL 8, 1933

Of the reams of publicity which the big networks and a few of the advertising agencies are kind enough to send this old fellow every day, he finds most enthralling the personal items about radio's bright stars, intimate details of their private lives, inside information as to how they prepare their valuable contributions to our culture, and occasional samples of the spontaneous, off-the-mike waggishness that seems to be their chief characteristic and that must keep their friends and associates in gales of torpor.

It bothers my conscience that only we reviewers and a limited number of employees of local stations have access to these fascinating reports and I would fill this space with them if it were not against Ye Quainte Editor's principles to pay for stuff written with scalpel and adhesive. He knows, however, that ordinarily I earn what I get, no matter how much he cuts me, and I am sure he won't protest if just this once I do a little judicious copying from the press-agents, particularly as he is bound to realize that what I copy is more entertaining than anything that might come out of my own desert-minded head.

For example, McCann Erickson, Inc., which handles the "Five Star Theatre" programs, sponsored by Standard Oil, mailed me this bit shortly after the Southern California temblors:

"It takes more than an earthquake to jar Groucho Marx. As soon as the wires from the west were clear, Groucho sent the following message to Max Gordon in New York: 'Dear Max You can't have your quake and eat it. Everybody fine. Love.'"

Of course Mr. Gordon was anxious to come back with something equally side-splitting, but not being a comedian himself, consciously, he "delegated Solly Ward, new member of the Five Star Theatre troupe, to answer Groucho, which he did as follows: 'Dear

264

Groucho Your telegram would have been funnier if you had sent some slides along with it. Anyway we are still shaking with laughter and everybody says "California, Here We Stay." ' "

Mr. Gordon signed this, but proved himself a man of honor by seeing that Mr. Ward got credit for it with McCann Erickson's mailing list, and Groucho must have known without being told that it was the work of a brother comic.

Groucho is not the only Marx who refuses to save all his drolleries for the microphone. Again I quote McCann Erickson, Inc.: "Everything was ready to start the rehearsal of Groucho and Chico Marx' latest radio skit—except that Chico was missing. Just then he drove by the low, open window of the radio studio on the way to park his car. 'Hullo, boss. 'Lo, Missa Dimp,' he called as he went by. A moment later he bustled into the studio. 'Why isn't the rehearsal going on?' he asked with mock indignation. 'Didn't I give you my opening lines as I went by the window?' "

This one is even funnier than it reads if you can picture to yourself the mock indignation.

The National Broadcasting Company's press department is full of items concerning its star tenor, James Melton, and always follows them with: "Melton, who is six feet two and one-half inches tall and weighs 198 pounds, played football at Florida, Georgia and Vanderbilt Universities and between broadcasts still gives his handball and squash opponents a lot of punishment."

No doubt the squash and handball are part of his preparation for future football activities at Tulane, Sewanee, Louisiana State, and Alabama, and whoever happens to be coaching the Army sixteen years from now can count on at least one experienced substitute lineman unless James, or Jimmy as I call him, decides to put in a few years at Duke or V.M.I. on the way up.

One of his alma maters had a course in elementary grammar, and when, as a Reveler, he was asked to sing "My Silent Love," he made the first line "I reach for you as I'd reach for a star," instead of "like I'd reach," as Mr. Heyman, the lyricist, had written it. This enraged the Lyric Writers' Union, membership in which is limited to boys and girls who graduated from school at the age of three. They insisted that "like" was right because it was wrong and also because it was harder to sing, but Jimmie and the other Revelers stuck to "as" and, owing to their value as pluggers, the union decided to bury its natural prejudice against literacy.

Jimmie's Southern origin is noticeable in his speech; also in his chivalry, even to members of his own sex. For instance, there was an occasion when he knew he was going to be with me. He knew that he could outsing me, outplay me on the piano, outtalk me on any subject. He knew that he was much better looking. He knew I would feel painfully inferior unless I had one small advantage, and he learned from our prospective host, Mr. Grantland Rice, that I was inordinately proud of my height, six feet one and three-quarters inches in shoes, which I was wearing at the time. What did he do? He deliberately went to some specialist and had himself shortened so that when I met him he wasn't within two and a half inches of his N.B.C. publicity size and I stood up and gloated over him all evening.

Jimmie has been a "featured guest" on all the post-Jolson Chevrolet programs. They had better make him permanent; they need him. It certainly can't be his salary that causes them to hesitate, not the way they throw money around. Frank Black's orchestra, almost unique in that it is composed largely of musicians, doesn't work for room and board, and the master of ceremonies, Jack Benny, is said to rate $2,750.00.

Radio fans are now wondering what comedian they expect to engage. One night last month, I suspected that Mr. Benny himself might be trying out for the job when he got a noiseless laugh with a gag that was brand-new, at least to me. Someone asked him what his 1932 income had been and he said $80,000. "That's some sugar!" exclaimed the someone. "Sugar!" replied Mr. Benny. "That's diabetes!" I have one about gastric ulcers which I will send him when I have worked it out.

We're All Sisters Under the Hide of Me

Do Not Disturb, N. Y.

May 6, 1933

Nearly a year ago this department was expressing its admiration for the line "Let come what may" in the refrain of Allie Wrubel's nursery rhyme, "As You Desire Me." It struck me as perfect when it first came over the air, but in order to make sure of its perfection, I tried to improve it and asked my four spawn to do the same. Our efforts, including "Leave come what may," "Let may what come," "How come leave may," etc., were cast aside as inferior to the original, and the latter was ranked high gun (a high-gun expression) in our love nest until we heard an anthem entitled "It's Just a Little Street," or "Where Old Friends Meet," or both.

As in Mr. Wrubel's number, the stand-out line of this one occurred in the midst of the proceedings. It was, as I recall it, "Although I'm rich or poor, I still feel sure I'm welcome as the flow'rs in May." Once more I summoned the whippersnappers and conferred with them on a possible substitute for "Although" which would convey a similar meaning and add to the sublimity of the lyric. My own candidate, "What ho," was voted down as too risqué, but before that defect was discovered by a prowling helpmeet, the boys thought old daddy had again come through in a pinch, and John, the eldest, was about to lead the famous victory yell— "Old Daddy! Old Daddy!" (All respire.)

Consideration was given to "Except," suggested by James (Jake the Barber) Lardner, and to "Suppose," which David (Winnie-the-Pooh) Lardner submitted. Both were discarded for not being in modern usage as conjunctions. Bill (Jake the Barber) Lardner was in one of his ribald moods and would offer nothing but "Hotcha," which didn't even scan. John (Winnie-the-Pooh) Lardner finally hit on a couple of likely ones—"Unless" and "Until"—and now, when the five of us get together for a sing, we frequently employ one or the other, preferably the other, as a replacement for "Although." Thus: "Unless I'm rich or poor, I still feel sure," and so on. But we do this merely for variety, not because we think we have improved on "Although."

The "Little Street" enjoyed a long radio life, a fact that ought to silence those pessimists who argue that a song can't last unless it's got something. However, it is seldom heard now, and the foregoing discussion was just a prelude to some stuff about the song "Night and Day," which continues to thrive on its own merits and because Freddie Astaire refused to believe the obituary notices of "Gay Divorce," the show in which it is featured.

You must know that Mr. Cole Porter, lyricist of "Night and Day," shares the mantle of W. S. Gilbert with Ira Gershwin, Lorenz Hart, Irving Caesar, Irving Berlin, Joseph V. McKee, Howard Dietz, Bert Kalmar, George M. Cohan, Gus Kahn, Primo Carnera, and George Herman (Columbia Lou) Gehrig. Well, it seems to me that in this number, Mr. Porter not only makes a monkey of his contemporaries but shows up Gilbert himself as a seventh-rate Gertrude Stein, and he does it all with one couplet, held back till late in the refrain and then delivered as a final, convincing sock in the ear, an ear already flopping from the sheer magnificence of the lines that have preceded. I reprint the couplet:

> *Night and day under the hide of me*
> *There's an Oh, such a hungry yearning, burning inside of me.*

So what? Well, I have heard the song only by radio, and those whom I have heard repeat the refrain have sung that immortal couplet the same both times. Fortunate friends who have seen "Gay Divorce" report that the number is generously encored and reprised, and as a matter of course, most of the encores are pedal, not vocal. When they are vocal, the words are not changed.

Again, so what? Well, just as the apparently perfect lines in the Wrubel song and the "Little Street" courted an attempt at improvement, so did this superb couplet of Mr. Porter's, and though the attempt is as much of a failure as the others, the fact that the

song is still being sung on stage and air encourages me to publish
a few modifications to which Freddie and the radio artists are welcome if ever they tire of the original.

This time my own kiddies were left out of the conference, most
of them being away at school, taking a course in cuts. A little niece
of mine, Miss Ann (Jake the Barber) Tobin of Niles, Mich., was the
only party consulted. We agreed that there must be no needless
trifling with the impeccable five words—"There's an Oh, such a"—
which begin the second line; they should stand as written except
where our rhythm made changes imperative.

Well, then, here is the first variant from Little Ann's pen, with
spelling corrected by uncle:

Night and day under the rind of me
There's an Oh, such a zeal for spooning, ru'ning the mind of me.

And another, wherein she lapses into the patois:

Night and day under the peel o' me
There's a hert that will dree if ye think aucht but a' weel o' me.

And now a few by uncle himself:

1. Night and day under the fleece of me
   There's an Oh, such a flaming furneth burneth the grease of me.
2. Night and day under the bark of me
   There's an Oh, such a mob of microbes making a park of me.
3. Night and day under my dermis, dear,
   There's a spot just as hot as coffee kept in a thermos, dear.
4. Night and day under my cuticle
   There's a love all for you so true it never would do to kill.
5. Night and day under my tegument
   There's a voice telling me I'm he, the good little egg you meant.

As usual, the space is nearly all gone before I have said anything.
There may be enough left to admit that Jack Benny was recently
very funny in a Jekyll and Hyde sketch; to express the opinion that
Joe Cook, in two trial heats, has convinced me that he is as valuable
a radio comic as any sponsor is likely to find; and to report that Mr.

John Underwood of Buffalo listened-in on the Washington baseball opening and heard Ted Husing speak of Maxie Bishop, Joey Kuhel, and Lukey Sewell, and is indignant because he didn't state that Pressey Roosevelt had thrown out the first ballie.

Hail to the Chief

Do Not Disturb, N. Y.

May 27, 1933

Today, Graham, the program is going to be different. In place of picking on Mr. Vallée's taste in songs or his sponsor's taste in advertising, I intend to deal principally with the mountain's visit to Mahomet, the former having been ordered by his personal physician to snap out of it and move around regardless of inflated feet, and consort with somebody besides waiters, maids, bellhops, and George S. Kaufman, no matter if he could find no better substitute than a radio comedian.

Well, it happened that I could find no better substitute than a radio comedian, since a call on him meant combining business with slumber, the business being to acquaint myself with the truth concerning this new radio venture of his (I am referring to Mr. Wynn) which you probably know all about, but news of which was published while I was out of a newspaper's reach; and the chance for slumber coming while he tried to explain why the new venture was bound to be a success, it being an old habit of mine, and one of the many that made me what I am today, to doze off while people are trying to explain why things are bound to be a success.

Mr. Wynn telephoned me, in confidence, that the name of the new concern was the Amalgamated Broadcasting System, that that was also the name of the building in which it was housed, that the building was at 501 Madison Avenue, and that he would see me at once if I sent my name in. I learned later that he would have seen me just as at once if I had sent in the name of George Spelvin or Earl Benham. There is likely, however, to be a slight delay for any visitor on account of the fact that the System occupies three entire floors and the boy assigned to locate the boss has to go over each with a vacuum cleaner. The room where the vacuum makes the most noise is either where Ed is or where he ain't.

I had the good luck to find him in his private office. Anybody has got to have good luck to find him in his private office. Calling it an office is like referring to Russia as a building plot. Relays of dog teams take you from the entrance to Mr. Wynn's desk. He has no idea that his radio idea will flop, but if it should, he can certainly get even on this last-named piece of furniture, renting out one-sixteenth of it as a public dance hall, another sixteenth as a roller rink, and the remaining seven-eighths as the Chicago World's Fair Grounds in case inclement weather makes it desirable to hold that event under cover, where it probably ought to be.

If "office" is a reticent title for Mr. Wynn's headquarters, the descriptive adjective "private" is putting it mildly, to say the least. You can't possibly get into the place without pushing any one of the five or six entrance doors, and during my brief half-hour's stay (or maybe it just seemed that long), during which the orders were that we must not be disturbed, the list of other visitors included a priest, an interior decorator, a tapestry putter-upper, a tapestry taker-downer, Mr. Wynn's righthand man, whose name, believe it or no, is Mr. Ota Gygi, Mr. Wynn's son, Keenan, and a woman from a laundry who doesn't shrink. Moreover, no one is permitted to speak to Mr. Wynn on the telephone personally without asking for him by name. Thus you can't talk to Mr. Wynn by asking for Mayor O'Brien or Nellie Revell. When all the employees have been on their jobs a little longer and things are clicking properly, Mr. Wynn will be as secluded as a bell captain.

This was the first time I had seen the Perfect Chief since he decided to let his hair grow long again. Just now it is at the annoying stage where you have to pin it in the back, but it will be ready to braid in another week or two. In front it is still a great deal like the writer's except that the scalp is naturally curlier.

On the chance that you already know the Amalgamated System's scheme, I will report it as briefly as possible. There will be enough daily programs of big-time acts to supply, at a reasonable rental, the small independent stations in towns like Kalamazoo, Americus, Oconomowoc, and Tucson which can't afford what the two big networks charge them at present and are obliged to depend largely on local talent and phonograph records. If these stations can obtain sponsors for the acts, so much the better for them, but the advertising must be limited both as to time and number of words and must come only at the beginning or the end of the program, or both, but never in the midst of it.

Thus, at the beginning: "The following fifteen-minute program, by Ray Perkins and Victor Arden's Orchestra, is given you with the compliments of Richter's Drug Store." Or at the finish: "The program to which you have just listened was given you with the compliments of Richter's Drug Store. Advertisements of merchandise sold at this store will be found in the Niles *Daily Star*." Naturally, Mr. Wynn will perform on some of these programs himself. So will other stars whom you now hear only over the two big networks. I can't tell you who they are. I don't know. Possibly because I didn't ask.

"If they want to do more advertising than that," said Mr. Wynn, "it will have to be done in a kidding way. No radio advertising ought to be serious."

Which was my first intimation that any had been.

"You know," he continued, "I have always had a heroic strain in me. My primary motive in this venture is to save the actor. My secondary motive is to save the little fellow—the small, independent station that can't exist unless some scheme such as mine is brought to its rescue."

"What if you fail?" I asked, in a stupor to hear what reply I would get from one who had always had a heroic strain in him.

He led me to the window and pointed down.

"Twenty-five stories," he said.

"I'm sorry," I replied, "but I don't believe I have time for more than one right now, especially if it's about Mahatma Gandhi."

"Can't I tell one about Mahatma Gandhi if it isn't about his clothes?"

"Why the plural?" I said. "You can tell just one about him if it isn't about his clo."

"Well," said Mr. Wynn, "once there was a little girl and her father bought her some gumdrops and she left them in the house while she went out to play. Tired of playing, she went back into the house. The gumdrops had disappeared. No one had been in the house but her mother. The little girl, overwhelmed with grief, ran into the yard crying bitterly. 'Oh, Robinson,' said her father, 'why do you crusoe?' He called her Robinson. 'Because,' she said, 'Mahatma Gandhi.' "

The Perfect Radio Program

OUT TO LUNCH, N. Y.

AUG 26, 1933

Late last winter the McCann-Erickson advertising agency, handling in behalf of a flock of big oil companies the publicity for what it called the "Five Star Theatre," a series of five much better than average radio programs per week, including Groucho and Chico Marx and a condensed Aborn light opera, announced that one of its headliners, Solly Ward, was striving to select and assemble for his share of the entertainment a layout which might truly be designated "The Perfect Radio Program" and would present same to our eager eardrums as soon as the minor details of selection and assemblage had been attended to.

It is my recollection that I was out of touch with radio for a few weeks subsequent to this announcement, and inquiry among my operatives has failed to educe evidence that Solly ever tried to follow through. That he succeeded is beyond belief unless there was a stipulation that he himself, or McCann-Erickson, or some other individual or very small group should act as sole judge. To get as many as two people to agree on any radio program as perfect is impossible, as I shall presently prove by giving you my own idea of perfection and suggesting that when you have scoffed at it to your heart's content, you select one yourself and try to find a friend or acquaintance who will say you haven't made a single mistake.

There is no doubt in my far from humble mind that I could win a verdict of unqualified approval if a sponsor were judge. His ideal program would begin with two minutes of the drawing card— Fanny Brice, or Wynn, or Cantor, or Jolson; just enough time to prove that the big name was really there—and then proceed with fifty-eight minutes of talk by a "good" talker about the product being "advertised," talk that is always tiresome, often disgusting, and more often so childishly and manifestly untrue that large numbers of the listeners resolve not to buy the product or, if they have

275

been buying it, to switch to some other brand. Whenever I am bothered by the suspicion that my work is not as good as it was a year ago, I obtain comfort by repeating to myself the word "sponsor" until it becomes almost a cheer.

However, you, not a sponsor, are the judge of my Perfect Program, which you must admit has variety to make up for a lack of thrift:

Announcer: "This is Station WENC and the following program is sponsored by Fleischmann's Antiseptic Cigarette Oil. It comes to you every Saturday night, just an hour before bedtime. The oil is probably as good as any other oil you can buy. We have made no test to prove that statement, but it sounds reasonable because the well we get it from looks almost exactly like all the other oil wells we ever saw, and we have seen our full quota of oil wells. Now our program will open with George Olsen's music and Miss Fanny Brice." (One minute.)

George Olsen's orchestra, without the "railroad effect" theme, plays some new stuff, including a comedy song, dialect if possible, to be sung by Miss Ethel Shutta. Miss Brice, with a straight man, does some comedy dialogue written by someone who can write for Miss Brice. (Four minutes.)

Ohman and Arden, on two pianos, without an orchestra, playing early Gershwin or recent Schwartz or both. (Two minutes.)

Stoopnagle and Budd in dialogue that does not include any reference to Stoopnocracy. (Two minutes.)

Ben Bernie's orchestra, with Ben singing a refrain and making a remark or two. (One minute.)

Jack Pearl and Cliff Hall, doing the kind of stuff they did before they got to doing the kind of stuff they got to doing. (Four minutes.)

The Revelers in a medley of songs intended for quartets. No trick song or comedy song such as What's-his-name playing the rumba on his tuba or any song in which the melody is sung by the bass. (Two minutes.)

Joe Cook, giving directions on how to get to his old home in Evansville from the C. & E. I. station. (Five minutes.)

Bing Crosby in a couple of his specials, with a good orchestra such as Denny's or Goodman's or Lopez's for him to fight it out with. (Four minutes.)

Ed Wynn, with Graham McNamee and Vorhees' band, telling some of those jokes it takes him thirty-one hours per week to write, and trying, as a stunt, not to use his favorite word for 1932–33— "underwear." (Ten minutes.)

Rosa Ponselle, singing an aria from the opera "Norma." (Two minutes and a half.)

Irvin S. Cobb, waiting for them to stop laughing before he starts his first story. (Half a minute.)

Burns and Allen, with Guy Lombardo's orchestra. We are crowded for time, but Burns and Allen rate as much as Stoopnagle and Budd and shall have it. Miss Gracie, at my request, is doing over twice as much singing as usual. Mr. Lombardo, in the minute allotted to him, will attempt to have his strings and saxophones in tune with his saxophones and strings for at least one encounter. (Five minutes.)

Ruth Etting, queen of the torchers, singing, perhaps, Irving Berlin's old "Remember." (One minute.)

Eddie Cantor and James Wallington in dialogue written by someone who knows how to write for Eddie Cantor. (Two minutes.)

A fellow named Lawrence Tibbett, singing in English a song called "Bendemeer's Stream," or, in Italian, the aria in "Traviata" which Daddy sings to the gal and which is virtually a complete history of France up to the time the United States entered the world War. (Two minutes.)

Fred Allen and Roy Atwell, in dialogue written by Fred Allen for Fred Allen, and something nobody will admit having written for Mr. Atwell. (Two minutes.)

Al Jolson in anything he wants to sing or say. (Two minutes.)

And the remaining eight minutes to the best band in the land, Marse Paul's, who, I hope, will give me all the "Music in the Air" and other recent Kern he can crowd into that all too brief period.

That's my dream program, ladies and gents. If a single one of you agrees with me *in toto*, I will gladly apologize and begin all over.

What the editors say about each other

Henry Morgan writes about Babette Rosmond:

Babette Rosmond and I have been friends for twenty years. She thought up this book. She is all right.

Babette Rosmond writes about Henry Morgan:

Although he is taller than I, Mr. Morgan has been my friend for twenty years. He has referred to himself as Peck's Bad Middle-Aged Man. He is more than that.